CW00661365

OCEANS
HEART OF OUR BLUE PLANET

Printed in China through Globalinkprinting.com on PEFC certified paper
Published by Earth in Focus Editions–a division of iLCP
2011 Crystal Drive, Suite 500
Arlington VA, 22202
www.ilcp.com

OCEANS
By Gregory S. Stone, Russell A. Mittermeier, Octavio Aburto-Oropeza, Claudio Campagna, Kent E. Carpenter, Laurence P. Madin, David Obura, Enric Sala, Cristina G.Mittermeier, Sebastian Troëng and Peter A. Seligman

ISBN: 978-0-9841686-6-8

10 9 8 7 6 5 4 3 2 1

Production Direction: Abbie Williams
Design: Stefan Gutermuth

Foreword by H.S.H. Prince Albert II of Monaco

COVER: A pod of long-beaked common dolphins (*Delphinus capensis*) glides across a darkening Sea of Cortez, Gulf of California, Baja California, Mexico. **Photograph by Ralph Lee Hopkins/ iLCP**

TABLE OF CONTENTS: A spawning aggregation of large fish, appropriately titled the big eye trevally (*Caranx sexfasciatus*), swims in a school directly at the photographer.

Photograph by Octavio Aburto/ iLCP

ACKNOWLEDGEMENTS

We would like to express our gratitude to the many people who have made contributions to this book, and have helped so much to make it the most dynamic and beautiful CEMEX Series book to date.

Our sincere thanks to the Board of Directors of the International League of Conservation Photographers (iLCP) for their support and guidance, including Wolcott Henry, Mark Lukes, Kathy Moran, and Shari Sant Plummer.

We are also most grateful to several different components of Conservation International (CI). From CI's Marine Subcommittee, we offer special thanks to William Wrigley, Jr. (chair), David Ellison, Harrison Ford, Jeff Gale, Gordon E. Moore, Claire Perry, Kenneth F. Siebel, and Rob Walton. From CI's Ocean Health Council, we thank Stone Gossard, Steve McCormick, Bart Sayle, Ted Waitt, William Wrigley Jr., and Heather Wrigley. From CI's Marine Division, we thank Ed Lohnes, Tim Noviello, Christy Olsing, Brittni Paris, and Debra Zeyen for their tireless work in bringing this book together. And from the President's office at CI, we are grateful to Ella Outlaw, Jill Lucena, and Paula Rylands for their ongoing support.

Our deep appreciation also to Dr. Richard Sneider and Fabian Oberfeld from One World for their support of this book; to Susan and Dexter Paine, Alan Dynner, Tom Haas and Byron Trott for their strategic input to and support for CI's marine program; to Dan Roe and Emma Patricia Gomez from CEMEX for continued assistance during the process of preparation; to Diana Cohen from the Plastic Pollution Coalition for providing feedback and information, and to Kerry Lagueux from the New England Aquarium for his expert input on illustrations.

We would like to give special recognition to H.S.H. Prince Albert II of Monaco for writing the excellent foreword to this book. His commitment to and leadership on marine conservation has been of global importance and sets a new standard. We also want to recognize the President of Kiribati, Anote Tong, for his creation of the Phoenix Island Marine Protected Area, now the world's largest World Heritage Site and highlighted in this book, and for his outstanding leadership on marine issues in the Pacific region as a whole.

We owe particular heartfelt thanks to our Editor, Ann Downer-Hazell, who has been relentless, creative, and totally committed to making this book a product of the highest quality, and who succeeded in uniting a wide range of stories and narratives into a single coherent voice.

We are indebted to the staff of the many photographers who contributed to this book for their kind and generous assistance and guidance: Deirdre Skillman, Art Wolfe Stock; Ashley Parada, National Geographic Image Collection; Nadia Hughes, National Geographic Image Collection; Jessica Licciardello, George Steinmetz Photography; Karolina Elijas, Wild Wonders of Europe; Meri Bell, Ocean Wide Images; Rachel L. Woolfson, Tim Laman Photography; Stella Freund, Jürgen Freund Photography; Renee Bish, Pete Oxford Photography; Michele Hall, Howard Hall Productions; Deanne Henninger, Carr Clifton Photography; Mark Jones, The Roving Tortoise Worldwide Nature Photography and Carla Boecklin, SeaChange.

Last, but certainly not least, we offer very special thanks to CEMEX for their unwavering support of this Conservation Book Series, of which this is the 19th volume. This is a collection unique in the history of conservation and one that has had enormous impact around the world.

CONTENTS

Chapter Six

Chapter Seven

FOREWORD

Palais de Monaco

May, 2011

What makes the oceans so fascinating, I believe, is that they speak of us. They speak of our origins, of course, and the first miracles of photosynthesis that led to the appearance of life on our Planet.

They also evoke the primitive animals—our very distant ancestors—that gradually moved out of the water to occupy dry land.

And they remind us that the marine element has always punctuated the history of humankind, just as it has defined our boundaries and harboured our dreams. From the first Mediterrenean civilisations to the great discoveries of the Modern Era, from Phoenician merchants to international trade in the 19th century, to every major step in Man's history has corresponded to a new mastery of the seas.

Century after century, Man has succeeded in taming this seemingly infinite giant.

But the dimension—and even the nature—of this rising domination gradually changed. The last few decades in particular have witnessed a reversal in the balance of power. Globalisation has resulted in a change of scale for the world as a whole, including the oceans.

This salt-laden immensity, whose power and mystery were perceived by humans with whims of fate long, has become a fragile sanctuary, already ravaged on all sides. And mankind, once frail and insignificant, has grown into a destructive factor with limitless power.

Global warming, acidification of the oceans, rising sea levels, reduced biodiversity, endangered ecosystems, threatened polar reaches, overfishing, pollution: the oceans are often the first victims of all the ills we inflict on our Earth.

It remains difficult, nonetheless, for us to measure the scope of this reversal. And we too often forget that the sea remains the indispensable source of life for us all, and the generator of its great equilibria.

If the oceans speak of our origins and our past, they also speak of our future, how best to preserve and improve it.

Whether for biodiversity, which is given a major role in this work, climate change or simply natural catastrophes, no future is conceivable for humankind if it is not built on respect for the oceans.

This is why conservation of the seas is so important—and also why it is so daunting. Indeed, this is a mobile world with no regard fror human frames and borders, and infinitely complex universe still poorly known.

Our task today is thus, to improve our knowledge, and share it widely with our fellows to make everyone understand the urgency of concerted sustainable global action, in a spirit of harmony with the elements that shape our existence.

This book's force is in that it brings to light this harmony day after day and year after year, making it palpable, protecting it, and inciting it.

And this book's force and value lie in offering so complete an approach of what remains the true salt of life on our Blue Planet. I have no doubt it will make a useful contribution to sharing this essential message.

H.S.H. Prince Albert II of Monaco

A TRIBUTE TO DR. SYLVIA EARLE

Dr. Sylvia Earle is one woman whose work has become synonymous with Ocean Conservation. Her advocacy for all things living, especially for those living beneath the thin blue line that defines the surface of our global ocean, is nothing short of inspirational.

When TED2009 asked Dr. Earle to articulate a wish big enough to help change the world, she said: "I wish you would use all means at your disposal—films! expeditions! the web! more!—to ignite public support for a global network of marine protected areas, hope spots large enough to save and restore the ocean, the blue heart of the planet." We listened. The authors, photographers, and publishing partners would like to pay tribute to the woman who has stirred millions of people with her passion, knowledge, compassion, and commitment. She continues to show us that The Heart of our Blue Planet beats with force, and this book is our humble contribution toward sharing and making her wish come true.

ABOVE: An edible sea urchin, (*Echinus esculentus*) rests on a large piece of kelp off the Atlantic coast in Salstraumen, Bodö, Norway. Sea-urchins are spiny-skinned invertebrates that are in the same phylum as sea lilies, starfish, brittle stars, and sea cucumbers.
Photograph by Magnus Lundgren/ Wild Wonders of Europe.

PRECEDING PAGE LEFT: The dwarf minke whale (*Balaenoptera acutorostrata*) exists only in the Southern Hemisphere. The one seen here was photographed off the Great Barrier Reef in Australia, where they are commonly seen between March and October.
Photograph by Jürgen Freund/ iLCP

RIGHT: A chambered nautilus (*Nautilus pompilius*) photographed in Osprey Reef, Coral Sea, Australia. The nautilus has survived relatively unchanged for millions of years and is often considered a "living fossil." **Photograph by Gary Bell/ Oceanwide Images**

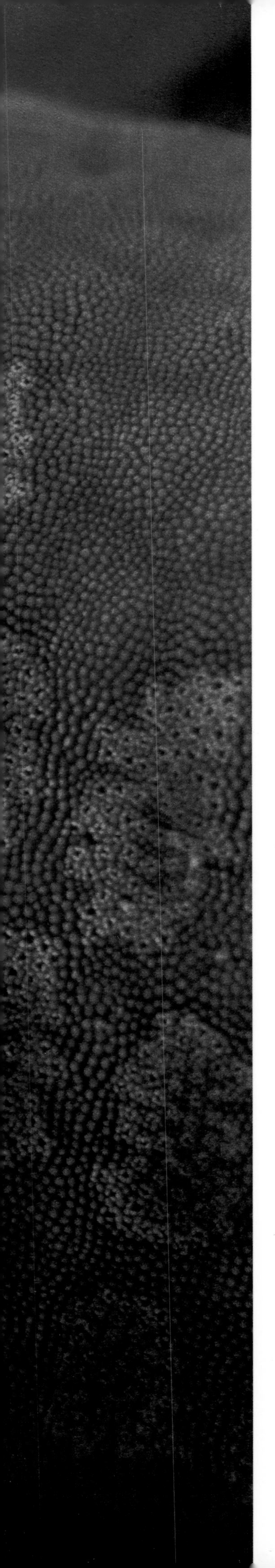

A MESSAGE FROM CEMEX

Within the realm of current scientific knowledge, planet Earth is unique in the entire universe. This is certainly true within our own solar system. The abundance of water on Earth's surface is an exceptional feature that distinguishes our "Blue Planet" from others. About 70 percent of its surface is covered by oceans that contain roughly 97 percent of the planet's water. Scientists believe that life originated on Earth thanks to the abundance of liquid water—beginning on the ocean floor about two billion years ago. Since then, life has evolved in many forms, inhabiting not only the oceans, but also the land and the air. At present, there are over 1.7 million living species, of which approximately 50 percent are marine organisms.

Beyond the species that inhabit them, the oceans are essential to all living organisms on Earth. Thanks to the oceans, clouds and rainfall are produced, allowing vital water to reach all terrestrial ecosystems and human communities. The oceans support life on our planet by moderating Earth's climate and producing 70 to 80 percent of the oxygen we breathe through the plants that inhabit marine ecosystems.

We have dedicated the 19th edition of the CEMEX Conservation Book Series, *Oceans: Heart of Our Blue Planet*, to raising awareness about the critical importance of our planet's marine ecosystems. The objective of this book is to gather the world's leading experts in marine ecosystems together with world-renowned nature photographers to create an engaging and compelling piece of literature that conveys the beauty and wonder of our oceans, as well as the ever present threats to them.

CEMEX is greatly honored to have published this new book in collaboration with such highly respected organizations as Conservation International, the Wildlife Conservation Society, National Geographic, Old Dominion University, the Woods Hole Oceanographic Institution, Scripps Institution of Oceanography, Coastal Oceans Research and Development in the Indian Ocean (CORDIO), New England Aquarium, Code Blue, and our publishing partner, the International League of Conservation Photographers. Our collective goal is to engage readers and build awareness of the most critical issues affecting our oceans and our planet. With key illustrations, maps, and diagrams, this call to action aims to improve ocean governance and management practices that are fundamental to supporting the role our oceans play in the health and sustainability of the Earth.

We recognize the value of our planet's oceans. With this in mind, through the CEMEX Philippines Foundation we partnered with Conservation International to launch the Adopt-A-Species Program in 2007. Under this program, we spearheaded the adoption of the whale shark, (*Rhincodon typus*), a Vulnerable species on the IUCN Red List. As a second phase of the program, we partnered with the Batas Kalikasan (Law of Nature) Foundation to help revive the rich ecosystem of the Visayan Sea, which is situated in the Coral Triangle, acknowledged by international experts as the global center of marine biodiversity.

CEMEX is a global building materials company that provides products of consistently high quality and reliable service to customers and communities across the world. We advance the well-being of those we serve through our relentless focus on continuous improvement and our efforts to promote a sustainable future. We sincerely hope this book will inspire actions to help maintain healthy oceans for the sustainability of our planet and society.

LEFT: A brittle star rests comfortably (*Ophiothrix sp.*) on blue starfish, (*Linckia laevigata*). Busuanga, Philippines. **Photograph by Zafer Kizilkaya**

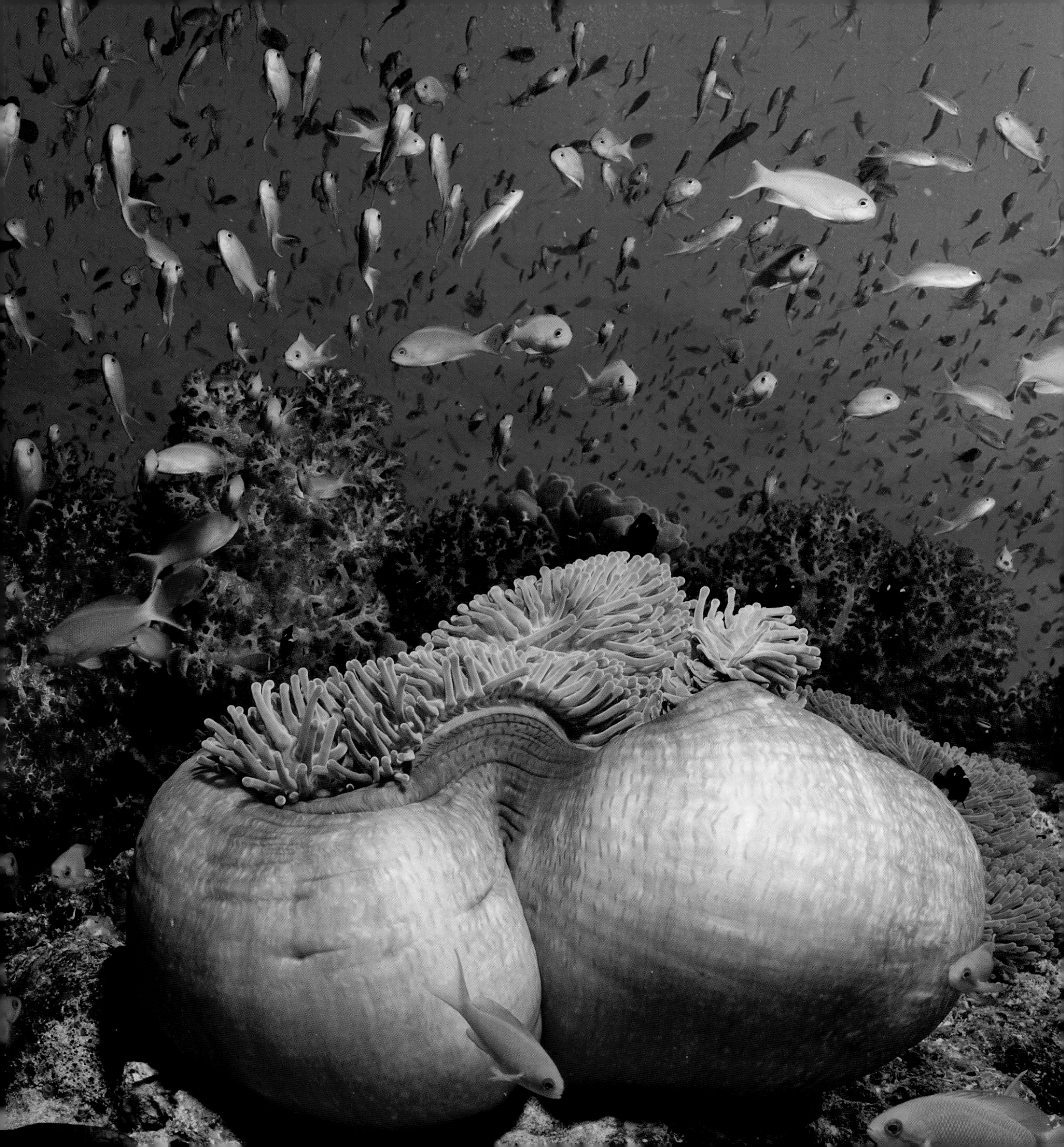

PREAMBLE

There is a thin blue line that separates what we know and understand about the oceans—what lies above, what the eye beholds—from what we cannot see—the mysteries of life teeming below. Our beautiful beaches, rugged shorelines, endless expanses of blue. To all appearances, life in the ocean is good, all is well. The picture is perfect—beautiful waters, busy fishermen, happy swimmers.

Underneath the peaceful mirror of water, however, lies a growing sea of concern and trouble. For those who dare look, the news is not so good and almost everywhere, too frightening to hear. The fish that once swam in abundant schools are being mined. Not to quench hunger among our planet's poorest, but to make pet food, to feed pigs and as luxury food for wealthy people in far off places. Entire stocks of top predators—sharks, swordfish, tuna—have been extirpated to make soup or sandwiches, and our generation may bear witness to extinctions of entire species that are not only good to eat, but also a key component of a healthy ecosystem.

Underneath the thin blue line we can see growing signs of climate change—corals dying as they endure warmer water; planktonic creatures that make up the foundation of the food chain are disappearing as the rich cool waters where they thrive become more acid with every new infusion of carbon dioxide.

In the Arctic, where the thin blue line was until recently covered in thick ice, we are now witnessing an unprecedented grab for mineral and fish resources. Industrialized nations are hurrying to exploit, pollute, slaughter and gain from a previously pristine ecosystem.

Over the next 10 years what we do preserve the ocean's ability to provide vital ecological services like oxygen production, carbon sink and food, may be the most important thing we do over the next 10,000 years. We need to realize that Earth is an ocean planet and we are all ocean creatures. If we fail to protect and understand the vastest, most important ecosystem on our planet and the role it plays in our survival, we will be making a catastrophic mistake.

So what can you do? Read this book, order the pasta, and most importantly, take every opportunity to stick your head under the thin blue line....you might hear whales singing or see a concert of bioluminescent creatures; fellow travelers on our journey through space.

Cristina G. Mittermeier
Founder and Fellow of the iLCP

LEFT: In the Fiji islands a giant anemone sits surrounded by bright orange Damselfish (*Hypsypops rubicunda*).
Photograph by Keith Ellenbogen/ iLCP

FOLLOWING SPREAD: A lemon shark (*Negaprion brevirostris*) makes his way through the twilight off the coast of the Bahama islands. These sharks inhabit the warm waters off the eastern seaboard and other tropical areas feeding on seals, fish, and small crustaceans.
Photograph by David Doubilet/ iLCP

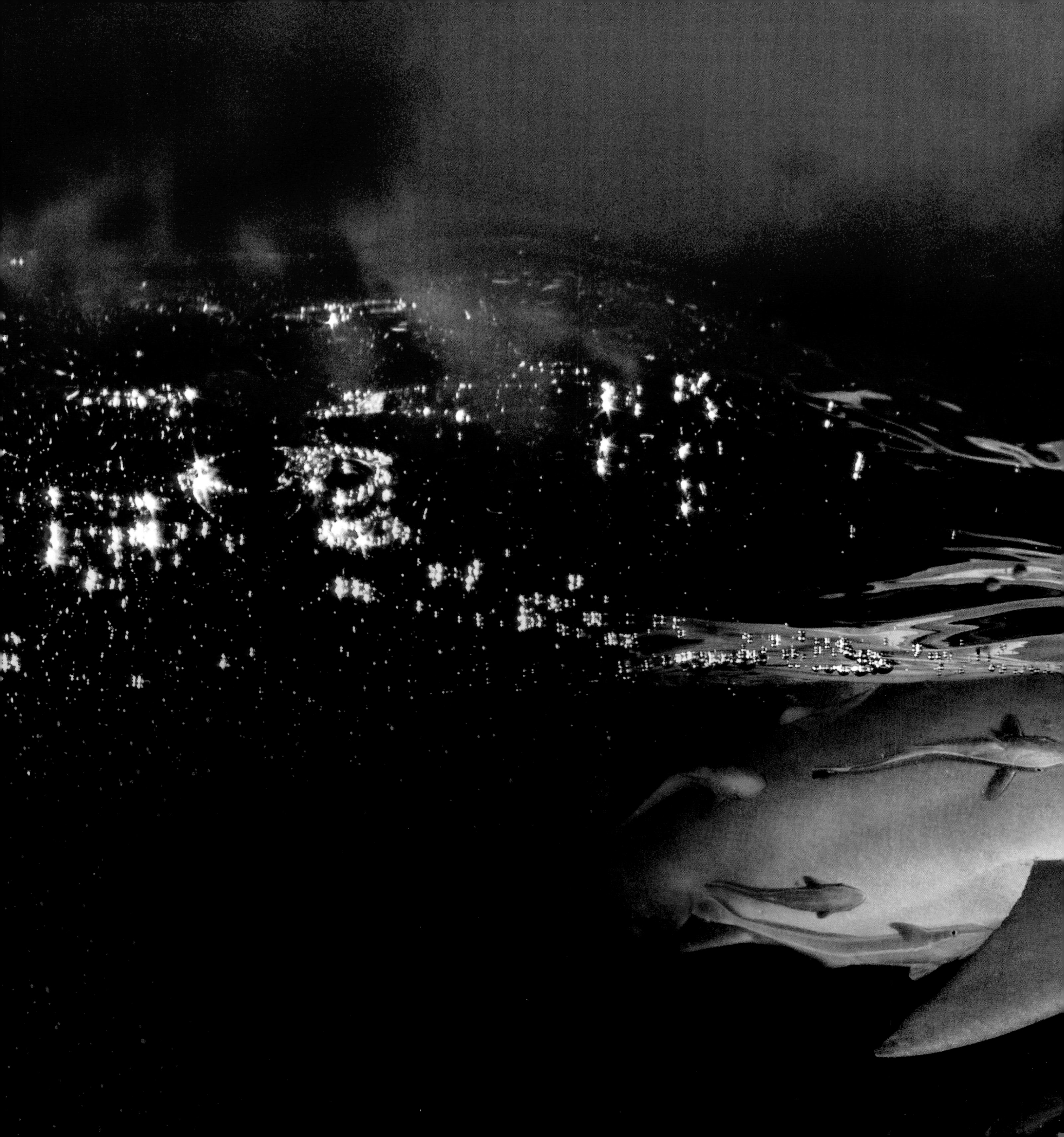

Gregory S. Stone, Russell A. Mittermeier, Octavio Aburto-Oropeza, Claudio Campagna, Kent E. Carpenter, Laurence P. Madin, David Obura, Enric Sala, Sebastian Troëng, Peter Seligmann, Carin J. Ashjian, Guilherme Dutra, Steven K. Katona, Roderic Mast, Scott Henderson, Mark Erdmann, and Andrew A. Rosenberg

INTRODUCTION

It is one of the most famous images of the twentieth century—the photograph of Earth taken in 1968 from the *Apollo 8* spacecraft as it orbited the Moon. When inventor and futurist R. Buckminster Fuller first saw the now iconic "Earthrise" image, he coined the phrase "Spaceship Earth" (Fuller, 1969). To Fuller, that image and that phrase perfectly expressed the complete dependence of humanity on our water planet.

Water makes life on Earth possible, and every drop of it comes from and returns to the ocean. For centuries we have taken the ocean for granted, viewed it as inexhaustible, unknowable; a vast, briny deep. Humankind ventured forth upon the sea in boats, at first tentatively hugging the shoreline but eventually venturing across long distances of open water to colonize the whole planet (Balter, 2008; Fagundes et al., 2008). We built bigger boats still, for whaling, fishing, and trade. Kings and queens sent armadas out onto the oceans, and explorers set sail to map and claim new lands. But the ocean remained mostly unknown, largely unmapped. For centuries, we imagined that its depths held monsters.

The ocean entered human culture through oral legends of sea-gods, then entered written literature, fine art, and song. In the English language alone it has left an indelible mark. Since the Industrial Revolution, our knowledge of the ocean has undergone a transformation, as first diving equipment and then submersibles opened the depths to scientific scrutiny and the popular gaze. What scientists found was life, unsuspected in its strangeness and variety, its resilience in the face of extreme environments barren of nutrients and cover, dealing with problems of buoyancy and pressure not faced by life on land.

Faced with the demands of life at sea, marine life forms evolved such amazing adaptations as swim bladders, gills, transparency, and bioluminescence. They developed suction devices and glues to anchor themselves to rocks to survive in the tidal zone. They formed symbiotic relationships, coral reefs, which form the only living structure visible from space. They developed astonishing

LEFT: A diver is encircled by a school of barracuda (*Sphyraena barracuda*) off the coast of Papua New Guinea, in the Coral Triangle, the wealthiest region for marine biodiversity on the planet.
Photograph by David Doubilet/ iLCP

The ocean continues to surprise us. The urgent question of the twenty-first century is, can we surprise ourselves, and address the looming challenges posed by overfishing and climate change?

forms of camouflage and crypsis. They exploited every marine niche, even "black smokers," hydrothermal vents on the ocean floor, where a whole food chain was based, not on the energy of the Sun, but on the energy from the Earth's core. But only in the last thirty years or so have we been able to see the ocean as a series of interconnected biomes—marine habitats with vastly different assemblages of animals and microscopic algae. The new science of biomes has profoundly changed the view of marine ecology—how all the biomes of the ocean are interconnected and interrelated, and how they are responding to the enormous pressures modern society is placing on the oceans.

Over the last two generations, conservationists have been taking a new approach to conservation in the ocean. In the 1930s and 1940s, conservation pioneers such as George Wright, Ben Thompson, and Aldo Leopold (Wright and Thompson, 1935; Leopold, 1941; Leopold, 1949) championed a new approach to conservation on land. In the 1970s, during high-profile battles over logging and water and grazing rights, this new way of managing ecosystems was further developed by the thinking and writing of Lynton Caldwell and Frank Craighead Jr. (Caldwell, 1970; Craighead, 1979). By the early 1990s, the approach was being called *ecosystem-based management* (Grumbine, 1994; Yaffee, 1996), or EBM. EBM put people and ecosystems at the center of conservation plans. Ecosystem-based management approaches were adapted for use in the marine realm partly through the passage in the United States in 1976 of the Magnuson-Stevens Fishery Conservation and Management Act (Public Law 94-265) and the adoption in 1992 in Rio de Janeiro of the United Nations Convention on Biological Diversity (United Nations, 1992). By the mid 2000s, a true sea change was underway. The urgency of multiple crises in the ocean was becoming apparent and, in response, leading conservation biologists and institutions were proposing EBM plans (US Commission on Ocean Policy, 2004; McLeod el al., 2005; Cogan et al., 2009).

The challenges we face in the twenty-first century are daunting and the choices stark. It is no longer a fight to save a whale here, a collapsed fish stock there. Now whole ecosystems hang in the balance, ecosystems that provide us with the air we breathe, the water we drink and that waters our crops, and much of the food we eat. It is time to view our humanized ocean in a whole new way.

We wrote this book because we believe a biome view of the ocean and ecosystem-based management offers the best chance for creating management plans that can address serious threats to the world's oceans. We've assembled fifty-four of the leading researchers around the world to tell the story of

RIGHT: A beautiful reef scene featuring red-tooth triggerfish (*Odonus niger*), in Komodo National Park, Sunda Sea, Indonesia. **Photograph by Zafer Kizilkaya**

a Conservation International initiative launched in 2004 called *Seascapes*. Seascapes are targeted "hotspots" of biodiversity where, we believe, a few strategic actions can literally make a world of difference.

In each Seascape, representatives from the governments of surrounding nations work with stakeholders and partner organizations (often multinational corporations or NGOs) to establish good governance and restore ocean health at scale. This model was pioneered in the three initial seascapes then expanded to the current nine. These critical Seascapes extend beyond country boundaries, creating opportunities for governments, multinational corporations, and others to work together to conserve the seas and the diverse marine life that is the lifeline for people living near their shores. The ongoing challenges they faced and the hard-won successes they have achieved thus far are detailed in the pages that follow.

The story unfolds in three acts. In the first act (chapters 1–4), we are introduced to the concept that healthy oceans are necessary for healthy humanity, indeed, for the survival of our planet. We learn of the different ocean biomes and the great diversity of life found within them, from viruses to the blue whale and including the "flagship" species that play such a crucial role in bringing the plight of our oceans to a wide constituency.

Act Two (chapters 5 and 6) is the heart of the book. We learn about the CI Seascapes initiative and then visit each seascape in turn. The seascapes section is really a book within a book, an atlas of these crucial hotspots where the conservation battles of the twenty-first century will be lost or won—we think won.

The final act is the chapter on management—in which we are reminded that we cannot manage the ocean, only our human actions. But the ultimate message of the book is that targeted local action that brings together stakeholders from all walks of life can enact change on a global scale. The images of the International League of Conservation Photographers bring the ocean, in all its unexpected beauty and raw energy, violence, and tranquility, to vivid—and vividly human—life.

We are still making discoveries about the life in the ocean that shares this planet with us. The Census of Marine Life, a decade-long endeavor that concluded in 2010, brought to the public notice the "yeti crab" and other wonders. The ocean continues to surprise us. The urgent question of the twenty-first century is, can we surprise ourselves, and address the looming challenges posed by overfishing and climate change? People everywhere have the power to bring change to their own Seascape and the mosaic of seascapes that is our water planet.

LEFT: An abandoned truck sits in shallow water in Puerto Natales in the Chilean Patagonia. Pollution and garbage from coastal cities, shipping lanes, chemicals, and sediments that make their way to the sea from inland agriculture and mining areas threaten marine species and degrade their habitats.
Photograph by Carr Clifton/ iLCP

ABOVE: A pair of sooty terns (*Sterna fuscata*) flies over Atol das Rocas, off the coast of Brazil. Its remote location provides protection for this atoll, which remains largely pristine; an ideal location to study undisturbed biological processes.
Photograph by Luciano Candisani/ iLCP

ABOVE: A group of brown pelicans (*Pelecanus occidentalis*) coated in oil awaits cleaning after the spill caused by the explosion of the Deepwater Horizon Oil Platform in the Gulf of Mexico. Hundreds of thousands of birds, reptiles, fishes, and invertebrates were directly affected by the spill.
Photograph by Daniel Beltrá/ Greenpeace/ iLCP

ABOVE: With Atlantic bluefin tuna's (*Thunnus thynnus*) population having dropped as much as 90% in some areas, efforts are being made—not without controversy—to rear these highly prized fish in captivity. Here we see Atlantic bluefin tuna in a seine net off the Turkish coast in the Mediterranean Sea. **Photograph by Richard Hermann**

LEFT: A Japanese fishing ship crew cuts and cleans recently caught bluefin tunas, the most valuable commercial fish in the world, Eastern Mediterranean, Turkey. **Photograph by Zafer Kizilkaya**

FOLLOWING SPREAD: Fisheries and Oceans Canada is the government agency responsible for managing inland fisheries in Newfoundland and Labrador, where this fishing camp in Bateau Cove, Northwestern Newfoundland, Canada, was photographed at sunset.
Photograph by Carr Clifton/ iLCP

Steven K. Katona, Benjamin S. Halpern, and Gregory S. Stone

HEALTHY OCEAN, HEALTHY PEOPLE, HEALTHY PLANET

Based on observations from the Hubble Space Telescope, the National Aeronautics and Space Administration (NASA) estimates that there are 125 billion galaxies in the universe. Our galaxy alone contains 10 to 100 billion stars. New observations indicate that 30% of stars have planets, suggesting that there may be at least 3 billion to 30 billion planets just in the Milky Way. Yet we only know of a single planet with a liquid ocean and where life exists: Earth. Why does our planet have an ocean, and how important is it to life here?

The children's story, *Goldilocks and the Three Bears*, is often used to explain why life evolved on Earth, but not on other planets in our solar system. Just like the porridge Goldilocks chose, our planet is "not too hot, not too cold, but just right." This is because Earth is neither too near the Sun nor too far from it, but instead lies within a narrow habitable zone. This explanation is known as at the Rare Earth Hypothesis. The central feature characterizing our habitable zone is the potential for water to exist in all three of its phases. Liquid water, water vapor, and ice each are essential to life on our planet.

Earth's size is also "just right"—large enough that its gravitational mass prevents escape of most gases into space. On the early Earth, water vapor and other gases were brought to the surface by volcanism, introduced from space by impacts from icy comets (Hsieh and Jewitt, 2006), attached to the dust particles from which Earth formed (de Leeuw et al., 2010), or manufactured through oxidation of an early hydrogen atmosphere. Under the influence of Earth's gravitational pull, these gases accumulated and formed the planet's atmosphere. Water falling as rain or snow then accumulated to form the ocean, lakes, glaciers, and ice caps so important to life and climate. Scientists increasingly believe we will find other planets in the universe with liquid oceans that may harbor life, but so far we know only one: Earth.

Earth's ocean has probably existed for at least 2 to 3 billion of our planet's 4.5 billion years of existence, but with dramatic changes. Powered by the heat of Earth's core, enormous currents of molten magma push crustal plates around the globe, continuously altering the location of continents and

LEFT: We are running out of easy answers. Oyster farming, generally considered a benign form of aquaculture, becomes contentious with seashore conservation in Point Reyes, California, where the two activities are vying to occupy the same space. **Photograph by Jason Bradley/ Bradley Photographic**

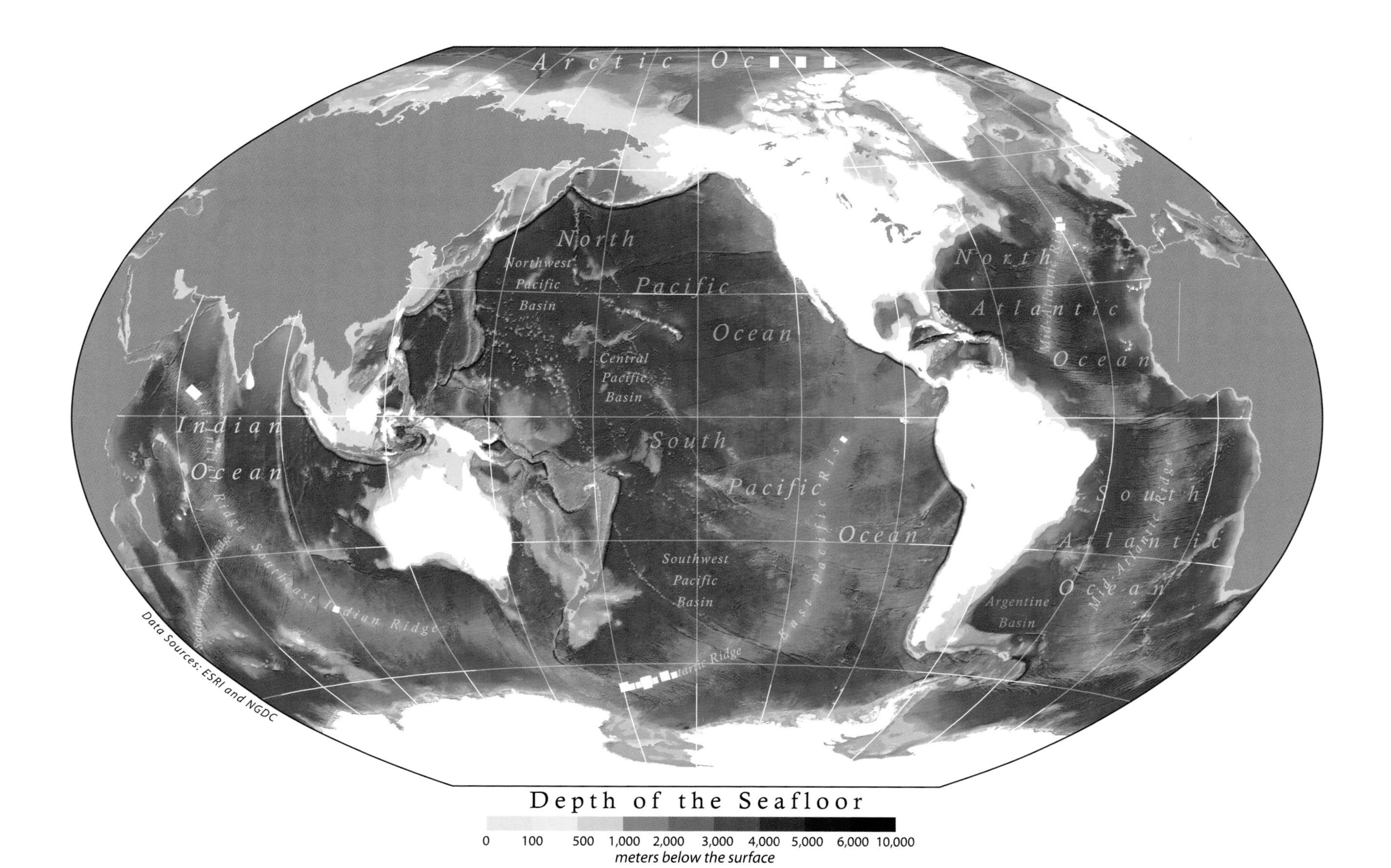

the size and shape of the ocean. Erosion, volcanism, outflows from hydrothermal vents, as well as impacts of meteorites and asteroids, have changed the ocean's physical, chemical, and biological characteristics—usually slowly, but sometimes rapidly and dramatically. For example, sea level has varied by more than one hundred meters during the past few million years and higher latitudes have experienced periods of complete ice cover as well as periods when there were no polar ice caps at all.

The Earliest Life

Simple single-celled bacteria and plants probably evolved in the ocean two billion years ago, proliferating in tide pools or deep in hydrothermal vents. Nearly 1.5 billion years later, the first marine animals appeared, and in the succeeding 550 million years species have evolved, flourished, given rise to new species, and gone extinct. Extinctions usually occur gradually over time, but on five occasions catastrophic events caused the abrupt mass extinction of at least 50% of marine species. The most dramatic extinction event occurred about 250 million years ago at the end of the Permian Era, when more than 90% of all marine species vanish from the fossil record. The most recent occurred at the end of the Cretaceous Era, 65 million years ago, when widespread extinction of species occurred in tropical reef communities and elsewhere.

Ten million years later, the Paleocene-Eocene Thermal Maximum occurred, perhaps as a result of massive release of methane hydrate previously trapped at the base of continental shelves. Temperatures increased rapidly for about one thousand years and continued more slowly for about 30,000 years, rising 5° C in the tropics, up to 9° C at high latitudes, and 4° to 5° C in bottom water (Zachos et al., 2005). As methane oxidized to carbon dioxide, it dissolved into the ocean, acidified it, and caused mass extinction of bottom-living Foraminifera and probably other shell-building organisms of the ocean floor.

To ask whether the ocean was unhealthy during those cataclysmic times is a question without an answer. The ocean simply was, and any plants and animals that could not adapt or did occupy a niche in a sheltered habitat perished.

Ancestors close enough to us to be called human, genus *Homo*, have existed for more than two million years, and our own species, *Homo sapiens*, evolved about 200,000 years ago. Some 40,000 years ago, the ancestors of all non-African people first migrated out of Africa, walking or rafting along the ocean's shores all the way to Australia, then colonizing the rest of

ABOVE: **Bathymetry of the world's oceans.** The depth of the seafloor varies from the shallow coastal waters (shown here in light blue) to oceanic trenches as deep as 10,000 meters (shown in dark blue).

the Pacific, Asia, India, and Europe.

Our first slight effects on the ocean probably began some ten thousand years ago, when soil erosion or wastes from our herding, agriculture, and early settlements entered the Tigris and Euphrates rivers and flowed to what is now the Persian Gulf. The Mediterranean Sea would have experienced similar effects as human communities spread into its watersheds, and coastal communities began to harvest fish, shellfish, and other marine organisms for food or other uses. In most places, however, cumulative human impact was still inconsequential.

Seafaring may have begun when ancient Polynesians voyaged from Melanesia to Samoa and Tonga, but such small expeditions left no significant impact on such a large ocean. Things began to change after 1500 BC, when the Phoenicians began developing trade throughout the Mediterranean. Their galleys were followed by the fleets of the Greek and Roman empires and, a thousand years later, those of Italy, Spain, Portugal, and France. These ships and others undoubtedly left trails of human waste and, when vessels sank, toxic waste, such as cargoes of mercury to be used in gold mining. During the 1400s, large Chinese expeditions to Malaysia, Arabia, East Africa, and perhaps beyond may have caused similar impacts. Fouling organisms attached to the hulls of these ships were likely transported to new areas to become some of the first marine invasive species.

During this same period, the growth of cities along coastlines and rivers, especially in Europe, India, and Asia, must have affected their coastal waters with silt from erosion, with organic waste from human settlements and livestock, and toxic waste from mining, dyeing, tanning, and metalwork operations. Even so, human impact on the ocean remained local, and the still-low number of humans on the planet—about 500 million according to estimates summarized by the U.S. Census Bureau—kept these localized impacts globally insignificant.

The first ocean-wide effects of the human presence may have begun in the tenth century AD, when Norsemen exploring Greenland and the lands beyond killed significant numbers of walruses, and in the eleventh century AD, when Basque fishermen sailed progressively further from the coast of Spain. Their pursuit of cod (*Gadus* spp.) and bowhead and right whales (*Balaena mysticetus* and *Eubalaena* spp., respectively) eventually brought them to Newfoundland in the sixteenth century. Commercial fishing for those species during the subsequent three centuries by ships from other European nations and America nearly caused their extinction. Steller's sea cow (*Hydrodomalis gigas*) and the great auk (*Pinguinus impennis*) were hunted to extinction, among other species.

Scientists increasingly believe we will find other planets in the universe with liquid oceans that may harbor life, but so far we know only one: Earth

Is the Ocean Healthy?

Today's ocean covers 71% of the globe and contains nearly 1.34 billion sq km of water (310 million sq mi). Its average depth is approximately 3,800 m, but its greatest depth, 10,924 m (35,840 ft), located in the Challenger Deep of the Mariana Trench off the Philippine Islands, could hold Mt. Everest with a mile of water over its peak. The ocean makes up 98% of the viable habitat on our world. Its waters hold more biomass—more microbes, algae, and animals—than any other place on the planet. Life thrives throughout its enormous volume, from the surface to the deepest trenches. Countless organisms ranging in size from the tiniest viruses and bacteria to blue whales, the largest animals our planet has produced, engage our interest. New species (and sometimes new genera and families) are discovered every time a scientific expedition explores new regions or depths. For example, between 2000 and 2010, during the Census of Marine Life, 2,700 scientists from eighty countries spent 9,000 days at sea on 540 separate expeditions. By the end of the decade-long census they had described 5,300 new species. The 210,000 known marine species display a dazzling variety of forms, structures, physiological adaptations, and a stunning array of genetic capabilities. Imagine what surprises will come from the several million species Census of Marine Life scientists believe remain to be discovered. This richness, the result of billions of years of evolution, is a biological legacy of incalculable value.

Now, as our civilization is growing and evolving so quickly, we must ask whether we are guarding this treasure satisfactorily. Will we bequeath to future generations the same opportunities and potential that the ocean provides to us? How will we know if we are accomplishing such a goal?

What Should We Measure?

Like a fund of funds in the investment world, the ocean is an ecosystem of ecosystems. Investment analysts have created standard measurements to assess the financial health and performance of their funds, and those standards are used worldwide. In contrast, no standard measures exist to evaluate ecosystem health or performance, and without such standards we can't know whether the ocean we leave to posterity is as "healthy" as what our generation inherited.

The question of whether the ocean is healthy only begins to make sense with the arrival of the Anthropocene Era (Zalasiewicz et al., 2010) in which human activities rival or supersede geological factors as the major agents of change on a planetary scale. Within this context, one may judge that the ocean is "less healthy" because high levels of carbon dioxide released by human activities are causing sea temperature, sea level, and ocean acidity to increase, with serious consequences for life on the planet. Because these and all other significant stressors of today's ocean are primarily anthropogenic, we could perhaps define "ocean health" with reference to a baseline status when such human-caused stressors were absent. However, that benchmark is not realistic. Our human population is now so large and our effects so pervasive that there is little chance that the ocean will ever revert to such a pristine condition. Ocean health is a human construct, and so it is only meaningful if people are made part of the equation. For better or worse, we humans are now a significant part of the ocean's life and vice versa, and therefore it is now most useful to consider human activities and the ocean as one coupled and mutually dependent system. It is the health of that coupled system that we must evaluate.

A growing number of projects are attempting to evaluate ocean health at different scales using a variety of methods. In 2005 the United Nations General Assembly passed a resolution calling for a Regular Process for Global Reporting and Assessment of the state of the marine environment, including socioeconomic aspects. In 2008, the first global map of the ecological impact of humans on the marine environment was published (Halpern et al., 2008). The Global Environmental Fund in collaboration with the United Nations Educational, Science, and Cultural Organization (UNESCO), the United Nations Environment Programme, and other entities, has begun a Transboundary Waters Assessment Program to develop indicators and methods for evaluating the linkages among five water systems: rivers, lakes, groundwater basins, the open ocean, and the areas recognized as Large Marine Ecosystems. A number of transoceanic research expeditions are underway to evaluate aspects of ocean health. These include the Antinea Foundation's Changing Ocean Expedition, which will in this decade evaluate environmental change at fifty sites worldwide. Noteworthy regional studies are available on the health of Chesapeake Bay (Burke, Litt, and Fox, 2000), the Baltic Sea (HELCOM, 2010), and indiSeas, a comparative study by EUR-OCEANS member institutions to develop indicators for fishing and evaluate the exploitation status of marine ecosystems, beginning in the eastern North Atlantic Ocean (Shin and Shannon, 2010).

Ocean Health at a Global Scale

Recognizing the need for a comprehensive and single method to evaluate ocean health at a global scale, Conservation International, the National Geographic Society, and the New England Aquarium are creating the Ocean Health Index. Through collaboration with scientists at the National Center for Ecological Analysis and Synthesis, the University of British Columbia's Sea Around Us initiative, and scientists from the International Geophysical-Biophysical Program, Scripps Institution of Oceanography, Woods Hole Oceanographic Institution, and many other organizations and laboratories, the Ocean Health Index will assess ocean health as a function of the status and trends of both ocean health and its relationships to economic and social aspects of human well-being.

In 2002, UNESCO defined Ocean Health as a "reflection of the contemporary condition, trend and prospect for improvement of the marine environment from the perspective of adverse anthropogenic effects and with respect to the ocean's ability to provide ecosystem services that benefit human well-being." Based on this definition, the Ocean Health Index project states that "a healthy ocean is one that sustainably maintains the ecological structure and function necessary to support uses or intrinsic features valued by humans." The Index evaluates the status and progress of ocean health with reference to ten social goals, such as provision of seafood, maintenance of cultures and traditions, support of marine livelihoods, biodiversity, and clean water. The first iteration of the index is scheduled for completion in early 2012.

Ecosystem Services

When we define ocean health in such an anthropocentric context and utilitarian manner, we make explicit the fact that humans rely on the water and life of the ocean for a variety of essential natural services, often called ecosystem services (Daily et al., 1997; Beaumont et al., 2007; Ruckleshaus and Chan, 2007). The most important of these have been categorized by function into four groups (Millennium Ecosystem Assessment, 2005), as follows:

PROVISIONING: This category includes plants and animals taken from the sea for human consumption (food provision); and other marine organisms extracted for all purposes except consumption (natural products or raw materials provision).

SUPPORTING: This includes mediation by marine organisms of storage, cycling, and maintenance of the availability of nutrients (nutrient cycling); and the extent to which ecosystems can absorb recurring natural and human perturbations and continue to regenerate without degrading or flipping to alternate states (resilience and resistance).

REGULATING: This includes the role of marine organisms in balancing and maintaining the chemical composition of the atmosphere and oceans (gas and climate regulation); habitats provided by living marine organisms (biologically mediated habitat); and dampening of environmental disturbances by biogenic structures (disturbance prevention and alleviation).

CULTURAL: This includes cultural value associated with the marine environment expressed in religion, folklore, art, and cultural or spiritual traditions (cultural heritage and identity); cognitive development such as education and research associated with marine organisms (cognitive values); and refreshment and stimulation of the human body and mind through engagement with living marine organisms in their natural environment (leisure and recreation).

Some of the general benefits listed, as well as others specific to the ocean, accrue to all of nature, some are shared by people and other organisms, and others specifically benefit humanity.

Benefits that accrue to nearly all life, including people, include:

CLIMATE MEDIATION: The ocean moderates Earth's climate in four main ways. First, moisture evaporated from warm surface waters is the major component of the heat-trapping blanket that keeps Earth warm, raising its temperature about 60°C above what it would otherwise be. Second, because it takes a lot of energy to raise the temperature of water, the ocean is Earth's largest heat sink, buffering and tempering the climate not only of coastal regions but also of our whole planet. The ocean has absorbed 80% of the heat produced by climate change. Third, planktonic plants as well as mangrove forests, seagrass meadows, salt marshes, and tropical coral reefs fringing the ocean's coasts actively absorb from the atmosphere the other major heat-trapping gas—carbon dioxide—sequestering some of it in sediments for long periods. Thanks largely to those organisms, the ocean has absorbed about 25% to 30% of the carbon emitted into the atmosphere by human activities, reducing the rate of global warming. Fourth, pressure and cold temperatures keep in place huge reservoirs of methane (CH4) that exist as clathrate, an ice-like form of methane hydrate, at the base of continental slopes all around the world. Methane's immediate heat-trapping effect is twenty-three times greater than that of a similar amount of CO_2, but over the course of its lifetime in the atmosphere, its effect is even stronger, as it traps seventy times more heat than does CO_2. Even slight warming of water in the vicinity of methane hydrate deposits could release enormous quantities of methane, causing runaway global warming.

WATER FOR DRINKING AND GROWING: Clouds and rainfall produced by water evaporated from the ocean are the source of water for all terrestrial biomes and human communities.

WINDS AND WATER CURRENTS: Differences in the heating between different parts of the ocean, and between the ocean and the land, help produce the winds that stir oxygen into lakes and seas, the ocean currents that distribute nutrients to stimulate production of aquatic plants, the heat that tempers coastal climates, and the refreshing sea breezes enjoyed by coastal residents.

OXYGEN FOR RESPIRATION: The photosynthesis of plankton, seaweeds, and plants of the ocean's other fringing ecosystems produce 70% to 80% of the oxygen we breathe.

These "common" services are truly priceless. They could not be replaced on any meaningful scale by human artifice or device. We, and most of nature, would not exist without them.

Another set of benefits accrues mainly to people. These services can be valued economically (Farver, Costanza, and Wilson, 2002; Ruckleshaus and Guerry, 2009), because we know the approximate costs of human actions that would be needed to replace them—at small scale at least. They include:

FOOD: The ocean is the main source of animal protein for one billion people.

NATURAL PRODUCTS: Different cultures harvest wood from mangrove forests, building blocks or roof tiles from coral blocks, sand from beaches, or agar from seaweeds. The huge deposits of petroleum that fuel contemporary civilization are derived from oil droplets that were stored as energy reserves by single-celled planktonic plants and the small planktonic animals that ate them in ancient seas. Marine plants, animals, and bacteria are also sources of antibiotics, anticancer agents, anesthetics and adhesives used in medicine, as well as genetic material and animal models important in seeking cures for heart disease, cancer, leukemia, cystic fibrosis, and other ailments (Carté, 1996; Jah and Zi-rong, 2004; Villa and Gerwick, 2010). As just one example, the first antiretroviral medication approved for the treatment of HIV and AIDS, Azidothymidine (known as AZT), is derived from the marine sponge *Cryptotethya crypta.*

NUTRIENT REGENERATION: The ocean's vast populations of plants and bacteria recycle carbon, nitrogen, water, and other substances central to life. Within limits they are also able to break down human wastes.

COASTAL PROTECTION: The ocean's fringing ecosystems (mangroves, wetlands, seagrass beds, and tropical coral reefs) protect coastal cities, villages, and their residents from hurricanes and tsunamis.

CULTURAL DIVERSITY: Different cultures have developed a variety of different relationships to the ocean. The social, economic, and spiritual expression of these differences contributes to the adaptability and intellectual richness of our species.

INCOME AND LIVELIHOODS: The ocean generates tens of millions of jobs and billions of dollars in revenue through industries including fishing, tourism, recreation, dining and hospitality, construction, and ship and boat building, among others.

The first attempt to value ecosystem services in economic terms estimated their global annual value at US$33 trillion (Costanza et al., 1997). Nearly US$21 trillion (63%) of that estimated annual value was contributed by marine systems, especially coastal systems (US$10.6 trillion). For context, the annual global total of all gross national products at the time of that analysis was about US$18 trillion. Subsequent studies are ongoing to evaluate ecosystem services for nations or regions. For example, Hussain et al. (2010) calculated the net present value of ecosystem services for waters of the UK out to the continental shelf to be £10.3 to £22.7 billion (about US$16 to US$35 billion), which the authors considered an underestimate because it did not include several categories of services. This value was at least seven times greater than the estimated costs of administering or maintaining the services.

Ocean Stressors

Stresses of many kinds now affect the ocean and its natural populations, biodiversity, and habitats, compromising their abilities to thrive and jeopardizing the ecosystem services they provide. The major threats are overfishing, habitat destruction, global warming (climate change), ocean acidification, pollution, and invasive species. They are causing widespread decline in marine biodiversity and environmental quality, challenging the ocean's ability to provide benefits fundamental to human health (Chivian and Bernstein, 2008) and well-being.

OVERFISHING: Overfishing is the dominant immediate threat to marine biodiversity and future human food sources. Lack of appropriate regulations, poor enforcement of existing regulations, excessive bycatch, excessive fishing capacity spurred by inappropriate government subsidies, and illegal, unregulated, and unreported fishing have reduced fish populations

ABOVE TOP: At Jewelmer pearl farm in Palawan, Philippines, pearls are cultured by transplanting a tiny piece of mantle tissue of an oyster shell into the shell of a young oyster. This graft forms a pearl sac and precipitates calcium carbonate into this pocket. Over time, this grows into a pearl. After cleaning, oyster cages are returned to the ocean. **Photograph by Jürgen Freund/ iLCP**

ABOVE BOTTOM: According to the traditional technique for the crafting of *yaeyama jofu,* woven fabric is dried in the sun and then finished by bleaching in the sea water on Ishigaki in Kabira Bay, Okinawa, Japan. The dumping of various chemicals for whatever reason has a cumulative effect on marine life. **Photograph by Karen Kasmauski/ iLCP**

LEFT: A Gentoo penguin (*Pygoscelis papua*) entangled in fishing net. Lost or abandoned fishing gear can continue killing wildlife for months or even years and is nearly indestructible. Falkland Islands. **Photograph by Frans Lanting/ iLCP**

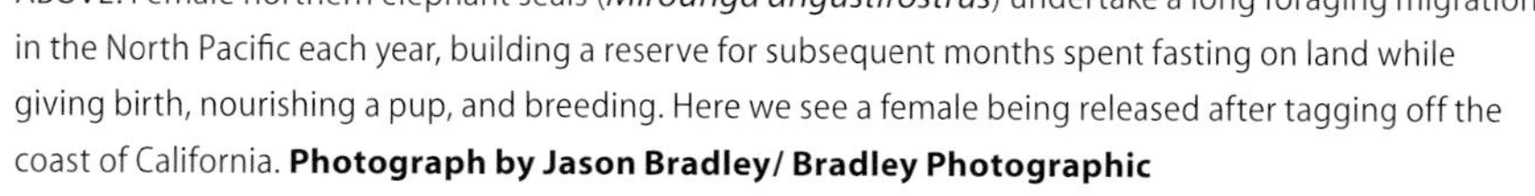

ABOVE: Female northern elephant seals (*Mirounga angustirostrus*) undertake a long foraging migration in the North Pacific each year, building a reserve for subsequent months spent fasting on land while giving birth, nourishing a pup, and breeding. Here we see a female being released after tagging off the coast of California. **Photograph by Jason Bradley/ Bradley Photographic**

RIGHT: A man in a dhow, a traditional sailing vessel, crosses a coral reef at high tide, Diani, Kenya. **Photograph by Thomas P. Peschak/ iLCP**

worldwide. Of the large fish that supported past fisheries, 90% by biomass are gone (Myers and Worm, 2003; Pauly, Watson, and Alder, 2005). All productive fishery locations are being harvested at or beyond their maximum capacity (Swartz et al., 2010). In 2010, aquaculture harvests for the first time equaled the harvest of wild-caught fish, and it is important to regulate that industry carefully lest it replicate the mistakes and excesses that have characterized the history of fisheries.

HABITAT DESTRUCTION: The destruction of ocean habitats seriously reduces or eliminates biodiversity and biological production for decades, centuries, or, in some cases, for a thousand years or more. Major causes of habitat destruction are fisheries (including aquaculture), oil and gas production, and coastal development. The fishery practice of dragging heavy trawls across the ocean bottom causes the most widespread damage to habitats, burying or killing most benthic organisms and destroying the ecological structure of the bottom. Trawling on seamounts destroys centuries-old cold-water coral communities whose complex architecture shelters fish populations and their prey (Stone et al., 2003). On tropical coral reefs, dynamite or cyanide are too frequently used to harvest fish for food or for the aquarium live-trade, with deadly effects on the reefs.

Oil and gas production destroys habitats through drilling, dispersal of drilling mud and wastewater, and oil spills associated with drill platforms and transportation of crude oil by ships and pipelines. Coastal development degrades ocean health and services by destroying fringing ecosystems, such as mangroves, salt marshes, seagrass meadows, and tropical coral reefs.

Damage can be direct, as when mangrove forests are cut down to make space for marinas, hotels, shrimp aquaculture, or other uses. Indirect damage occurs when construction, deforestation, or poor agricultural practices cause soil to erode, smothering reefs or seagrass meadows, or retarding their growth by absorbing light that they need for photosynthesis. Similarly, excessive nutrients released by those projects or by poor sanitary waste treatment can overfertilize coastal waters, stimulating harmful (and sometimes poisonous) algal blooms. After the algae die, their decomposition by bacteria can reduce the amount of oxygen in the water to levels at which fish and shellfish cannot survive, creating so-called dead zones.

GLOBAL WARMING: Climate change presents a more insidious threat, because its progress is slow and invisible. Short-term, small-scale changes in weather patterns confound the layperson's ability to recognize broader changes in climate. Global warming's lack of immediacy weakens the motivation of politicians and regulators to take action to mitigate climate change. However, this threat is relentless and pervasive. It will in time significantly reduce the ocean's primary productivity, the food base upon which all life in the ocean depends; change the distribution of marine populations; decimate tropical coral reefs and the biodiversity they support; and dislocate the marine industries and economies that depend on these resources.

Whereas overfishing and habitat destruction can be remedied by creation and enforcement of relatively few specific, targeted regulations, the causes of global warming are distributed worldwide. Modern civilization's excessive (and wasteful) reliance on fossil fuels burned for electrical power, heat for buildings, transportation (cars, trucks, airplanes, ships) and manufacturing, as well as gases from the burning of forests to clear agricultural land, results in the emission of carbon dioxide (CO_2) and other heat-trapping gases. At the same time we are raising the level of CO_2 on the "source" side of the equation, human actions are reducing the Earth's capacity to absorb CO_2 on the "sink" side. These sink-reducing actions include deforestation, which reduces the capacity of natural systems to absorb and store CO_2. Without radical improvement in all of those sectors, global warming cannot be halted.

OCEAN ACIDIFICATION: The ocean's absorption of 25% to 30% of anthropogenic carbon emissions comes at a cost. When carbon dioxide dissolves in water, it forms carbonic acid (H_2CO_3), which acidifies the water (reduces its pH). Mathematical models indicate that the average pH of the ocean was 8.2 at the start of the industrial revolution in 1750. Since then it has dropped to about 8.1, and is becoming more acid at the rate of about 0.1 pH unit every 30 to 50 years. The current rate of acidification is ten times faster than during the last major mass extinction of marine life 55 million years ago—an extinction that appears to have been caused by very high concentrations of CO_2 and intense ocean acidification.

Small decreases in pH are more significant than it seems, because the pH scale is logarithmic, with each full pH unit expressing a tenfold increase in acidity (or alkalinity). Thus a 0.1 pH unit decline actually represents a 30% increase in average ocean acidity. This more acidic seawater is more corrosive to the calcium carbonate shells of marine organisms such as clams, oysters, mussels, starfish, sea urchins, corals, and many others. Increased acidity requires these and other calcifying organisms to use more energy to make and maintain shells, leaving less for reproduction and growth. Worse yet, at pH levels predicted for coming levels of atmospheric CO2, larvae of these organisms and others crucial to marine food webs may not be able to mature and produce viable adults.

INVASIVE SPECIES: Species are deemed invasive that are not native to a particular habitat or ecosystem, but have been transported there deliberately or accidentally by human means. Such invasions in marine habitats typically result when species hitchhike on the hulls of ships or in their ballast water. In other cases, invasions occur when species are deliberately introduced for food or other uses, are transported on brood stock used in aquaculture, and

LEFT TOP: Ghost nets are lost or discarded fishing gear that continues "fishing" on its own for months or even years, like this gill net in Baja California, Mexico, with several drowned California sea lions in it. **Photograph by Howard Hall/ Howard Hall Productions**

LEFT BOTTOM: A Stellar sea lion pup (*Eumetopias jubatus*) also known as the northern sea lion, in Vancouver Island, British Columbia. This species, found in the northern Pacific, is the largest of the eared seals and the only member of its genus. **Photograph by Paul Nicklen/ National Geographic Stock/ iLCP**

ABOVE: Sperm whales (*Physeter macrocephalus*) are among the deepest diving mammals on the planet. These, the largest of the toothed whales, can dive to depths of over 2,500 feet and then surface to rest. This pod is doing that in the Azores off the coast of Portugal. Traditionally hunted for their spermaceti, these whales are now making a slow recovery.
Photograph by Magnus Lundgren/ Wild Wonders of Europe

ABOVE: Whale bones and a portion of whale rib at sunset, Barrow, Alaska. Coastal indigenous people in the Arctic still have a traditional culture based on subsistence principles. The Inuit who live there rely on the land and the ocean as their primary source of food. The International Whaling Committee allows the harvest of some fifty bowhead whales every year in Alaska.
Photograph by Karen Kasmauski/ iLCP

when hobbyists dump fish from home aquarium tanks. Because the transported species are new to their new locations, native organisms have not co-evolved with them and often do not have the ability to prey on them. Therefore, the alien populations can grow and spread rapidly, often outcompeting native species and causing significant ecological change and negative economic consequences.

Nearly 350 examples of harmful invasive species have been catalogued, among them the alga *Caulerpa*, which is blanketing areas of the bottom in the Mediterranean Sea, excluding most other species; the European green crab, *Carcinus maenas*, which has reduced populations of edible soft-shell clams (*Mya arenaria*) on both the east and west coasts of the United States; the comb jelly, *Mnemiopsis leidyi*, which caused catastrophic fishery declines in the Black Sea after its introduction from ballast water in the early 1980s; and the recent and ongoing spread of the red lionfish, *Pterois volitans* into the southeastern United States, Bahamas, and Bermuda.

Many other stressors also affect portions of the ocean and its life. Bacterial and viral pollution from human and domestic animal wastes discharged into coastal waters compromises the health of humans who contact the water while swimming or bathing, or who eat fish or shellfish taken from those waters, causing diarrheal diseases that can be fatal if not treated. Although not global in scope, this stressor is ubiquitous along coastlines, especially in developing countries.

Some other stressors seriously affect marine wildlife, but have fewer direct or indirect effects on humans. Ocean noise—from the propellers of large ships, explosions, air-gun discharges used for oil exploration, and powerful military sonar—can imperil marine life, especially cetaceans. Depending on loudness and pitch, such ocean noise can compromise long-distance communication among whales, possibly disrupt sonic communication among fish, and damage the inner ears, brains, and internal organs of deep-diving whales, causing death. Especially vulnerable are beaked whales in the genera *Ziphius* and *Mesoplodon*. Plastic floating in the water column is mistaken for food by marine turtles, albatrosses, and some whales, causing death by choking or gastric blockage. Particles of microplastics ingested by animal plankton could turn out to be a problem. Seals, whales, marine turtles, and some seabirds die from entanglement in nets, ropes, six-pack collars, and other plastic afloat or on the sea or on the bottom. Plastics also accumulate coatings of persistent organic pollutants that could further increase the danger from ingestion.

We already know that each environmental stressor does not act independently, but instead interacts with other existing stressors, often in synergy. For example, the stress caused by warming sea temperature exacerbates the stress caused by ocean acidification, and both increase the susceptibility of marine organisms to reduced oxygen levels, infection by pathogens, and physiological damage from contaminants. Populations exposed to those stressors have a reduced ability to grow and reproduce, making them more vulnerable to other pressures, such as overfishing. Conversely, mitigation of one stressor can therefore have a powerful effect by reducing an organism's vulnerability to a number of other stressors.

How Can We Restore Ocean Health?

Until now we have had a very incomplete and fragmented understanding of the stressors, impacts, status, and trends of ocean health, and perhaps even less awareness of their relationships to human health and well-being. Therefore, one of our first goals must be to organize and integrate that knowledge to provide a comprehensive view of our oceans' health. Completing the Ocean Health Index and other regional ocean assessment projects now underway, as well as the United Nations' proposed Regular Process for Assessment, will allow us to make sunstantial progress toward that objective.

Results from the Ocean Health Index and related projects will not answer every question or give an easy solution for every problem. Instead, they may be used to guide our course toward beneficial decisions and personal actions that will improve our relationships to the ocean, the health of marine species and habitats, and human well-being. The goals around which the index is organized are the destinations toward which we must sail. Just as prevailing winds may keep a sailboat from steering directly toward a destination, we may not always be able to achieve those goals straightforwardly. Political or economic winds may force us to tack one way or another. Nevertheless, with those goals as compass points, each tack can bring us closer to increased prosperity for humans and the ocean, and the Ocean Health Index score will show what progress we've made and how far we still have to go.

The Role of Marine Protected Areas

Another strategy already proving its worth is the creation of Marine Protected Areas (MPAs). These areas are typically created by a nation in waters within its Exclusive Economic Zone (EEZ), but larger MPAs may be created in international waters by means of treaty agreements among nations. They may provide varying degrees of protection depending on their purpose. Some MPAs (or portions thereof) may completely exclude human entry or activities; others may allow entry and recreational activities, but prohibit extraction of living or mineral resources; still others may allow recreational, commercial, or other harvest of fish or other organisms with regulations specified by permits.

Regardless of location or level of protection, all such protected areas share the goal of protecting their habitats and species from one or more stressors. With a refuge from some stressors, populations may prove more resilient to those that lie outside the MPA's control, such as rising sea temperature or ocean acidification. By aiding the survival and growth of their marine populations, protected areas function as arks supporting their living cargo through the flood of challenges they face.

For example, a study of more than 120 no-take MPAs presented to the IUCN World Conservation Congress in Barcelona, Spain, in 2008, demonstrated without question that such areas restore marine species and ecosystems. What's more, benefits occur quickly. Biomass and population densities of fish and invertebrates show the greatest rate of increase during the first year of protection and reach average overall values within one to three years (Halpern and Warner, 2002). Additionally, there is hope that by creating groups of MPAs close enough together and with sufficient attention to the direction of wind and ocean currents, the ecological benefits of all areas might be increased. For example, recruitment from the drift of excess eggs or larvae and spillover of adults that swim out of a reserve may help replenish the populations of other accessible MPAs and adjoining areas.

We don't know how many marine protected areas will be needed as arks to weather the current storm of ocean stressors. The World Summit on Sustainable Development, held in Johannesburg, South Africa, in 2002, called for the creation of networks of MPAs representative of all marine ecosystems. Delegates to the fifth World Parks Congress held in 2003 in Durban, South Africa, recommended that at least 20% to 30% of every type of marine habitat be protected from fishing in order to restore habitats and rebuild fish stocks. Many experts suggest that even more area (20% to 40%) should be protected in order to achieve maximum benefits (Gell and Roberts, 2003). Balmford and colleagues (2004) estimated the annual worldwide cost of protecting 20% to 30% of habitats as US$5 billion to US$19 billion (more specifically, probably US$12 billion to US$14 billion), but noted that benefits from making global fisheries harvests sustainable and ensuring continued delivery of ecosystem services would provide substantial return on that investment.

Progress toward the 20% to 30% goal has been halting. The United Nations Convention on Biological Diversity set a goal of protecting 10% of marine areas by 2010, but delegates to its Tenth Conference of Parties (COP10, held in Nagoya, Japan, in 2010) postponed that objective until 2020. In any case, despite the creation by former president George W. Bush of a 139,793 square mile ocean reserve in the northwest Hawaiian Islands, Papahanaumokuakea Marine National Monument (Federal Register, 2006, 2007) and even larger (157,626 square miles) Phoenix Islands Protected Area, Republic of Kiribati (Stone, 2011), existing MPAs comprise less than 1% of the ocean. Much more rapid and dramatic action is needed if the potential benefits are to be realized. MPAs located in or near the most intensively harvested portions of the ocean are especially needed to function as refuges for commercially important species.

Returning the ocean to a prosperous state will also require renovating the fragmented systems by which we govern and manage it. At every level—high seas, EEZ, state, and local—regulations for ocean management form a tangled, confusing net. Even where laws exist, oversight and enforcement are often ineffective, and abuses abound. And of course, some locations have few laws and very weak management. We need a more coherent approach to management that extends through and beyond territorial boundaries so that the policies, laws, and enforcement enacted by neighboring nations are coordinated toward the same goals. The seascape model that Conservation International has helped to pioneer (Boyd et al., 2008; Pressey and Bottrill, 2009) is a successful method for stimulating such coordination among nations that share access and use of coastal regions. It is especially important to extend those goals to the "high seas," the 60% of the ocean that lies beyond national boundaries and must be managed by means of international treaties.

Many more targeted actions will be needed at every scale, but we will not make much progress if we cannot accomplish these big tasks: creating the indicators of ocean health and using them to measure progress toward sustainable goals; creating a robust worldwide network of MPAs as refuges from fishing and other major stressors; renovating the fabric and effectiveness of marine governance and management; and managing the ocean with awareness of the major drivers of global change that characterize our times.

These powerful drivers include growth of the human population toward 9 billion by 2050; human population migration toward coastlines and cities; increasing consumerism; increasing demand for food, fossil fuels, water, and other natural resources; inequitable distribution of wealth; the spread of poverty; and dislocation caused by global warming and the effects of climate change.

Finding ways to control the growth and intensity of those drivers and the stresses they create poses an enormous challenge to humanity. The ocean's health—indeed, the health of ecosystems and people everywhere on the planet—depends on the success of those efforts. The fates of nature and people are intertwined as never before. We, and much of life on Earth—both in the ocean and on land—will flourish or perish together. Happily, there is still time to flourish if we act quickly, intelligently, and resolutely. The good news is that decision makers are exhibiting an unparalleled willingness to listen, learn, and act as they increasingly recognize the links between human well-being, economic costs, and the marine environment.

Evidence for this progress is the increasing popularity of marine managed areas (Orbach and Karrer, 2010) and ecosystem-based management (McLeod and Leslie, 2009). Ecosystem-based management (EBM) recognizes the links between marine ecosystems and human societies and between economies and institutional systems. EBM finds links among species in an ecosystem and the ocean places linked by the movement of species, materials, and ocean currents. One form of EBM, Coastal and Marine Spatial Planning, applies those concepts to create integrated, forward-looking, and consistent decision-making to balance multiple, cumulative, and potentially conflicting uses for the oceans (White House Council on Environmental Quality, 2010).

We consider the many efforts now focused on ocean health to be waves of awareness of the central importance of the ocean to life on earth, including our own. We believe that these waves are combining to form a groundswell of energy leading to a new age of ocean health, a planetary scale, generations-long commitment to create a more harmonious, sustainable relationship between humans and the ocean that gave birth to us all.

RIGHT: High tide turns a palm tree into a swing in Betio, Tarawa, on the island nation of Kiribati. Sewage-tainted waters and floating household wastes are less visible at dusk.
Photograph by George Steinmetz/ iLCP

LEFT: Atlantic horseshoe crabs (*Limulus polyphemus*) emerge from the waters of the Atlantic Ocean at the mouth of the Delaware Bay to seek mates and release their spawn, a ritual they have been repeating for millions of years. **Photograph by Piotr Naskrecki/ iLCP**

FOLLOWING SPREAD: Bowhead whales (*Balaena mysticetus*) like this one photographed in the Canadian Arctic, can live to be 200, but most adult whales are around 60 at time of death, with some individuals much older. This massive creature may have been born before the beginning of the industrial revolution, which sadly may be the cause of its demise, as emissions of carbon dioxide contribute to the melting of its icy home.
Photograph by Paul Nicklen/ National Geographic Stock/ iLCP

Laurence P. Madin and William Hamner

OCEAN BIOMES

Ecologist Frederic Clements first introduced the concept of biome to the field of ecology in 1916, though he didn't fully develop the idea until he published *Bio-Ecology* in 1939 (Clements 1916, 1939). Today the word is generally used to refer to a community of plants and animals living together and typical of a particular climate or region, whether on land or in the sea.

In 1975, ecologist Robert Whittaker described nine discrete terrestrial biomes where similar patterns of climate, primarily annual precipitation and average annual temperature, have selected for astonishingly similar adaptations of plants and animals from genetically unrelated lineages via convergent evolution. These biomes offer us a window on the ways that species interact via competition, predation, and mutualism, and how evolutionary lineages have been shaped by chance and history (Ricklefs, 2007). Thus there are tropical rainforest biomes in Africa, Indonesia, Central America, and Hawaii with plants and animals that exhibit startling biological similarities in form and function to equable climate and lots of rain, even though these rainforests have been separated for millions of years and by thousands of kilometers. Similarly the desert biomes of Arizona and Madagascar are full of plants adapted to extreme temperature and lack of rain, both with spiny stems and tiny leaves, but the New World cacti (family Cactaceae) are genetically unrelated to the Old World spurges (family Euphorbiaceae).

In convergent biomes, unrelated species evolve so that they use and partition habitats and resources in similar ways, producing communities that achieve an ecological equilibrium (Futuyma, 2005). In Australia the marsupial lineage gave rise to equivalent animals (many now extinct) to placental mammals found elsewhere. Thus Australia has, or once had, marsupial forms of mice, wolves, squirrels, tapirs, lions, moles, and so on (Flannery, 1994; Johnson, 2006). And since deserts select for desert organisms, we understand that desert biomes encompass all temperate deserts everywhere on earth. The existence of discrete, convergent biomes provides evidence that there are discrete rules for ecology at the community level. Repeated, independent convergence is one of the most important categories of proof of evolution (Darwin, 1859; Cuthill, 2005; Futuyma 2005).

Yet ecologists were slower to apply this important concept to the most extensive habitat on Earth: the ocean. Even while ecologists were gaining

LEFT: A brood of jellyfish is stirred by the swift tidal currents of the Douglas channel, one of the many fjords found in northern British Columbia. These long, narrow inlets host a rich and diverse marine flora and fauna that provide livelihoods for local First Nations. **Photograph by Thomas P. Peschak/ iLCP**

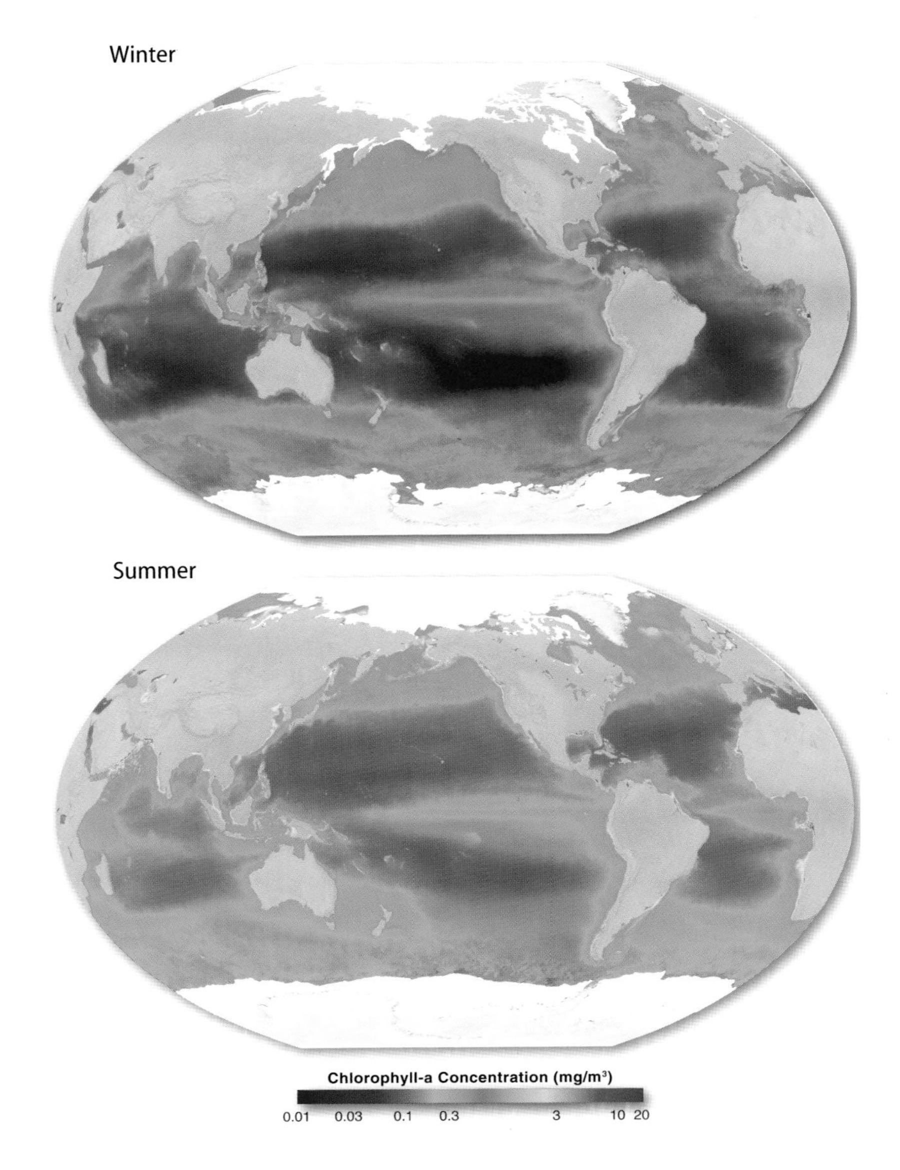

The Ocean: Two Dimensional and Three Dimensional Habitats

The ocean is the largest living space on earth, with over 1.37 billion cubic kilometers of water and with an average depth of 3.7 km (Robison, 2009). The organisms that occupy this vast space are among the most numerous of Earth's creatures but also some of the least understood. Oceans are predominantly three dimensional, highly stratified, constantly moving and energetically dominated at the surface by microscopic, drifting single-celled algae, and tiny zooplankton. Terrestrial habitats are essentially two dimensional, thinly stratified, and spatially structured by multicellular plants—large, rooted shrubs and trees. Aerial terrestrial habitats are inhabited by insects, birds, and bats, but these animals still must feed and reproduce on land. In contrast, the ocean includes the vast biomes of the open ocean and the deep sea, where organisms spend their entire lives perfectly buoyant in three-dimensional space (Dawson and Hamner, 2008). There are also many substrate-dependent benthic biomes beneath the surface of the sea, of which the kelp forests and tropical coral reefs most resemble biomes found on land. In this overview we pay particular attention to the defining characteristics of the three-dimensional biomes of the water column that make up the vast majority of Earth's ocean.

important insights into community structure and function in terrestrial environments, aquatic biomes were not differentiated much beyond freshwater, marine, and estuaries. Over the course of the last two generations, this view of the marine biome has changed; we now know the ocean is a mosaic of highly varied biomes. Several factors contributed to changing the former view of the ocean as a single, all-encompassing biome. Conceptual and technological advances allowed the development of methods, including scuba diving, samplers, cameras, and underwater vehicles that enabled marine scientists to explore and document the great variety of ocean habitats and improve sampling of their biota (Anon., 2000). Pioneers like William Beebe, Jacques Cousteau, Rachel Carson, and Eugenie Clark did much to bring the variety of ocean wildlife and the importance of ocean issues before the public through their popular writings, early photography, and documentaries (Kroll, 2008). By the 1990s, the ocean was viewed—by scientists at least—as an underwater world with biomes analogous to the rainforests, deserts, and prairies found on land (Gopnik, 1995). Evolutionary biologists had compiled a list of examples of convergent evolution among marine species as diverse as shark and whales, seals and marine iguanas, and jellyfish and squid.

Benthic Biomes

Most terrestrial biomes can be recognized from afar and explored from within by humans. By contrast, when we view oceans from above, from the shore, or from the deck of a ship, they all look alike—flat, fluid, and full of empty blue water, with nothing big enough to see. During the past fifty years, however, scientists have explored the ocean from within, via scuba, submersibles, and remotely operated vehicles carrying cameras. This has opened one ocean biome to exploration that had previously been poorly known: the benthos.

Benthos is from the Greek and means "the bottom of the deep sea." In the marine sciences, it is used to describe the flora and fauna found at the ocean bottom and within the bottom sediments. Many benthic biomes are defined by differences in global climate, substrate, or dominant vegetation (Bertness et al., 2001). Like terrestrial biomes, these environments are two dimensional with characteristic biota and convergent communities of benthic animals at fixed locations on the sea floor. Benthic biomes in shallow water are readily recognized and easily relocated. In the relatively shallow waters of the continental shelf and slope, or around ocean islands, familiar benthic biomes include estuaries, intertidal zones, and coral reefs. Even though tropical Atlantic coral reefs include many different species than Pacific coral reefs, both are readily recognizable as coral reefs. Similarly, along temperate shores, there are kelp forest biomes along the coasts of different continents. In polar regions, benthic environments are often richly populated due to the high seasonal productivity of the overlying water. But they are also subject to darkness for half the year and the risk of being scraped clean by passing icebergs. An

ABOVE: **Seasonal variation in ocean primary production.** Production in polar regions varies greatly between the northern winter and summer. Tropical waters close to the equator show much less variation in primary production throughout the year.

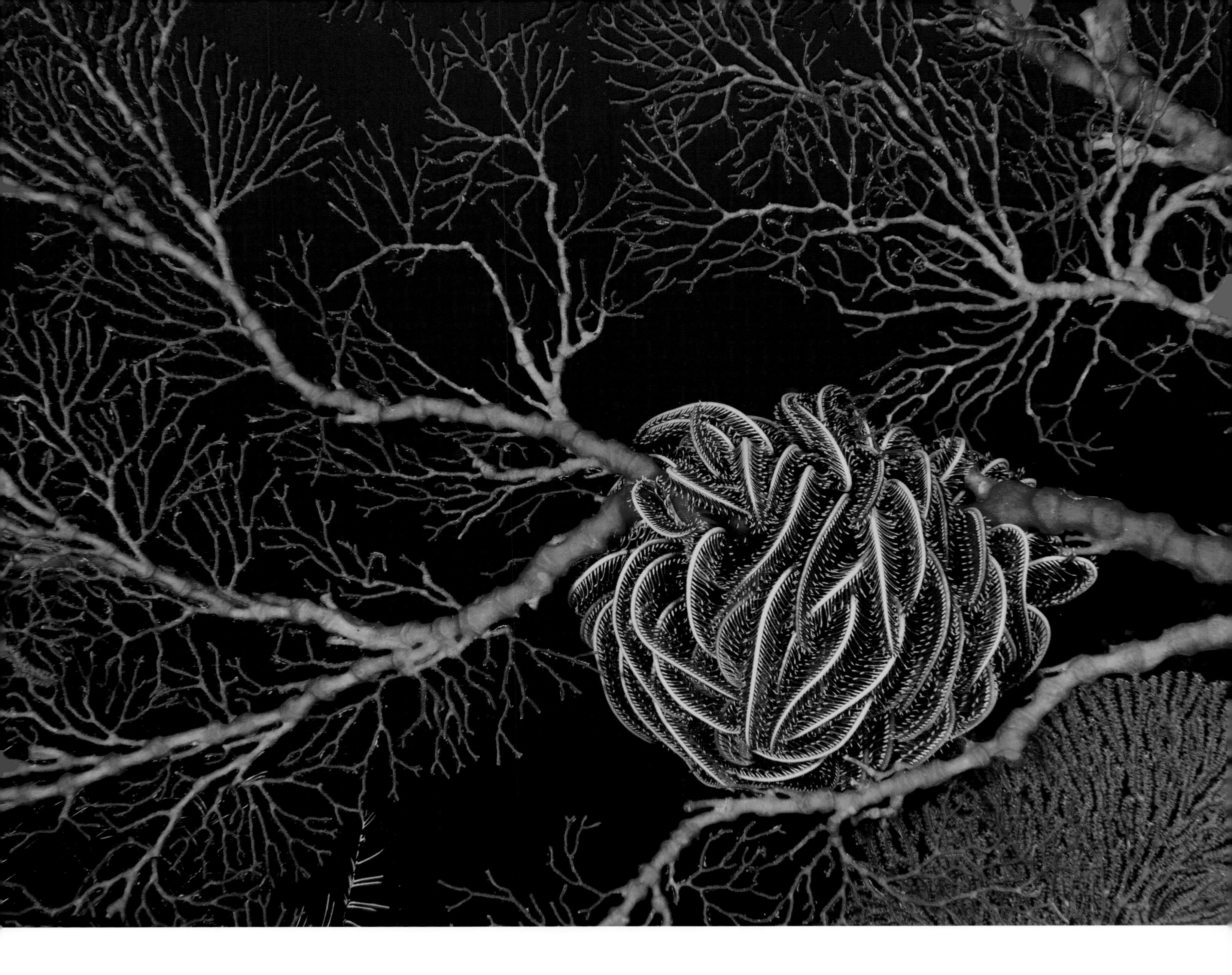

ABOVE: Crinoids, like this feather star (*Comantheria briareus*) photographed on a red fan coral in Raja Ampat, West Papua, Indonesia, were immensely abundant during the Paleozoic Era. Today, they still have a wide distribution in all oceans and are a common feature in many benthic biomes.
Photograph by Jürgen Freund/ iLCP

unusual upside-down benthic habitat is found on the underside of the ice sheet, where diatoms grow and are grazed by a variety of animals.

Researchers have defined several distinct biomes in the deep sea (Ramirez-Llodra et al., 2010). The largest of these is the extensive abyssal plain that covers most of the ocean floor at depths between 4,000 and 6,000 meters. This plain is largely a flat, unbroken sedimentary environment with a large proportion of burrowing organisms. Along the rocky mid-ocean ridges, however, are the very different biomes of hydrothermal vents. Divorced by distance and evolutionary history from the solar-fueled life of Earth's surface, hydrothermal vent environments have convergent communities of microbes and animals that derive their energy and nutrition from the hot chemical compounds that flow from chimneys and fissures in the volcanically active ridge spreading zones.

Seamounts are another distinct deep-sea biome, generally with enhanced biomass and diversity relative to surrounding plains, and often having highly endemic faunas. Estimates based on the slight bulges in sea level above seamounts, which can be detected by satellites, suggest there may be 100,000 seamounts in the world ocean, rising thousands of meters up from the plain, but not reaching the surface. Extending downward from the abyssal plain is yet another distinctive and poorly known deep-sea biome, the trenches, or hadal zone. Trenches are the deepest parts of the ocean, extending to 11,000 meters, and are an environment of extreme cold, darkness, pressure, and paucity of food. Another biome, perhaps the most remote of all benthic biomes in the ocean, awaits confirmation: the sub-crustal microbial environment. Based on limited data, scientists hypothesize that there may be a huge biomass of microbes, subsisting on chemical energy within cracks and fissures of the Earth's crust beneath the sea, perhaps extending kilometers beneath the ocean floor, and rivaling all other large biomes in total biomass (Schippers et al., 2005).

Pelagic Biomes

While terrestrial biomes are defined largely by their type of vegetation (Whittaker, 1975), the open ocean defies such classification. The pelagic zone covers all those ocean waters not near the coast or the ocean floor—all the open ocean. Here producers are single-celled algae, invisible to the naked eye and seemingly far simpler than the plants of terrestrial biomes (Ricklefs, 2007). We know now, however, that small cyanobacteria, coccolithophores, and flagellates are very different from large diatoms and that different kinds of microbes and algae do create distinctive communities in the waters of the ocean where sunlight penetrates. In the nutrient-poor open ocean, small-celled photosynthetic cyanobacteria and flagellates form the bases of long, complex food webs whereas nutrient-rich conditions produce large diatoms supporting simple, short food chains (Ryther, 1969; Falkowski et al., 2004; Berger, 2007).

At each step in a food chain, as much as 90% of the energy is lost to respiration and growth. In a short food chain with two steps—for example, *diatoms–krill–whales*—only 1% of the original energy in the diatoms would be available to the whale for growth or milk production for the calf. In a chain with five or more steps—such as *flagellate–copepod–arrow-worm–fish larva–comb jelly–sunfish*—a 90% loss per transition means that only a minute fraction of the original energy remains for consumption by the top consumer, the ocean sunfish, *Mola mola*. These long food chains are therefore not very productive, and cannot support many large individuals at the top.

Cyanobacteria, flagellates, coccolithophores, and diatoms all engage in photosynthesis, but smaller cells absorb nutrients, grow, and reproduce more rapidly, and they also sink slowly because of their high surface-area-to-volume ratio. Many dinoflagellates (Phylum Dinoflagellata) are both photosynthetic and heterotrophic. Although they swim with their flagella to find food, they cannot swim very far because they are so small. These and other members of the nanoplankton usually measure under 20 micrometers. Their heterotrophic foods include dissolved and particulate organic materials, other cells, and bacteria. This "dual fuel" metabolism gives dinoflagellates an advantage during periods when lack of movement in the water column means fewer nutrients flow their way (Falkowski et al, 2011).

Diatoms generally are larger—in the size range of 20 to 200 micrometers. While they grow more slowly, a large vacuole inside the cell wall allows diatoms to store nutrients over the course of several cell divisions. Diatoms cannot swim, and with cell walls of silica glass, these microplankton are heavier than seawater, which causes them to sink. Yet most remain near the sea surface suspended by turbulence in the upper water column, and they thrive particularly during periods of upwelling (Falkowski et al., 2011). The silicate cell walls may also provide protection from microscopic grazers like copepods.

These differences create two biomes based on pelagic algal vegetation. One, typical of the central open ocean, is dominated by small cyanobacteria, coccolithophores, and flagellates that form the base of long food chains. Another, typical of coastlines and regions of upwelling, is dominated by larger diatoms, short food chains, and more large animals like fish and whales. Although the coastal biome covers much less area than the open ocean, its higher productivity provides most of the fish caught for human use.

Oceanic Gyres and Vertical Stratification

The flow of water and nutrients shapes all the ocean biomes. The movement of water, in the form of oceanic gyres, is caused by the rotation of the Earth, by a phenomenon known as the Coriolis effect. These gyres create distinct biomes that persist over time. In some areas, flows of the great ocean currents produce upwelling of nutrient rich water from the depths to the sunlit surface, supporting the diatom biomes with their short food-chains. In other locations, the great currents create the large,

LEFT: Benthos is a word from the Greek that means "the bottom of the deep sea." Benthic biomes, like this sandy flat off the North Sound of the Cayman Islands in the Caribbean, are home to a wide variety of plants and animals, like this southern stingray (*Dasyatis americana*).
Photograph by David Doubilet/ iLCP

FOLLOWING SPREAD: A group of chin-strapped penguins (*Pygoscelis antarcticus*) surveys the sea from the precarious safety of an icy floe. Antarctica is one of the most extreme biomes on our planet: It is the coldest, the driest, and the windiest continent, and every species that lives here is exquisitely adapted to these conditions. **Photograph by David Doubilet/ iLCP**

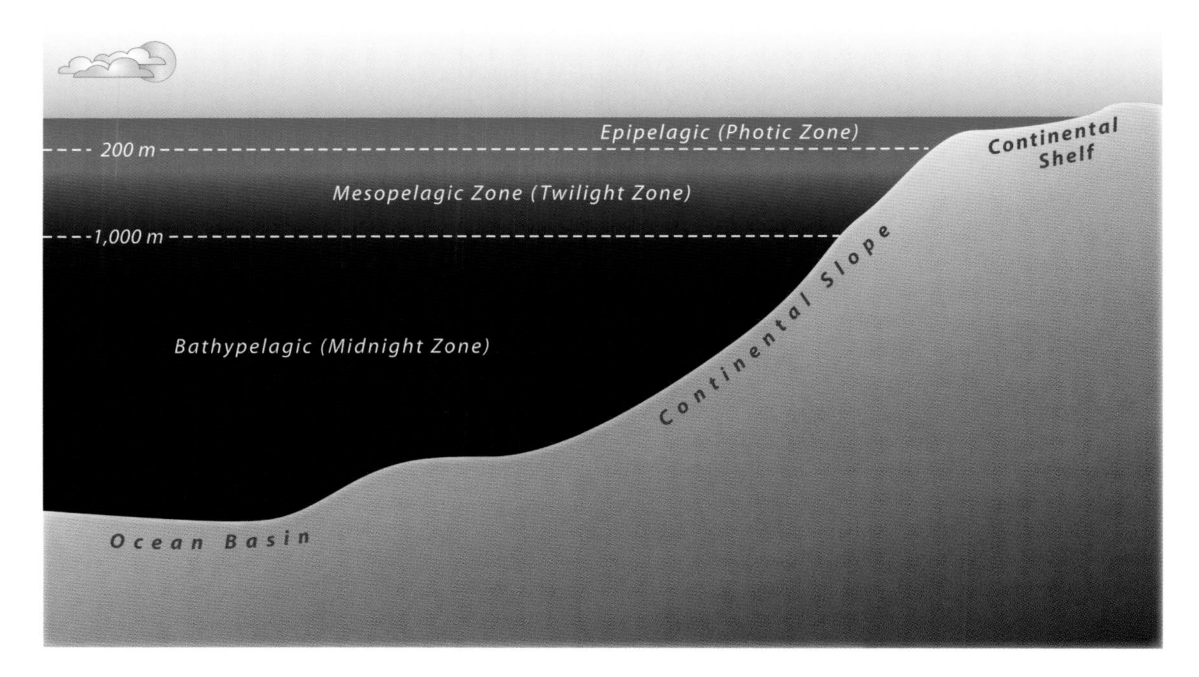

low nutrient water masses of the central ocean, home to the tiny cyanobacteria and flagellate biomes that produce exceptionally long food-chains (Ryther, 1969; Lipps and Mitchell, 1976; Berger, 2007; Falkowski et al, 2011). There are also major seasonal changes in the patterns of ocean primary productivity across the globe.

Vertical gradients of light and temperature affect the distribution, behavior, and life histories of pelagic organisms. Light is strongest at the sea surface and fades with depth. Sunlight warms the sea surface and fuels photosynthesis. The epipelagic (or photic) zone, with enough light for algal growth, extends to about 200 meters, but light often penetrates to 1,000 meters at intensities sufficient for vision (Johnsen, 2007). The upper 1,000 meters is home to a wide variety of herbivorous, predatory, and scavenging animals—many bioluminescent and many that make daily vertical migrations.

Surface waters are often of uniform temperature, bounded by a lower thermocline where temperatures drop rapidly, creating a density difference. Organisms sensitive to temperature or density differences may be restricted to a region above or below the thermocline, and small organisms and particles accumulate at the boundary between the two water densities, unable to penetrate into deeper, denser waters. Flakes of detritus, called marine snow, are sometimes also caught within density discontinuity layers. Density of seawater is also a function of salinity. Fresh water from rainfall, rivers, and melting ice dilutes seawater, reducing its density, whereas evaporation from the ocean surface causes salinity, and density, to increase.

Other discontinuities and boundaries result from the horizontal movement of water in the open ocean. Convergent fronts between water masses, such as the west wall of the Gulf Stream, can create very distinct barriers, separating adjacent horizontal water masses and often accumulating large and small organisms. Areas of horizontal divergence along coastlines or between adjacent great currents along the equator generate upwelling and nutrient enrichment at the sea surface. Throughout this book, we will see how such upwellings are exploited by biome communities.

Latitudinal and Longitudinal Gradients

There are two great ocean asymmetries—from polar regions to the equator and the Atlantic versus the Pacific Ocean—associated with the shape of the oceanic basins, rotation of oceanic gyres, and the persistent upwelling of nutrients (Berger 2007; Falkowski et al., 2011). Diatom blooms occur in polar regions during the Arctic and Antarctic summers but not in winter because of insufficient light and winter sea ice, shown in white in the satellite images, whereas the tropics are aseasonal, with constant light and warm surface waters. The oceans are also markedly asymmetric from east to west, with western basins containing far more species and genera than eastern basins (Longhurst and Pauly, 1987). Trade winds in the tropics blow warm surface waters to the west, producing deep thermoclines in the western Pacific and Atlantic oceans and shallow thermoclines in the eastern basins. Most upwelling is seasonal, with diatoms dominating during periods of nutrient enrichment and dinoflagellates and coccolithophores dominating during periods of reduced upwelling. Along the equatorial divergence in the eastern Pacific, the west and northeast coasts of South America, and on the west coast of Africa upwelling occurs all year long. Access to the Arctic Ocean by deep Pacific currents is inhibited by the continental shelf in the Bering Straits, whereas the far north Atlantic is open at depth to the Gulf Stream, which warms the eastern Arctic Ocean, Iceland, and northern Europe.

Survival in the Open Ocean

Terrestrial animals escape predators by hiding, burrowing, flying, and running; growing large or acting aggressive; finding safety in herds or flocks; or by becoming nocturnal, small, or dangerous (Elton, 1939). In the open ocean, there is no cover comparable to the complex topography and vegetation found on land. Single-celled phytoplankton are too small to provide vegetative cover for oceanic animals. In the water column there are no rocks or trees to offer protection, no soil for burrowing, no place to hide from predators. Yet we can categorize epipelagic oceanic animals into groupings similar to terrestrial animals on the basis of the protective system of the prey (Elton, 1939; Hamner et al. 1975; Zaret, 1975; Hamner, 1995). The epipelagic community is organized primarily by the attenuation and diurnal pattern of sunlight, and by the absence of vegetative cover, and it is shaped by predation.

However, life has adapted to this absence of cover in the pelagic biome. In 1972 we initiated a scuba-diving program in the open ocean—the "blue water" of the Florida Current off Bimini, Bahamas—to investigate the attributes of oceanic animals that help protect them from predators (Hamner, 1974; Hamner et al., 1975; Hamner, 1995). We could distinguish several groups of

ABOVE: **Ocean light zones.** The amount of light in the ocean diminishes with depth and profoundly influences species and ecosystems along the light-dark gradient.

animals having convergent attributes for protection from predators.

GELATINOUS ZOOPLANKTON. We observed and collected jellyfish, comb jellies (*ctenophores*), salps, and other taxa, which are relatively large, slow, gelatinous, transparent invertebrates. They can live near the sea surface during the day because they are invisible, protected from predators by the transparency of their tissues. Gelatinous taxa are genetically unrelated, and transparency has evolved repeatedly and independently via convergent evolution (Johnsen, 2007).

NET-ZOOPLANKTON. Blue water is also home to smaller creatures such as copepods, appendicularians, invertebrate larvae, and fish larvae that are collected only with fine-meshed nets—thus earning them the name net-zooplankton. These tiny animals are typically about 1 millimeter long, having converged on a small body size that is difficult for most vertebrate predators to see. As divers, we could rarely see them either, but they were always there when we towed a plankton net through the water. Ultimately it is this group of inconspicuous organisms that feed all the larger creatures in the sea.

SCHOOLING FISH. We also saw schools of fish while blue-water diving in the Florida Current off Bimini. These fast and silvery fishes were always uniform in size, between 2 and 20 centimeters. In the Antarctic we saw instead vast schools of krill (*Euphausia superba*) with schooling behaviors that parallel those of sardines. Schooling offers an effective defense against most pelagic predators, because these visual hunters cannot easily target and capture individual prey within the protection of the surrounding school (Hamner et al., 1983; Hamner, 1995).

NEKTON. Fish and other animals large and strong enough to move at will through the water include potentially aggressive animals like sharks, as well as tuna, dolphin fish, billfish, penguins, seals, and both toothed and baleen whales. There has been repeated and independent convergent evolution at sea for high speed, visual predators. We have seen more sharks in the open sea while diving than other large predators probably because many sharks are just curious; most are not aggressive toward blue-water divers. We did not anticipate when we began blue-water diving, however, that floating neutrally buoyant in the open sea would make us feel so vulnerable to predators.

MICRONEKTON. Diving at night, we saw nocturnal animals like krill, mid-water fishes, and small squids. The micronekton are between 2 and 10 centimeters long, often darkly pigmented, and easy to see. They are relatively fast swimmers and many engage in daily migrations through the water column, with unrelated species having very similar sizes and behaviors. During the day they hide from predators at twilight depths between 200 and 1,000 meters. When dusk falls, they swim rapidly toward the surface to feed on small zooplankton. Just before dawn they return again into deeper, darker water, completing their daily migration.

These observations of gelatinous zooplankton (Hamner et al., 1975) revealed at least three trophic levels: grazer-herbivores, primary carnivores, and secondary carnivores. One of our most unexpected findings was that large gelatinous grazers use nets and filters made of mucus to capture a broad range of sizes and types of food particles that span several trophic levels, including algae, protozoans, net-zooplankton, and detritus. Marine snails known as pteropods use mucus sheets, nets, and strands to collect, concentrate and transport food particles (Gilmer 1972, 1974; Lalli and Gilmer 1989). Other animals using mucus nets include pelagic tunicates, salps, doliolids, pyrosomes, and appendicularians (Madin 1974; Alldredge and Madin, 1982), as well as the larvae of prosobranch snails (Gilmer, unpub. obs.) and polychaete worms (Hamner et al., 1975). These strategies can produce very high rates of particle filtration, making large gelatinous animals disproportionately effective grazers in the water column.

We have learned recently (Sutherland et al., 2010) that salp mucous feeding-webs can capture a remarkably broad size-range of particulates, including submicron particles–less than 1/1000th of a millimeter. Epipelagic open ocean waters are frequently dominated by phytoplankton and bacteria that appear too small to be captured by most filter-feeding animals (Riisgård and Larsen, 2010), yet salps apparently can survive and grow on a diet exclusively of bacteria, viruses, and minute organic particles. These pelagic tunicates consume food items that are four to five orders of magnitude smaller than themselves, bypassing several entire trophic levels and producing short food chains in nutrient-poor waters where long and inefficient food webs are the norm (Sutherland et al., 2010).

This use of mucus by gelatinous grazers

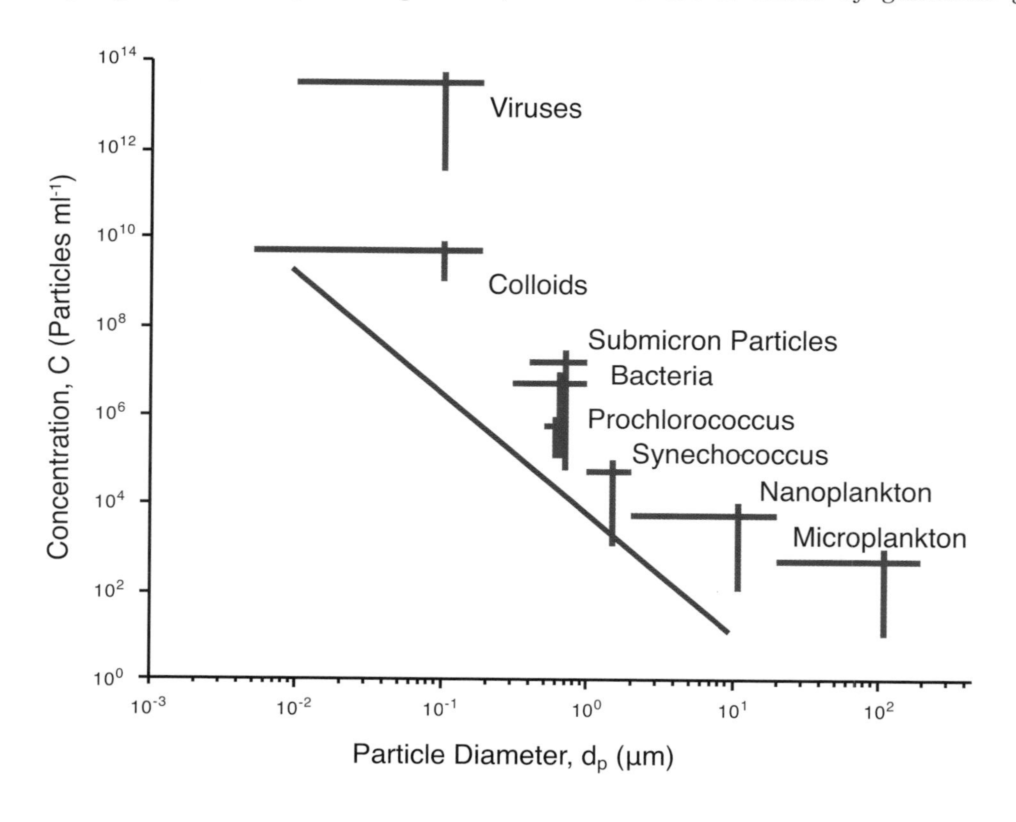

RIGHT: Size of particles in the upper ocean. The green line shows regression of microphytoplankton concentration versus cell diameter.

contributes to production of marine snow when mucous feeding structures become clogged and discarded, heavy with waste material. The resulting marine snow sinks away from surface waters (Nishizawa et al., 1954; Alldredge, 1972; Wangersky, 1974; Hamner et. al., 1975). In the thirty-five years since our initial discussion of marine snow (Hamner et al., 1975), its role in microbial metabolism, as a food resource, and a component of the ocean carbon cycle has been widely studied.

Gelatinous predators in blue water include sea jellies (medusa), siphonophores, comb jellies (ctenophores), marine snails (heteropods), sea butterflies (pteropods), and arrow worms (chaetognaths) (Hamner et al., 1975). With both specialized predators and generalists that consume many kinds of prey, the food chains in these open water biomes become tangled food webs. It is often difficult to assign a single trophic status to these animals, and it is clear that the gelatinous blue-water zooplankton is not a "dead end" to the flow of energy and materials, but a complex and often changing food web with unexpected trophic interactions, linking to both microbes and tiny particles on one hand and to large pelagic fishes like tuna on the other. Indeed, gelatinous grazers and predators can sometimes unexpectedly overwhelm entire pelagic ecosystems, such as occurred in the 1980s, when a North American ctenophore accidentally introduced via the ballast water of a ship ate all the fish larvae in the Black Sea, eliminating almost all commercial fishing in the surrounding six nations (Daskalov, 2002). Removal of top predators from the Black Sea through decades of overfishing may have left his ecosystem ripe for invasion by the jellyfish (Llope et al, 2010).

The Deep Water Column

Below the epipelagic biomes lie the largest two oceanic environments, the midwater, or mesopelagic, zone and the bathypelagic zone (Ramirez-Llodra et al, 2010). Extending to about 1000 meters in all oceans, the mesopelagic is defined by the penetration of light—not enough to support plants but adequate for animals to see. The slight day/night difference in this twilight region allows many species to migrate upward at night for feeding in surface waters and then to retreat into cover of darkness in the depths by day. Most of the animals here are bioluminescent, producing light for many purposes, including predator defense, prey attraction, and mate recognition. Without new food production at these depths, the animal communities of the midwater are composed mostly of detritivores and predators (Johnsen, 2007).

Sunlight does not penetrate below 1000 meters, and here the midwater realm gives way to the deep-sea biome, a zone of eternal darkness lacking even many bioluminescent organisms (Robison et al., 2010). This, finally, is the largest biome on earth, containing 73% of all the water in the ocean (Ramirez-Llodra et al., 2010). The deep sea is extraordinarily constant in its properties across all ocean basins and the species that live there are widely distributed, with few barriers to their distribution. So little is known of this environment that it might almost be another planet, yet it has likely existed for hundreds of millions of years much like it is today. Over the last forty years, deep-sea biologists around the world have used improved technologies to remotely view and sample these very deepest environments. Scientists are beginning to shine a light on this dark, cold, and remote realm (Hesler and Sanders, 1967; Tunnicliffe, 1992; Tyler, 1993; Van Dover, 2000; Rex and Etter, 2010).

Polar Biomes

There has been repeated and independent convergent evolution of marine mammals in response to the relatively recent evolution of diatoms and the productive biomes they support. Diatom-dominated food chains appear to have evolved at least twice, once along the continental shelves that surround the Arctic Ocean and once along the edges of the Antarctic continent via independent and convergent evolution, creating two distinctive polar versions of the diatom-dominated, short food-chain pelagic biome. During the Miocene, from 23 million years ago to 5 million years ago, pelagic cetaceans and pinnipeds radiated into many adaptive types in response to the availability of new sources of food related to global cooling, upwelling, and diatom blooms (Lipps and Mitchell, 1976; Falkowski et al., 2004; Berger, 2007; Marx and Uhen, 2010).

In the Arctic, the cetacean consumer is the bowhead whale *Balaena mysticetus*, a unique right whale in the Family Balaenidae that lives only in northern boreal waters. The bowhead feeds primarily below the sea surface, gathering copepods using its enormously long baleen in high-speed ram-filtration (Simon et al., 2009). Arctic waters and extensive northern continental shelves also provide benthic feeding areas for grey whales (*Eschrichtius robustus*), walrus (*Odobenus* spp.), belugas (*Delphinapterus leucas*), and narwhals (*Monodon monoceros*), other large marine mammals that do not occur south of the equator. Antarctic waters, in contrast, produce dense diatom blooms that are exploited by Antarctic krill, the largest of the euphausiids (Hamner et al, 1983). Antarctic krill are harvested most effectively by penguins and by eight species of rorqual whales and humpback whales in the Family Balaenopteridae, whales that engulf entire schools of krill into an enormous throat pouch, then expel the water, retaining the krill on relatively small baleen plates before swallowing.

We know now that polar diatom-dominated biomes have evolved at least twice because marine Arctic apex predators are so different from those in the Antarctic and because copepods dominate in the Arctic while euphausiids and salps dominate the Antarctic. These habitats, poles apart, are both examples of the pelagic polar biome, with evolutionary convergence among the largest creatures on earth in response to a food resource based on some of the smallest. Eventually, we also will be able to distinguish between nutrient-poor open sea biomes because the pelagic animals of the Pacific and Atlantic Oceans are markedly different and because western oceans are far richer than the corresponding fauna to the east (Longhurst and Pauly, 1987).

LEFT: Pelagic biomes cover all those ocean waters that are not near the coast or the ocean floor. Out in the nutrient-poor open ocean, as shown in this image from Antarctica, small-celled photosynthetic cyanobacteria and flagellates form the bases of long, complex food webs, invisible to the eye but critical to all life on Earth. **Photograph by Chris Linder/ iLCP**

What Biomes Mean for Marine Conservation

Each of the ocean biomes is a particular habitat type occupied by communities of organisms adapted to the physical properties and food resources of that habitat. With a new understanding of the nature of marine biomes, we are beginning to assemble a more complete picture of the structure and functioning of the diverse communities that live in the ocean, and the ways in which their component species interact with their surroundings and each other. Viewing the ocean's ecosystems as biomes is essential if we are to recognize and manage human impacts on the ocean. As we'll see in later chapters in this book, most ocean biomes around the world are under pressure from powerful anthropogenic stressors—fishing, pollution, habitat destruction, and increasingly the effects of global climate change. The biome concept provides a framework for understanding diverse ecosystems on a much broader and more general scale, improving our scientific understanding of how ocean systems work, and helping us design better ways to lighten or reverse our impacts on the life of the ocean.

RIGHT: During the first few hundred million years, the surface of our planet was extremely hot, while rampant volcanic activity spewed volatile gases into a newly forming atmosphere. A significant portion of these venting substances consisted of water vapor. This vapor formed dense clouds that rained incessantly on the Earth, where they instantly were converted back to vapor by the intense surface temperatures, as shown here in Hawai'i Volcanoes National Park.
Photograph by Art Wolfe/ Art Wolfe Stock/ iLCP

FOLLOWING SPREAD: Kingman atoll, in the Central Pacific, is one of the last "untouched" shallow water coral reef systems in the world. It also harbors the largest population of giant clams (*Tridacna maxima*) in the Central Pacific ocean. These clams have been severely depleted in most areas of the world. **Photograph by Brian Skerry/ National Geographic Stock/ iLCP**

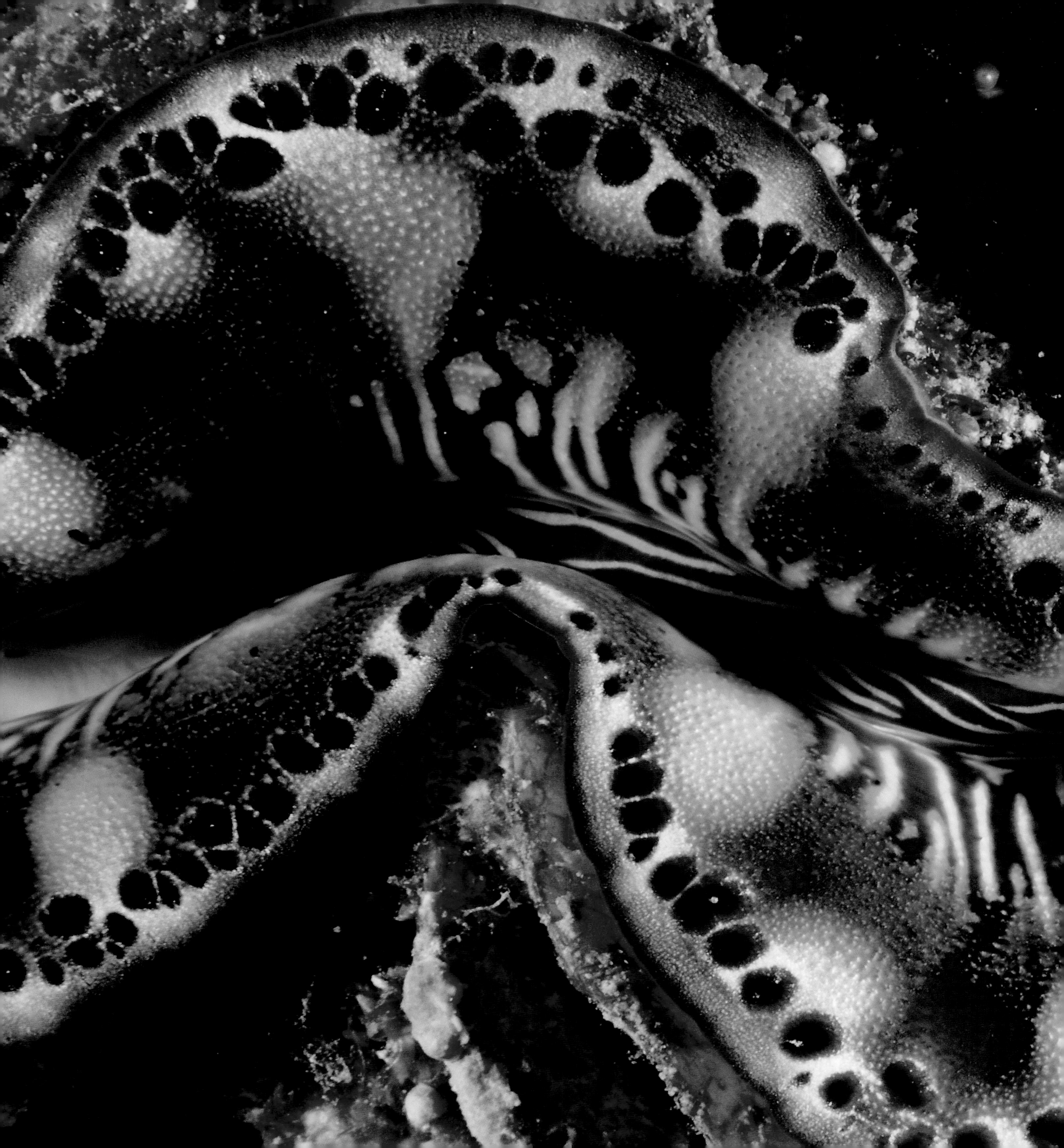

Kent E. Carpenter, Beth Polidoro, Heather Harwell,
and Jonnell Sanciangco

OCEAN BIODIVERSITY

The early formation of oceans on our planet resulted in an environment that engendered complex life forms and the foundations of Earth's biodiversity. Over 4.6 billion years ago, heat and gravitational forces transformed Earth from a ball of homogenous space dust into a dynamic sphere, with layers stratified by elemental density and inner heat. In the early days of our galaxy, orbits around our sun were more chaotic, and celestial bodies wobbled considerably before settling into a more defined path. One such planetary body, a little smaller than Earth, collided with our planet shortly after Earth's surface had formed. The heavier metallic elements from this gargantuan missile pierced the Earth's surface, reaching the molten core and being incorporated into it. The missile's lighter rocky mantle recoiled from the impact, hurtling back into space and forming an orbital ring of dense debris around the early Earth. These floating fragments eventually coalesced into the single moon that plays an important role in ocean rhythms.

During the first few hundred million years, the surface of our planet was extremely hot while rampant volcanic activity spewed volatile gases into a newly forming atmosphere. A significant portion of these venting substances consisted of water vapor. This vapor formed dense clouds that rained incessantly on the earth, where they instantly were converted back to vapor by the intense surface temperatures. The vapor simply returned to the clouds, as the surface of the earth was too hot to allow a liquid state to form. By 4.5 billion years ago, the earth cooled, water began to accumulate on the surface, and a constant rain lasted for perhaps 20 million years. Subsequent erosion of rock brought copious salts and other elements into the pooling water. Most of the ocean water on Earth today had formed by around four billion years ago, some 600 million years after our Earth formed.

The ancient oceans that covered most of our planet provided the necessary conditions for life to evolve. The thermal and physical properties of water moderate temperature and climate and allow vital elements, nutrients, and wastes to move about, combine, and dissociate in an aqueous milieu.

LEFT: The giant Australian cuttlefish (*Sepia apama*) is a solitary animal that can be found in waters up to 100m deep off the coast of Eastern and Southern Australia. This charismatic creature is also the largest of all cuttlefish, reaching up to one meter in length, and its ability to change color to match its background makes it both mysterious and endlessly fascinating. **Photograph by Michele Hall/ Howard Hall Productions**

The basic organic compounds such as simple sugars, amino acids, and nucleotides can spontaneously form in water, given energetic input in the form of light, heat, and lightning strikes. The fossil record for the very earliest life is woefully sparse, and therefore just where and how life first formed is left to speculation. All life on Earth shares the same basic energetic pathways, methods of replication, and building of organic forms, indicating that all life on Earth evolved from a single common ancestor. Furthermore, the fact that all forms of life on our planet rely on internal saline water strongly suggests that the first simple, self-replicating organisms arose in our ancient oceans.

The oldest fossils are complex bacteria-like organisms dating to around 3.5 billion years ago, although life may have formed several hundreds of millions of years earlier. Most importantly, evidence suggests

Coral reefs are often compared to rain forests in their ecosystem complexity and capacity to support life

that some of the earliest complex life forms were photosynthetic. Their prevalence in our oceans allowed Earth's atmosphere to evolve from one nearly devoid of oxygen to one able to sustain aerobic life. The earliest single-celled life forms most likely survived by consuming energy-rich organic molecules that arose spontaneously in water. The supply of these organic molecules would eventually have been depleted had life not evolved photosynthesis and the capability to form energy-rich organic molecules from inorganic molecules. Photosynthesis also allowed oxygen to accumulate in our atmosphere, which began in earnest around two billion years ago. Accumulation continued until around 400 million years ago, when gas composition reached a steady state in our atmosphere that is similar to present day. This allowed animals, the first multicellular, nonphotosynthetic organisms, to evolve around 900 million years ago. As oxygen accumulated in our atmosphere in increasing amounts, enough became available to support animals larger than those composed of a few hundred cells. These first animals were marine, since land animals did not arise until around 450 million years ago. Ancient oceans also gave rise to the most unique spike in animal diversity, the so-called Cambrian explosion, which started somewhere around 540 million years ago. This was the age of the trilobites (class Trilobita) and numerous bizarre marine animals that have long since gone extinct. However, the Cambrian explosion gave rise to all major anatomical animal designs; nearly all animal phyla arose during this time (Marshall, 2006), and all but one animal phylum has marine representatives.

After the Cambrian, marine diversity continued to increase with periods of relatively slow diversification and rare mass extinctions (Alroy et al., 2008). Five mass extinctions stand out in the fossil record (Alroy, 2008) with the largest being the Permian-Triassic extinction that occurred around 250 million years ago with losses of up to around 90% of marine species (Knoll et al., 2007; Jacobsen et al., 2009). The causes of these two massive extinctions are still debated, but massive volcanism, release of greenhouse gasses, and subsequent climatological changes and anoxia in the oceans are implicated in the environmental disruptions that brought about the extirpations (Knoll et al., 2007; Algeo et al., 2011). The most recent of the big extinction events occurred around 65 million years ago at the Cretaceous-Tertiary boundary, when nonfeathered dinosaurs became extinct. This extinction event was likely caused by a massive asteroid impact that forced dust into the atmosphere, cutting off sunlight, hindering photosynthesis, and causing climate change. In the marine realm, between 80% and 90% of species went extinct; these rates were higher for warm water coral species that relied on photosynthetic symbionts (Jablonski and Raup, 1995).

Extinctions are followed by periods of diversification, and since the Cretaceous-Tertiary mass extinction, biodiversity has increased very rapidly (Alroy et al., 2008). After the Cambrian explosion, the number of genera of marine invertebrates in the fossil record hovered below one thousand for nearly 350 million years. In the last 100 million years, this has jumped to over 2,500 genera. Examination of the magnitude and causes of the big five mass extinctions that are evident from the fossil record has led to comparisons of our current extinction crisis caused by humankind's interaction with nature (Glavin, 2007; Alroy, 2008; Carpenter et al., 2008). The human triggers of current extinctions, however, are profoundly unrelated to the geological triggers in past mass extinctions events. The study of past extinctions, therefore, does not help predict either mechanisms of change currently taking place in the biosphere or likely paths of recovery. Nevertheless, rates of recovery can be estimated from geological history. At current extinction rates, it will require approximately ten million years for marine biodiversity to recover (Alroy, 2008). However, if current rates of extinction continue to rise and eventually rival the largest Permian-Triassic extinction event, it will take around forty million years for marine biodiversity to recover.

Marine Biodiversity Today

Of the approximate 1,868,000 species that make up global described biodiversity (Reaka-Kudla, 1997) marine species comprise about 15%. Of the thirty-six total phyla found within the animal kingdom, only ten are found on land, and only one is exclusively terrestrial. By comparison, fifteen of the world's animal phlya are found only in the marine environment. Recent calculations place the total number of described marine species somewhere between 230,000 (Bouchet, 2006) and 250,000 (Goombridge and Jenkins, 2000), although synonymy and conflicting estimates of unicellular eukaryotes make pinpointing this number rather difficult. Contrary to the popular opinion that new species encounters are rare, between 1,300 and 1,500 new marine species are currently described each year (Bouchet, 2006). Indeed, taxonomy remains a very active field of research, especially within the marine realm. In fact, Bouchet (2006) estimates that at the current rate of new species descriptions, it will take anywhere from 250 to 1,000 years to complete the inventory of marine biodiversity. As a consequence, the total number of marine species (described and undescribed) is not known, and estimates span orders of magnitude, from 200,000 to more than ten million species (Grassle and Maciolek, 1992).

Although advances in information technology have made it much easier to compile and update species catalogues and produce authoritative taxonomic lists, we are still a long way from having a comprehensive global checklist of everything that lives in the oceans. Unequal coverage among taxonomic groups remains a problem. For example, the 110 described species of marine mammals have been very well studied, yet they represent less than 0.05% of the total number of known species that inhabit the oceans. The global inventory of both bony and cartilaginous marine fishes (16,475 species) is also relatively well established. On the other hand, there are an estimated 12,000 marine nematodes (phylum Nematoda) and annelid worms (phylum Annelida) and 15,000 flatworms (phylum Platyhelminthes). Together, these three invertebrate phyla make up almost 17% of all marine biodiversity (Bouchet, 2006). Unfortunately, to date there has been no comparable effort to produce a global inventory of these groups.

The most diverse phylum in the marine realm is Mollusca, which includes the world's cephalopods, gastropods, and bivalves. These 52,525 extant species (Bouchet, 2006) account for about 23% of all marine life. Coming in at a close second are the crustaceans (lobsters, crabs, shrimp, barnacles, krill, and amphipods) at 44,950 species, representing 19% of all known species in the oceans. Such groups have received moderate attention from researchers, and regional taxonomic lists are becoming increasingly common.

Microbial species richness has not been properly quantified at global scales, therefore these groups—such as bacteria and viruses—are often left out of marine biodiversity tallies. Recent studies, however, suggest that microbial diversity may be vast. Venter et al. (2004) found 1,800 distinct microbial species in only 1,500 liters of surface seawater in the Sargasso Sea. They also suggested that this was a gross underestimation of true species richness (due to the limitations of their methodology) and estimated that the actual total was on the order of 48,000 unique species. Though our methods of identifying microorganisms are constantly improving, the alpha and global diversity of prokaryotes and protists will probably remain unknown for years to come (Bouchet, 2006).

Although we may have a relatively poor grasp of absolute marine biodiversity, a great deal can be learned from spatial analyses of available data. There are three major paradigms concerning the spatial organization of marine biodiversity. Perhaps the most widely accepted is the latitudinal gradient of species richness (e.g., Gray, 1997; Roy et al., 1998), which states that species richness increases as one moves from the poles to the tropics. This idea was first formulated in the late 1960s (Sanders, 1968), based largely on small-scale studies. However, its plausibility has remained significant, particularly given that terrestrial researchers had come to similar conclusions regarding biodiversity patterns on land. Although new data representative of large scales have been collected from coastal areas in the Northern Hemisphere, validating that there is indeed a cline from the Arctic to the tropics, a similar gradient in the Southern Hemisphere has not yet been validated (Gray, 2001).

The second hypothesis put forth by Sanders (1968) was that, contrary to prevailing belief, diversity in the oceans increases with depth (at least to 2,000 m, the limit of his study). This idea was expanded upon to include a subsequent decrease in diversity with increasing distance from the continental rise toward the abyssal plain (summarized by Levinton, 1995). This idea has also been challenged, and it remains unclear whether or not the species richness of the deep sea is higher than that of coastal areas (Rex and Etter, 2010; Gray et al., 1997). This uncertainty also speaks to the large, lingering gap in our knowledge of the biology and ecology of the deep sea.

If current rates of extinction continue to rise and eventually rival the largest Permian-Triassic extinction event, it will take around forty million years for marine biodiversity to recover

The final paradigm used to explain patterns of marine biodiversity refers to a longitudinal gradient, in which species richness decreases as one moves west to east in the tropical Pacific and Atlantic. This gradient is largely due to patterns in coral reef biodiversity, which is highest in the Indo-Malay-Philippines Archipelago or Coral Triangle and decreases radially from there across the Pacific and Atlantic (Veron, 1995). The mechanism or mechanisms behind these paradigms remain hotly debated but likely include some combination of biological interactions, area, energy productivity, species ranges, and evolutionary factors (Gray, 2001).

The biggest repositories of marine biodiversity are coral reefs. Though they occupy just 0.1% of the surface of the planet, they harbor an exceptionally high number of species, including numerous reef fishes, crustaceans, sponges, hydroids, mollusks, echinoderms, and many others. Coral reefs are often compared to rain forests in their ecosystem complexity and capacity to support life (Bouchet, 2006). Reaka-Kudla (1997) estimated that coral reef biodiversity amounts to about 93,000 described species, or almost 34% of all marine life. She also suggested that coral reefs contain a very high number of undocumented species, concluding that the true number of species on global coral reefs is at least 950,000. Indeed, tropical waters remain relatively understudied, particularly compared to the temperate waters of the Northern Hemisphere.

Though much remains to be discovered in the tropics, even less is known about the deep sea, which some argue may rival the biodiversity

ABOVE TOP: Sea anemones are a widely distributed group of animals that are related to corals. Here, the fleshy green tentacles of a colony of anemones in Namena Marine Reserve off the coast of Fiji are seen feeding on zooplankton at night. **Photograph by Keith Ellenbogen/ iLCP**

ABOVE BOTTOM: "A face only a mother could love" is how some have described wolf eels (*Anarrhichthys ocellatus*). A common denizen of rocky reefs and stony bottoms throughout the northern Pacific, these fish are popular with divers. This large specimen, photographed in Browning Pass, Vancouver Island, British Columbia, had a head the size of a volleyball.
Photograph by Paul Nicklen/ National Geographic Stock/ iLCP

LEFT: Skimming the surface off the coast of the island of Holbox in the northern Yucatán peninsula, a whale shark (*Rincodon typus*) filter-feeds on fish spawn and other planktonic creatures. This gentle and harmless shark has become the main attraction for a fast-expanding tourism industry in the region. **Photograph by Brian Skerry/ iLCP**

ABOVE: Sponges, like this elephant ear sponge (*Lanthella basta*) photographed in Raja Ampat, West Papua, Indonesia, are an important component of the benthic community, especially on coral reefs.
Photograph by Jürgen Freund / iLCP

ABOVE: A pink dorid nudibranch (*Chromodoris bullocki*) or sea slug, photographed off Bali, Indonesia.
Photograph by Gary Bell/ Oceanwide Images

of coral reefs. The harsh conditions of the deep, first thought to preclude life, are now considered to provide a very stable environment that promotes highly specialized species that are able to coexist despite their limited resources. Estimates of deep-sea diversity are surrounded by uncertainty and remain controversial. However, the sheer expanse of deep ocean bottom, coupled with studies showing high species richness in some areas (e.g., Rex and Etter, 2010; Grassle and Maciolek, 1992), suggests that both hard and soft substrate communities of the deep sea may indeed contain very high diversity.

There are other marine ecosystems besides coral reefs that support high numbers of species. Shellfish reefs are often considered the temperate analog of coral reefs, providing habitat for numerous species not found elsewhere. Seagrass beds, kelp forests, mangroves, and salt marshes also boast high species richness, and often serve as nursery grounds for the next generation of marine life. Although often overlooked, soft sediment benthic communities can also be extremely diverse.

The Center of Marine Biodiversity

A hotspot is defined as an area of relatively restricted geographic range that contains an extraordinarily high concentration of biodiversity and endemism. The first authors to apply this concept to the marine realm found eighteen hotspots, based on the distribution patterns of 1,700 reef fishes, 804 coral species, 662 mollusks, and 69 species of lobster (Roberts et al., 2002). These areas ranged in size from Easter Island (164 sq km) to the entire Great Barrier Reef of Australia. Though the methodology has since been modified, the identification of marine hotspots remains an integral part of conservation efforts around the globe.

No place on the planet contains more marine species than the Coral Triangle, a region that extends from central Indonesia to Papua New Guinea and the Solomon Islands northward to the Philippines (Allen and Werner, 2002; Briggs, 2005). For example, the Coral Triangle has 605 species of zooxanthellate corals, which amounts to 76% of the world's species complement (Veron et al., 2009). The potential mechanisms behind this epicenter of marine life are complex and include factors such as the geological setting, physical environment, and numerous ecological processes. Within this hotspot, Carpenter and Springer (2005) have identified the central Philippines as the "center of the center" for fish diversity, based on Geographic Information System (GIS) mapping overlays for 2,983 marine organisms, including 2,047 shore fishes. Allen (2007) has since corroborated this. Unfortunately, this part of Southeast Asia is also among the most threatened marine regions of the world. The extremely high density of human inhabitants and consequent effects of overfishing and careless land use make the species inhabiting the Coral Triangle vulnerable to heightened extinction risk (Allen, 2007). With current extinction rates climbing far above background levels, the possibility of species going extinct before they have even been described is very real.

Current Rates of Extinction

As the human population continues to grow, we are placing more and more pressure on marine species and ecosystems. It has been estimated that no area of the ocean is free from current human impact and influence (Halpern et al., 2008). There is growing concern that a broad range of marine species could be under increased threat of extinction and that marine biodiversity is experiencing potentially irreversible loss (Roberts and Hawkins, 1999; Dulvy et al., 2003; Jackson et al., 2006) due to a number of direct and indirect anthropogenic impacts. These impacts include pollution, overexploitation of fish and marine invertebrates, climate change effects, invasive species, coastal development, and habitat loss (Cheung et al., 2009; Halpern et al., 2008; Lotze et al., 2006; Myers and Worm et al., 2003).

Current extinction rates for marine species are largely unknown, but are likely accelerating. Over recent decades, pressures on biodiversity have shown increasing trends (Butchart et al., 2010). The Global Marine Species Assessment (GMSA), a joint initiative of the Species Survival Commission of the International Union for the Conservation of Nature (IUCN) and Conservation International, has been working since 2005 to determine the extinction risk of thousands of key species, including marine fish, mammals, primary habitat producers, and selected invertebrates. Although assessments are ongoing, almost ten thousand species have been assessed based on IUCN Red List methodology (IUCN, 2001) as of 2010. Of these, approximately 15% were determined to have an elevated risk of extinction as they appeared as Critically Endangered, Endangered, or Vulnerable on the IUCN Red List of Threatened Species (IUCN, 2010). Almost one-third (28%) of assessed marine species are listed as Data Deficient. Many of these species may also be at elevated risk of extinction, but more data is needed to adequately determine just how threatened these populations are.

It is clear that some marine groups are more threatened than others. One in four species of the world's primary habitat producers, such as reef-building corals, mangroves, and seagrasses, are at elevated risk of extinction. Of the 845 species of reef-building corals, over 27% are in threatened categories, primarily due to increased bleaching and diseases driven by elevated sea surface temperatures, and exacerbated by a number of local anthropogenic disturbances (Carpenter et al., 2008). Of the seventy species of mangroves, 16% are at elevated risk of extinction as mangrove areas are cleared for coastal development and aquaculture and logged for timber and fuel production (Polidoro et al., 2010). Seagrass habitat is declining worldwide, primarily due to poor water quality associated with coastal development, pollution, and aquaculture (Short et al., 2011). Of the seventy-two species of seagrass, 14% are now at elevated risk of extinction. The loss of these species, and the habitats they collectively provide, will have serious repercussions for marine biodiversity as well as for the human populations that depend upon their resources.

In general, longer-lived marine taxa that reproduce slowly are at higher risk of extinction. Their populations recover slowly from the significant population declines caused by repeated impacts. Six of the seven species of marine turtles are at elevated risk of extinction.

ABOVE: Sea turtles, like this green sea turtle (*Chelonia mydas*), can be found in all oceans except for the polar regions. **Photograph by Jürgen Freund/ iLCP**

ABOVE: The sabellids are commonly known as "fanworms" or "feather duster" worms due to a colorful appearance of a tentacular branchial crown. The large fanworms never leave their tubes and are associated with shallow water, but smaller ones are able to move around and are common in deep seas.
Photograph by Octavio Aburto/ iLCP

FOLLOWING SPREAD: Scalloped hammerhead sharks (*Sphyrna lewini*) schooling in current with Barberfishes (*Heniochus nigrirostris*), Cocos Island, Costa Rica, Pacific Ocean.
Photograph by Avi Klapfer/ Jeff Rotman Photography

Protection of our declining marine species is one of the greatest challenges we face as stewards of our planet. The preservation and protection of our ocean resources, not only for the marine species they contain, but also for the food, products, and ecosystem services that they provide for billions of people around the globe, is an urgent priority

Their life history characteristics, particularly late sexual maturity and long juvenile stage, combined with the many threats from human activities in the sea and on land, contribute to their high risk. Sea turtles face threats around the globe and at all stages of their life cycle (Eckert, 1995). Marine turtles lay their eggs on beaches, which are subject to coastal development, sand mining, and other threats. The eggs and hatchlings are threatened by pollution and predation by introduced predators such as pigs and dogs, as well as collection by humans. At sea, marine turtles are faced with threats from targeted capture in small-scale subsistence fisheries, bycatch by long-line and trawling fishing boats, entanglement in marine debris, and boat strikes. Global climate change is now considered to be a serious, if not entirely understood, threat that is possibly skewing sex ratios (Hawkes et al., 2007) and contributing to the loss of nesting beaches (Fish et al., 2005) and foraging grounds (Chaloupka et al., 2008).

Almost one-third of the world's marine mammals are at elevated risk of extinction (Polidoro et al., 2009, Schipper et al., 2008). Marine mammals around the globe are threatened by accidental mortality from entanglement in fishing gear, by the effects of noise pollution from military and seismic sonar, and by boat strikes (Schipper et al., 2008; Reynolds et al., 2005). In many regions, marine mammals are also affected by habitat loss from coastal development and loss of prey or other food sources due to overfishing. Some still are recovering to historical levels after centuries of hunting; others are hunted still (Polidoro et al., 2009). Two marine mammals have already gone extinct in the recent past from relentless hunting and exploitation: Steller's sea cow (*Hydrodamalis gigas*) by 1768 and the Caribbean monk seal (*Monachus tropicalis*) by 2008.

The two most significant impacts on marine fishes are overfishing and habitat loss (Jackson et al., 2006; Dulvy et al., 2003). Approximately 17% of the world's 1,045 species of sharks and rays are at elevated risk of extinction primarily due to their capture in nets, both as the targeted species and as bycatch. Most shark species grow slowly, mature late, produce few young, and have low rates of population increase, making them highly vulnerable to depletion, and with a low capacity for recovery from overexploitation, such as the practice of shark finning (Stevens et al., 2000; Dulvy et al., 2008; Camhi et al., 2009). Shark fisheries have proliferated around the world during recent decades, and millions of sharks are caught each year for their fins—which are used to make the Asian delicacy, shark fin soup.

At least 13% of the world's 161 grouper species are now at elevated risk of extinction. Major threats from overfishing include targeting of spawning aggregations and uncontrolled fishing throughout the entire range of the species during the life span, from small juveniles to adults. For example, in Southeast Asia juveniles are sometimes the major fishery targets, as they are taken at sub-market size and grown-out in captivity until they reach market size.

Marine fishes that have higher turnover rates, such as blennies (suborder Blennioidei) or gobies (family Gobiidae), or those that are habitat generalists such as some species of butterflyfish (family Chaetodontidae) or angelfish (family Pomacanthidae), may have relatively lower rates of extinction. Currently, it is estimated that less than 5% of these species are at elevated risk of extinction (IUCN, 2010). However, these smaller-bodied fishes are not immune to extinction, especially those that have very small ranges and that are impacted by significant threats (Hawkins et al., 2000).

A Way Forward

Protection of our declining marine species is one of the greatest challenges we face as stewards of our planet. The preservation and protection of our ocean resources, not only for the marine species they contain, but also for the food, products, and ecosystem services that they provide for billions of people around the globe, is an urgent priority. The development of sustainable fisheries, including the elimination of harmful fishing or harvesting practices, the enforcement of current fishery regulations, and implementation of improved fishery technology, are essential to reduce the risk of extinction of marine species. We need to direct our efforts to reducing pollution and destructive development of coastal areas. The need to slow or reverse global climate change is becoming more important to protect our planet's resources and quality of life, not only for the survival of the plants and animals living in the ocean, but for those that live on land or in freshwater as well. The continued assessment of the status of marine species is essential for monitoring the impact of threats to the ocean's health and survival. As the largest biome on the planet, the state of the world's oceans and marine species will undoubtedly impact the fate of global biodiversity and humankind.

RIGHT: The banggai cardinal fish (*Pterapogon kauderni*) is commonly found in the shallow waters of sheltered lagoons and bays. This species is often seen seeking shelter between the spines of sea urchins but also among anemones, corals, stony hydrozoans, rocks, and even artificial structures such as jetties. **Photograph by Michael Aw/ iLCP**

FOLLOWING SPREAD: Regrettably, bluefin tuna (*Thunnus thynnus*), like the captive one seen here in an aquaculture pen, is better known as a sushi delicacy than an awe-inspiring, free-swimming ocean predator. One of the largest, fastest, and most beautiful of fish in the ocean, the bluefin tuna can weigh 454 kilograms and race across the ocean at speeds of up to 80 kilometers per hour.
Photograph by Solvin Zankl/ Wild Wonders of Europe

Roderic Mast, Michael Farrior, Arlo Hemphill, Scott Henderson, Brian Hutchinson, Olivier Langrand, Russell A. Mittermeier, and Bryan Wallace

MARINE FLAGSHIP SPECIES

A flagship is a symbol, named after the lead vessel in a sailing armada—typically the largest, fastest, or grandest ship of the flotilla—that flies the standard of its land of origin. Flagship species are iconic representatives of their ecosystems, distinguishing them from keystone species—those taxa that scientists believe play a disproportionately large ecological role relative to their abundance—and other such ecological monikers such as indicator, icon, umbrella, or sentinel species, apex predators, or "species of conservation concern." Flagship species are those charismatic creatures that capture human attention, pique our curiosity, and appeal to what E. O. Wilson calls *biophilia*, our "innate tendency to focus on life" (Wilson, 1984). The main value of flagship species is as centerpieces for facilitating communications and telling stories about conservation that can help to change the way people think and behave in their relationships to the natural world around them.

The ocean is the crucible of life on Earth, home to vast numbers of plants, animals, and microorganisms, with new taxa being described daily and countless millions still awaiting discovery (see Carpenter et al., this volume). Interrelated species, ecological processes, and abiotic factors combine in a vast tapestry to make the ocean an unfathomably complex whole. All species are important to the integrity of this fabric of life, and the removal of a single thread can begin to unravel the whole tapestry in ways scientists are only beginning to understand. We now know with certainty that humankind has adversely affected the world's oceans, and that limiting what we put in to and take out of the seas is of the utmost importance to avert untold species loss in the future, including potentially our own species. We must change human behavior to reverse our negative impacts on the ocean. This is the message, the standard that must be borne high as we move into the future.

Pandas, tigers, and great apes have been the flagship species of tropical forests for fifty years of conservation awareness efforts. They have served as the mascots of action campaigns that have changed the course of conservation history on land. In similar fashion, marine flagship species, some of

LEFT: Leatherback sea turtles (*Dermochelys coriacea*) one of the world's largest living reptiles, begin their lives on land. This hatchling, photographed as it makes its first trip to the ocean in Las Baulas National Park in Costa Rica, will go on to make epic migrations from its foraging grounds to its breeding grounds. Males will never leave the water again, but females will return to the beach where they were born to lay their eggs. **Photograph by Jason Bradley/ Bradley Photographic**

which are described herein, can help leverage social change by communicating the beauty, magnificence, and fragility of our seas, and by conveying the complex issues of ocean health to human societies that must take immediate actions, individually and collectively, to save the oceans.

Marine Mammals

Among the most captivating and charismatic species in the ocean, marine mammals have been used widely and effectively as flagship species in conservation campaigns for decades. The seals, sea lions, and walruses (pinnipeds in the families Phocidae, Otaridae, and Odobenidae), whales and dolphins (order Cetacea), dugongs and manatees (order Sirenia), the sea otter (*Enhydra lutris*), and the polar bear (*Ursus maritimus*) are among the best known.

At the forefront of public popularity are the cetaceans—the whales, dolphins, and porpoises. In North America, names such as Flipper, Shamu, and Willy need no explanation. These popular dolphins and orcas of television, theme park, and movie fame have become true pop-culture icons. Likewise, the highly successful Greenpeace "Save the Whales" campaign of the 1970s burned both the cetaceans and their real-world plight into the cultural memory of the West. Thirty-five years after this campaign began, the love affair between the popular media and cetaceans shows no sign of decline. In fact, in 2010, the feature film "The Cove," a story of a brutal dolphin hunt near Taijii, Japan, won the Oscar for best documentary at the Academy Awards.

Recognized for their beauty, grace, and intelligence, cetaceans are a diverse group of eighty-two species of whales and dolphins. Among these, the blue whale (*Balaenoptera musculus*) is the largest animal to ever exist, reaching lengths of thirty-three meters and weighing over one hundred tons. On the other end of the size spectrum is the vaquita (*Phocoena sinus*). This Critically Endangered porpoise measures 1.5 meters and weighs 50 kilograms; fewer than two hundred individuals remain, their range limited to the northern Gulf of California. Threatened primarily by accidental capture in fisheries, the vaquita became the flagship species for numerous campaigns that resulted in UNESCO declaring the upper Gulf of California a Biosphere Reserve in 1993. The similarly diminutive baiji (*Lipotes vexillifer*) was once the flagship for conservation efforts in China's Yangtze River, but has not been seen since 2004. Now considered functionally extinct, it has thus become a sobering symbol of the reality of major vertebrate extinctions in the twenty-first century.

Another well-loved group of marine mammals is the pinnipeds, which consists of thirty-three living species. Once seen as endearingly playful circus performers, they are now acknowledged as powerful oceanic predators, deep divers, and as the favored food of South Africa's great white sharks. As flagship species, they have played a powerful role. Harp seals (*Pagophilus groenlandicus*), found in the northern Atlantic and Arctic Oceans, have a spectacular white coat for the first fifteen days of life; these pelts were highly prized by furriers, and the harp seal pups were subject to a controversial hunt in Canada that was outlawed in 1987. The hunt is now closely regulated by the Canadian government and no longer poses a threat to the survival of the species (Lavigne, 2009).

There are three species of monk seal in the genus *Monachus*, one extinct and two rare species whose numbers are dangerously low. The last verified sighting of the Caribbean species (*M. tropicalis*) was in 1952, and in 2008 it was officially listed as extinct by the US government (Kovacs, 2008). The Mediterranean monk seal (*M. monachus*), with fewer than six hundred remaining individuals, is Earth's second rarest pinniped following the Saimaa ringed seal (*Pusa hispida saimensis*) and one of the most endangered mammals in the world. And the Hawaiian monk seal (*M. schauinslandi*) is considered Critically Endangered, with just over one thousand individuals remaining (NMFS, 2010).

Similar in appearance to the pinnipeds but more closely related to elephants are the sirenians, which are represented by four species of dugongs and manatees, all considered threatened with extinction (IUCN, 2010). Sirenians are herbivores that graze on rich expanses of seagrass in coastal estuaries, swamps, rivers, and coastal marine waters. The largest known sirenian of recent times was the Steller's sea cow (*Hydrodamalis gigas*), which grew to nine meters in length and possibly up to ten tons in weight. This gentle giant from the northern Pacific was extinct by 1768, just twenty-seven years after its discovery by European explorers. It too remains one of our most powerful reminders of the reality of extinction and serves as a clarion call to protect its extant cousins, particularly the closely related dugong (*Dugong dugon*) and the three species of manatee, the South American (*Trichechus inunguis*), the West African (*T. senegalensis*), and the West Indian (*T. manatus*), all of which face a variety of anthropogenic hazards, from boat-strikes to hunting to habitat loss and alteration. Such stressors have prompted the IUCN to give all four species a ranking of Vulnerable (IUCN, 2010).

The polar bear (*Ursus maritimus*) has emerged as one of the leading flagship marine species of the twenty-first century, having become synonymous with climate change in the face of disappearing Arctic ice floes. In 2011, members of the U.S. Geological Survey observed a polar bear that swam for nine days across the Beaufort Sea before reaching an ice floe 686 kilometers offshore (Durner et al., 2011). The bear lost 22% of her body weight and the life of her year-old cub in the epic swim, made necessary by disappearing ice floes that normally would have provided places to rest and platforms from which to hunt. As Arctic ice continues to decrease due to climate change, polar bears will face increasing challenges to their survival.

Another iconic marine species is the playful sea otter (*Enhydra lutris*) of the northern and eastern North Pacific Ocean. Throughout the eighteenth and nineteenth centuries, these animals were hunted relentlessly for their valuable fur, the densest in the animal kingdom. Their populations crashed from between 150,000 (Kenyon, 1969) to 300,000 individuals (Johnson, 1982) in the mid-1700s to fewer than 2,000 by the early 1900s (Kenyon, 1969), and by the turn of the last century experts believed they would certainly go extinct. In 1911 they were formally protected and since have recovered two-thirds of their former range, representing one

ABOVE: A female polar bear (*Ursus maritimus*) and her two cubs stand along basalt shores of Spitsbergen, Norway. Cubs this young are not yet expert swimmers and cannot remain in the cold water for long periods of time. The Svalbard archipelago has many glaciers, and bears can swim out to claim a platform of drifting glacier ice from which to grab an unsuspecting seal. However, due to rapid climate change, glaciers are rapidly receding and such ice islands are becoming fewer.
Photograph by Paul Nicklen/ iLCP

Flagship species are those charismatic creatures that capture human attention, pique our curiosity, and appeal to what E. O. Wilson calls biophilia, our "innate tendency to focus on life"

ABOVE: A female mako shark (*Isurus oxyrinchus*) is being definned at a shark fishing camp in Santa Rosalia, Gulf of California, Mexico. Sharks are killed worldwide, in part driven by the high price paid for shark fins on the Asian market. **Photograph by Brian Skerry/ National Geographic Stock/ iLCP**

of the greatest success stories in marine conservation. Less successful and lesser known is the distantly related marine otter (*Lontra felina*) of which fewer than 1,000 may survive today (Alvarez and Medina-Vogel, 2008).

Sea Turtles

The seven species of sea turtles found throughout the world's tropical and temperate oceans are among the most charismatic of marine species. Since their first appearance on Earth some 110 million years ago, they have weathered drastic changes in climate, shifting continents, even surviving the dramatic events that left the dinosaurs extinct. Yet today, the fate of these great evolutionary survivors hangs in the balance. Six of the seven species are ranked within the Endangered categories of the IUCN Red List, and they face the growing hazards of postindustrial human society: bycatch and entanglement in fishing gear; habitat loss due to beachfront development; pollution in the form of plastics that they ingest; hunting and poaching of adult turtles and their eggs for food, tortoiseshell trinkets, and the trade in aphrodisiacs. Moreover, global climate change remains a potent specter, threatening to raise sea levels and reduce nesting habitat. Global warming may even skew the natural sex ratios of these reptiles, whose sex is determined by the temperature at which their eggs incubate. New threats include diseases such as papillomatosis, caused by a widespread and potentially lethal virus not seen in sea turtles before the 1960s.

Sea turtles are found in nearly all ocean niches from near-shore habitats, seagrass pastures, and coral reefs where they forage and feed, to the open ocean, which they traverse in epic transoceanic migrations, and even the abyssal zones. Yet these consummate marine animals also remain tied to the land, since females must emerge to lay their eggs on tropical beaches.

The standout sea turtle is the leatherback (*Dermochelys coriacea*), the largest of all extant turtles, with specimens on record measuring more than three meters in length and weighing up to nine hundred kilograms. It achieves this heft feeding exclusively on jellyfish, an organism that is mostly water. Leatherbacks can make several dives each day to depths of over half a kilometer, where the extreme pressure, cold, and darkness preclude all but the most highly specialized life forms. Unlike most reptiles, leatherbacks can even maintain body temperatures higher than their surroundings, thus allowing them to ply cold waters where they search for their gelatinous prey. Sadly, leatherbacks have declined severely in the Pacific in recent decades (Spotila et al., 1996), due mostly to decades of egg harvest, the loss of eggs and hatchlings to introduced species such as dogs and pigs, and the loss of thousands of animals to fisheries bycatch.

One of the most compelling and primeval wildlife spectacles on the planet is the synchronous mass nesting of hundreds of thousands of olive ridley turtles (*Lepidochelys olivacea*) that occurs on a few remote beaches in Mexico, Costa Rica, and India (Mast and Rhodin, 2003). During these mass gatherings (called *arribadas*, from the Spanish for arrival), as many as 800,000 females emerge onto the beach to nest. This would be a daunting number for any predator except Man. Humans nearly extirpated the Kemp's ridley (*L. kempii*), another species in the same genus, in the Mexican state of Tamaulipas between the 1940s and the 1960s. After years of concerted effort by the Mexican and United States governments and nongovernmental institutions, populations of this Critically Endangered species finally appear to be on a gradual rebound (SWOT Report Vol. V, 2010).

Sharks and Their Relatives

Few other animals on land or sea evoke such a wide range of human emotions as sharks, from primordial fear to fascination and awe. We fear them as man-eaters, yet simultaneously we admire them for their majestic beauty, intriguing evolutionary history, and impressive biological adaptations.

The chondrichthyans—sharks, rays, skates, chimaeras, guitarfishes, and sawfishes—lack a bony skeleton. These cartilaginous fishes have occupied myriad ecological roles in ocean habitats for more than 400 million years. The many species of sharks—440 and counting—range from top predators on reefs and in the open sea to harmless bottom-dwellers. They range in size from the tiny **eight-inch-long** dwarf lanternshark (*Etmopterus perry*), to the whale shark (*Rhincodon typus*), the world's largest fish, reaching more than twelve meters. Sharks inhabit latitudes from the tropics to the polar regions, and they occupy the full spectrum of marine habitats from coastal to oceanic biomes. They fill unique and important ecological niches that make them critical for the healthy functioning of ecosystems (Ferretti et al., 2010). Moreover, like other long-lived marine megafauna, sharks are slow to reach maturity and reproduce (Schindler et al.; 2002; Calliet et al., 2005). These traits mean that shark populations grow slowly, are highly susceptible to pervasive human threats, and are slow to recover from population collapses (Field et al., 2009).

Stories about sharks abound in countless film, television, and popular media pieces, and the chance to experience sharks firsthand has become a sought-after attraction for scuba divers, generating millions of dollars in ecotourism revenue annually. Without a doubt, the most famous shark is the great white (*Carcharadon carcharias*), the inspiration for Peter Benchley's novel *Jaws* and the movies that followed. The great white is now the centerpiece of the cage-diving tourism industry in South Africa, Australia, and Guadaloupe Island, Mexico. Certainly one of the most spectacular marine wildlife phenomena is the sight of hundreds of scalloped hammerhead sharks (*Sphyrna lewini*) schooling in the eastern Pacific (Cocos, Galápagos, and Revillagigedo Islands), Australia, southern Africa, the Red Sea, and elsewhere (Mittermeier and Earle, 2003). More recent media stars among sharks include walking epaulette sharks of the genus *Hemiscyllium*. These small, highly specialized, bottom-dwelling sharks have adapted to life in low-oxygen tide pools. Rather than swimming, they wiggle their bodies from side to side and push off the bottom in a salamander-like gait using their paired fins as "feet." In 2008, scientists from Conservation International (CI) described two new species of epaulette shark from the Raja Ampat Archipelago, off the northwest tip of the island of New Guinea, considered the heart of the Coral Triangle and the global epicenter of marine biodiversity. The story of the walking sharks generated considerable media attention and a rash of online videos and stories that were viewed by millions. The scientific naming rights for one of these animals was auctioned at a charity fundraiser hosted by CI and HSH Prince Albert II of Monaco, raising a substantial sum that was used to help conserve the animal's habitat. The discovery of such a conspicuous animal as a shark, not to mention that there have been relatively recent discoveries of whales, underscores how little is known of marine species in general and how much remains to be learned of the countless millions of less conspicuous creatures.

Alarmingly, unsustainable exploitation by large- and small-scale fishing activities currently threatens numerous shark species with extinction. More than 30% of chondrichthyan (cartilaginous fish) species are Near Threatened or Threatened, with another 40% classified as Data Deficient, meaning that we simply don't have enough information to assess their status (Ferretti et al., 2010). One of the gravest hazards to their survival is shark-finning for shark-fin soup, a high-value Asian delicacy. This practice, which consists of slicing off a shark's fins and often discarding the shark itself, is believed to account for as much as a third of the targeted capture of sharks on a global scale—as many as 73 million sharks per year (Clarke et al., 2006). Combined with the bycatch of sharks in fishing gear and fisheries targeting sharks for meat, skin, and other products, this makes for unsustainable human pressure on several global populations.

ABOVE: The giant Pacific octopus (*Octopus doeflini*) is the second largest octopus in the world. With highly complex eyes that compare to human visual acuity and suckers that are also highly sensitive, these intelligent creatures have no problem discerning the world around them. **Photograph by Stuart Westmorland**

ABOVE: Manta rays (*Manta alfredi*) and bait fish in a feeding frenzy in the Hanifaru Marine Reserve, Maldives. **Photograph by Thomas P. Peschak/ iLCP**

FOLLOWING SPREAD: A couple of purple stars (*Pisaster ochraceus*) lie in the shallow water during low tide in the coastal waters of the Great Bear Rainforest, Canada. **Photograph by Thomas P. Peschak/ iLCP**

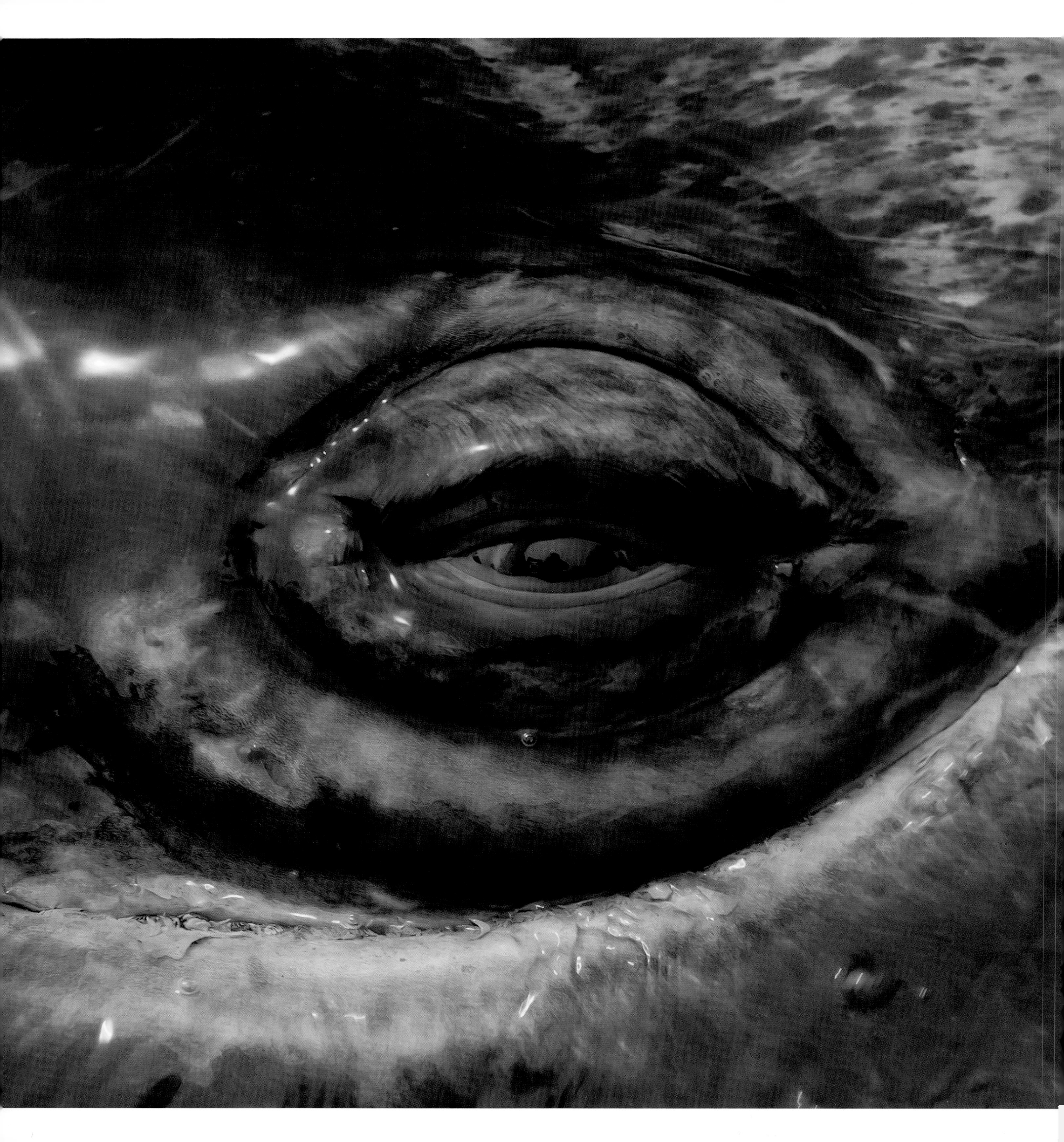

Tuna and Billfish

One of the most recognizable flagships for marine life as a whole is improbably a cartoon tuna fish. Charlie the Tuna, the advertising mascot for Starkist brand canned tuna, celebrated his fiftieth anniversary in 2011. Charlie's lifelong ambition was to be hooked and served as a "tuna of good taste," a fate that befalls six million tons of his kind each year, underwriting a US$6.4 billion a year industry (FAO, 2007) that accounts for 12% of the value of all marine fisheries (ISSF, 2010).

Regrettably, tuna is better known as a canned food staple than an awe-inspiring, free-swimming ocean predator that can weigh in at over 454 kilograms and race across the ocean at speeds of up to 80 kilometers per hour. Of the forty-eight species of tuna (family Scombridae), the skipjack (*Katsuwonus pelamis*), yellow fin (*Thunnus albacores*), bigeye (*Thunnus obesus*), and albacore (*Thunnus alalunga*) are the most commercially valuable. Of these, none can rival the economic value of the increasingly rare Atlantic bluefin tuna (*Thunnus thynnus*). In January 2011, a bluefin tuna sold at Tokyo's Tsukiji fish market for more than US$350,000. Such astronomic market value creates a powerful incentive for commercial vessels to track down the last individuals of dwindling, overfished stocks.

Like tuna, billfish are predators of the open ocean; although they tend to concentrate in certain areas, they do not school. Along with ten other species distributed across three genera, marlins are the holy grail of a burgeoning and multibillion-dollar sport fishing industry around the world, mainly based on the catch-and-release model.

The broadbill swordfish (*Xiphias gladius*), known as the "gladiator of the sea" for its long, wide, lance-like bill, inhabits depths to nearly one thousand meters (500 fathoms) within tropical and temperate waters around the world. The swordfish uses its large eyes to hunt in the murky depths and the broad bill to stun its prey. Catching a swordfish is the epitome of saltwater angling to many, and the world's record for a swordfish landed by rod and reel stands at 536 kilograms. Commercial fishing, which uses high-tech tools like GPS tracking and fish-finders, is putting increased pressure on billfish stocks as, like tuna, they are prized as a food fish as well.

Sailfish, of which there are two species in the genus *Istiophorus*, are distributed globally across tropical and temperate seas. These athletic fish win the gold medal of ocean sprinting, and can reach astounding speeds of one hundred kilometers per hour. That speed allows these three-meter-long fish to propel themselves out of the water in spectacular leaps. The sail, a greatly modified erectile dorsal fin, serves multiple functions, providing stabilization when swimming at high speeds and making this relatively slim fish look much larger to potential predators. The sailfish has even been observed using its sail like a matador's cape to herd prey fish into dense aggregations, making them easier to attack.

Sea Birds

Penguins, albatrosses, shearwaters, and petrels, along with some species of gulls and terns, are true marine pelagics, spending only a small fraction of their lives on the land. Much like sea turtles, pinnipeds, and horseshoe crabs, their link to the terrestrial world is typically limited only to a brief breeding season. The rest of their lives is spent far from land, cruising above and across the oceans of the world. Seabirds like the albatrosses, the Arctic tern (*Sterna paradisaea*), and the Wilson's storm-petrel (*Oceanites oceanicus*) are probably the greatest wanderers of all creatures. Their migrations are legendary, beating out the peregrinations of any land animals, and even those of the leatherback turtle and the great whales.

Among the most charismatic and universally loved and recognized seabirds are the seventeen penguin species (family *Spheniscidae*), all ideally suited for a marine existence. Their wings have evolved into flippers for swift propulsion under water, they boast thick fat for insulation, and dine exclusively on fish. Scientists know little of their lives at sea and indeed, penguins are seldom even seen at sea; when they do rest at the surface of the ocean, only their cryptically colored head and back are exposed, and they tend to dive rapidly when sighted (Harrison, P. 1996). The tallest and heaviest, and perhaps best known of all penguins—thanks in part to Luc Jacquet's 2005 Academy Award-winning film *La Marche de l'Empereur* (*March of the Penguins*), is the emperor penguin (*Aptenodytes forsteri*). Endemic to Antarctica, this elegant giant is famous for its mind-bogglingly long breeding trek of up to one hundred kilometers across the ice to form breeding colonies. The male and female take turns caring for their single egg and the subsequent chick against what appear to be insurmountable odds.

Of the twenty-two albatross species currently recognized, most breed in the sub-Antarctic and Antarctic territories, except for the four species restricted to the northern Pacific (IUCN, 2010). Albatrosses can use the wind to cover great distances while expending very little energy, using dynamic soaring and slope soaring, angling their wings and their flight path to best use the variation in air speed and direction near the wave tops (Dotson and Hyrenbach, 2001). This mastery of the wind allows them to cover vast areas in search of food. Modern telemetric devices have allowed researchers to learn that, when gliding with a favorable wind, the energy spent by an albatross in flight is equal to the energy spent by the same bird resting. Albatrosses also have a unique shoulder-locking tendon that allows them to maintain their wings fully stretched for flight without expending muscular energy. Laysan albatrosses (*Phoebastria immutabilis*), found in the Hawaiian islands, typically spend the first three to five years of their life in constant flight, never touching land, and they are believed to sleep while aloft!

LEFT: A gray whale calf (*Eschrichtius robustus*) makes eye contact with the photographer in the San Ignacio Lagoon, a place best known as the winter home to this once-endangered whale. Every year gray whales migrate over 10,000 miles between their summer feeding grounds above the Arctic Circle and the coastal waters of Baja California to have their calves. **Photograph by Ralph Lee Hopkins/ iLCP**

In March 2011, the 9.0 magnitude earthquake and tsunami that ravaged eastern Japan also unleashed a smaller tsunami on the other side of the Pacific, swamping the Northwestern Hawaiian Islands. The tidal wave killed an estimated 2,000 adult albatrosses and about 110,000 chicks in the Pacific Islands National Wildlife Refuge Complex. About a week later, a 60-year-old albatross named Wisdom and her recently hatched chick were spotted alive. Wisdom was first banded in 1956 at the age of five, and her latest chick is thought to be her thirty-fifth. Biologists estimate Wisdom has logged more than 4.5 million kilometers in flight during her lifetime, the equivalent of six round trips to the Moon (USFWS, 2011).

The southern royal albatross (*Diomedea epomophora*) and the wandering albatross (*D. exulans*) are the largest albatrosses, with wingspans of 3.5 meters. The latter can cover up to ten thousand kilometers in search of food for its chicks. Smaller species also log long-distance flights. The black-footed albatross (*Phoebastria nigriceps*) found off the coast of California is known to cover 5,067 kilometers in thirty-five days, and the gray-headed albatross (*Thallasarche chrysostoma*) from South Georgia has completed a full circumnavigation of the globe in forty-six days.

Fully eighteen of the twenty-two albatross species are in the Endangered status categories of the IUCN, and three of these are Critically Endangered. Together with other pelagic birds like shearwaters, albatrosses are severely affected by entanglement from long-line fishing. More than one hundred thousand albatrosses die every year as a result of this fishing practice, which is likely the single most significant anthropogenic hazard faced by these magnificent creatures. And as with sea turtles, mentioned above, seabirds are severely threatened by their inadvertent ingestion of the increasing amounts of floating plastic debris in the world's oceans, which can cause digestive blockages and high rates of mortality.

Marine Invertebrates

Invertebrates represent over 98% of all life on Earth, including the vast majority of marine species (MarineBio.org, 2011). Found in every available niche in the ocean, these members of the "spineless majority" often are responsible for building the very habitats in which multitudes of other creatures dwell. Tiny colonial corals create the vast reefs that have been called the "rainforests of the seas" for their high concentrations of life. Marine invertebrates include some of the smallest known forms of life, as well as some of the true giants. Even scientists do not have a grasp on the sheer numbers of marine invertebrates, and no global dataset yet exists for most of them (Bouchet, 2006).

Echinoderms, the sea stars and their relatives, are a ubiquitous symbol of life at the seashore, and their likeness is seen on everything from postcards to beach towels. An equally iconic group is the mollusks, especially the stunningly beautiful nudibranchs (shell-less gastropod sea slugs) and highly intelligent cephalopods—octopi, squid, nautilus, and cuttlefish. The giant squid (genus *Architeuthis*) and the colossal squid (*Mesonychoteuthis hamiltoni*) are the stuff of Jules Verne fame and the likely source of ancient mariners' tales of sea serpents and kraken, as they can reach lengths of over thirteen meters. The latter is the largest of all invertebrates, and has the largest eyes in the animal kingdom: twenty-eight centimeters diameter with a lens the size of an orange (Lilley, 2008).

Some of the most unique of invertebrates are the four species of horseshoe crab that have persisted on Earth for as long as 500 million years and are virtually unchanged for at least 200 million years (Nellaiappan and Sugumaran, 1996). Millions of Atlantic horseshoe crabs (*Limulus polyphemus*) leave the sea each spring to spawn en masse on the beaches of the Delaware Bay in the eastern United States. This ancient ritual is one of the greatest spectacles of the invertebrate world.

But it is in the deep sea where a treasure trove of new and unusual marine invertebrates awaits discovery. Some scientists have postulated that as many as 100 million new forms of life may lie within deep-sea sediments alone (Grassle and Maciolek, 1992). Some of these new abyssal species have captured the public's imagination, such as the "yeti crab" (*Kiwa hirsute*) discovered in 2005 in hydrothermal vents near Easter Island; within three months of its published description, it had been mentioned on over 200,000 websites (Bouchet, 2006). As we continue to dive further and longer into the deep, scientists will certainly continue to bring an ever-expanding menagerie of these bizarre discoveries to light.

Conclusion

History shows that the public is compelled by images of endangered wildlife, and over the past half-century we have seen many examples of how such images can catalyze change. Flagship species clearly influence individual and corporate philanthropy and government spending; spearheaded by conservation groups and governments, campaigns to save tigers, whales, primates, and other iconic species have generated hundreds of millions of dollars to establish protected areas and fund research, community development, anti-poaching efforts, and other activities that support and sustain biodiversity conservation from the ground-up and the top-down. Since 1976, Greenpeace's persistent campaigning on behalf of dolphin-safe tuna also has shown how flagships can effect changes to entire industries and can influence US and foreign policies—and even the public consumption of tuna, a popular food item. Flagship species can leverage change in attitudes and behavior at the individual, local, national, and global levels. Some argue that the kinds of global actions needed to save the oceans must be taken by governments. Yet, the decisions of governments are influenced by their citizens, and also by corporations and lobbies, that are in turn influenced by their customers, so the individual choices and changes in behavior do play an important role. It is not beyond us as individuals to be conscious of our place in Nature, to yield to our natural biophilia, to make wiser, more ocean-friendly choices in our lives. The stories and images of the flagship species with whom we share this planet are here to remind us that our own survival depends on how we choose to take care of them.

RIGHT: A whale shark (*Rhincodon typus*) swims languidly with an escort of colorful fish. Whale sharks migrate between Cocos, Malpelo, and Galápagos Islands, and possibly the coast of Ecuador. Satellite tagging is being used to track their movements. **Photograph by Pete Oxford/ iLCP**

FOLLOWING SPREAD:The emperor penguin (*Aptenodytes forsteri*) is the tallest and heaviest of all living penguin species and is endemic to Antarctica. It is also the bird that breeds in the coldest environment, with air temperatures down to -40 °C. **Photograph by Daisy Gilardini/ iLCP**

Sebastian Troëng, Peter Bryant, Guilherme Dutra, Mark Erdmann, Ginny Farmer, Scott Henderson, Keith Lawrence, Frazer McGilvray, Jonas Rüpp, and Romeo Trono

THE SEASCAPES APPROACH: SECURING HEALTHY OCEANS FOR THRIVING PEOPLE

By 2000 it was clear that some of the most outstanding marine regions in the world were under siege, facing rapid degradation and ecosystem collapse. Just as clear was the fact that old approaches were not going to save them. Conservation International developed the Seascapes Approach to stem the decline in ocean health in some of the most outstanding marine regions of the world, and to demonstrate that transforming the management of large ocean areas to benefit people and ecosystems is possible.

The term Seascape has been used by several organizations, including World Wildlife Fund (WWF), Wildlife Conservation Society, and Conservation International (CI), to describe a large area of ocean where species and habitats depend on and interact with each other. Conservation International's and partners' Seascapes Approach, formally launched in 2004, is a set of strategies, outlined as nine essential elements, that foster the effective management of large marine areas so that people can continue to benefit from the many services that healthy oceans provide while preserving the unique biodiversity of the world's oceans. Over the last decades, ocean scientists and marine conservationists have come to realize that ocean systems and human societies are interconnected; human societies simultaneously depend on and affect the ocean. The Seascapes Approach is a response to that realization. Wide-ranging ocean connectivity and global-scale climate change—along with ocean acidification, pollution, unsustainable fishing, and other pressures—mean that marine management must target large areas, from tens of thousands to millions of square kilometers, to be effective. This is much larger than what previously has been attempted through site-level marine management or by land-use management.

PRECEDING PAGE: Effective management of large marine areas is the lynchpin of the seascapes concept. Under careful management by the government of Kiribati, the Phoenix Island Protected Area (PIPA) will continue to provide citizens like these villagers with the many services healthy oceans provide. At the same time, PIPA and other marine protected areas around the world will preserve the unique biodiversity of the world's oceans. **Photograph by George Steinmetz/ iLCP**

LEFT: A school of yellow line scads (*Selaroides leptolepis*) seeks shelter under the shade of a fishing dock in Misool, Raja Ampat, West Papua, Indonesia. **Photograph by Jürgen Freund/ iLCP**

Beyond any nation's jurisdiction, the high seas cover almost half of the planet's surface and produce ten million tons of fish each year. This is where ocean governance and management remain the weakest, far from the coasts and outside the controls of national governments

At the same time, ocean governance rarely aligns perfectly with marine ecosystems or patterns of human use. While the Exclusive Economic Zones, or EEZs, of individual countries extend two hundred nautical miles (370.4 km) from the coast, the distributions of many marine species and some human uses extend beyond national jurisdictions into the high seas. In Ecuador, for instance, large fishing vessels in search of tuna ply the waters of the EEZ but also venture into the high seas between Ecuador's coastal waters and the Galápagos Marine Reserve. The tuna themselves move freely between international waters and the Eastern Tropical Pacific Seascape (encompassing the territorial waters of Costa Rica, Panama, Colombia, and Ecuador). Like other ecosystem-based management efforts (McLeod et al., 2005), the Seascapes Approach considers people as part of the ecosystem and seeks to address the cumulative impacts on the ocean by different sectors of society. We must consider ocean connectivity and governance when defining the boundaries of Seascapes. Within these boundaries, the Seascapes Approach strives to maintain ocean health so that ecosystem services, such as the provision of fish for food, can continue to benefit people now and for future generations.

Large-scale marine management requires the active involvement of a wide range of stakeholders—partnerships are central to the success of the Seascapes Approach. Nongovernmental organizations such as Conservation International make important contributions to Seascapes by providing technical support, obtaining external financing, facilitating partnerships and discussions among ocean interest groups, and by funding and guiding long-term ocean planning and marine conservation projects. Government agencies with authority, capacity, and resources to regulate and manage human impacts are fundamental to Seascape success. Communities that depend on ocean resources and, in some cases are the traditional owners of marine areas, arguably are the most crucial partners of all.

This is the case in the Bird's Head Seascape in eastern Indonesia, where community and family ownership of ocean areas is widespread. Strong local leadership is a key component of marine management success (Gutierrez et al., 2011). Private industries and companies can also be a force for positive change in Seascapes by ensuring that their operations do not negatively affect the ocean and by underwriting marine management. They also can generate employment and income for local communities and people through the sustainable use of marine resources, such as ecologically responsible wildlife tours or local fishing enterprises using nondestructive gear in accordance with sustainable fish quotas.

Universities have a role to play in the Seascape Approach as well. By promoting greater understanding of the ecology and socioeconomic conditions of Seascapes, researchers can foster innovation in ocean management in the present and educate ocean managers for the future. To enhance the impact of Seascapes, Conservation International collaborates with and provides grants to local, national, and global organizations and institutions. Around the world, over one hundred and fifty partner organizations are collaborating to ensure the success of the Seascapes program.

Genesis of the Seascapes Approach

The first Seascape was the Eastern Tropical Pacific, established in 2004 with major grants from the United Nations Foundation and the Global Conservation Fund (Bensted-Smith and Kirkman, 2010). In 2005, Seascapes were launched in the Sulu and Sulawesi Seas between Indonesia, Malaysia, and the Philippines, and in waters around the Bird's Head peninsula in eastern Indonesia. Also in 2005, marine conservation at a similar level of effort began in Abrolhos, Brazil, and over time this region has evolved into a fourth Seascape for Conservation International. Separately, Wildlife Conservation Society has also developed Seascapes in Antongil Bay (Madagascar), Glover's Reef (Belize), Karimunjawa (Indonesia), Kenya, New Ireland (Papua New Guinea), New York (USA), Patagonia and Southwest Atlantic (Argentina, Chile, Uruguay, Brazil, and UK), and Vatu-i-Ra (Fiji).

Investing in Diverse Ocean Jewels

Conservation International supports comprehensive marine conservation in four Seascapes, ranging in size from 95,000 square kilometers in Abrolhos, Brazil, to over two million square kilometers in the Eastern Tropical Pacific. These Seascapes cover a wide variety of ecosystems, from predominantly coastal areas with coral reefs and associated habitats in Bird's Head Seascape to oceanic islands and pelagic waters in the Eastern Tropical Pacific. They include the most diverse marine ecosystems on the planet: the Bird's Head and Sulu-Sulawesi Seascapes in the Coral Triangle; the cluster of Cocos (Costa Rica), Coiba (Panama), Malpelo (Colombia), and Galápagos (Ecuador) in the Eastern Tropical Pacific; and the unique mushroom-shaped reefs, the largest in the South Atlantic, in Abrolhos Seascape, Brazil.

The primary level of political and policy work ranges from local and provincial in Abrolhos and Bird's Head Seascapes to national and regional in the Eastern Tropical Pacific and Sulu-Sulawesi Seascapes. The pressure on marine resources ranges from extremely high in the Sulu-Sulawesi Seascape, where tens of millions of people depend on

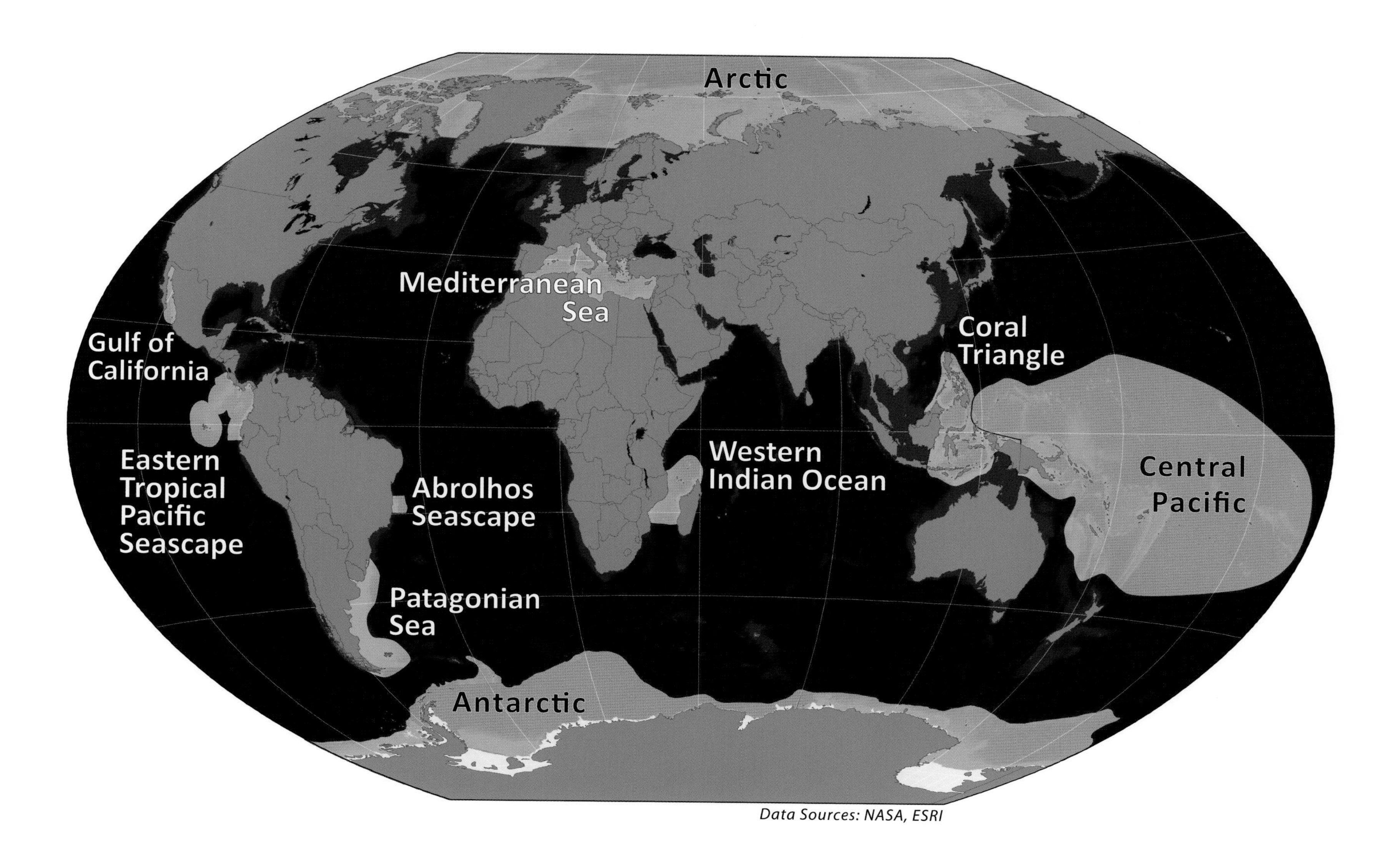

ABOVE: **Seascapes and ocean regions.** These areas cover polar, temperate, and tropical seas and represent a range of conservation challenges and opportunities.

the ocean for their immediate livelihoods and long-term survival, to the more sparsely inhabited coast along Abrolhos Seascape, where just 230,000 people live and work.

The investment is commensurate with the challenge facing ocean health. Overall, more than US$60 million has been invested in the four Seascapes since 2004 to conduct scientific surveys, develop new policies, train government officials and local communities in marine management, build public awareness about the importance of ocean ecosystems to human well-being, promote best environmental and social practices for private industry and companies, and to establish marine protected area trust funds and fees for marine ecosystem services. These activities have recovered marine species and habitats and improved the quality of life for all people. This and other successes makes the Seascapes program one of the largest, most effective, and efficient regional-scale marine management efforts in the world.

Nine Essential Elements to Turn the Tide

Despite the wide range of circumstances in the Seascapes, the Seascape managers must overcome many similar challenges. Over the past six years, the Seascape teams have converged on a framework of nine essential elements that allows sufficient flexibility to adapt to local conditions. The essential elements summarize the strategies necessary to effectively manage a large marine area. They are described below with general summaries on our experience to date. Highlights on how Conservation International and its partners are investing in the nine essential elements and are turning the tide in the four Seascapes are listed in Table 1. These four Seascapes and five additional marine regions are described in more detail later in this book in the Seascapes section.

1. Enabling legal framework of laws, conventions, regulations, and policies that facilitate marine conservation at local, national, and regional scales.

To date, much of the progress has been in the form of national and local policies to protect sensitive species and habitat while improving the management of fisheries and other marine resources. One key achievement has been catalyzing forty-three new or expanded marine protected areas across the four Seascapes. Together these areas extend 46,800 square kilometers, slightly larger than the area of the Netherlands. Several of these areas contain large no-take zones to protect highly sensitive areas, including those critical to fisheries recovery, and many are managed with the direct involvement of local communities and fishing associations.

2. Ecosystem-based management that advances large-scale marine ecosystem and species management through the use of multidisciplinary scientific information to inform effective planning, implementation, monitoring, and evaluation.

Research into ecological and genetic connectivity is important across all Seascapes. Socioeconomic research, including economic valuation of the benefits of ocean ecosystems—such as providing seafood, monitoring of governance to understand how natural resource management decisions are made, studies of local cultures and how these influence use of marine resources, and assessments of local livelihoods and how they depend on marine resources—is equally key to understanding human behavior and to helping design conservation strategies compatible with sustainable economic development. In all Seascapes, science results directly influence management decisions including marine protected area design and network expansions, and fisheries regulations and enforcement.

3. Adequate institutions and capacity, including personnel, infrastructure, and equipment, to make marine governance structures—governmental, private sector, and civil society—work effectively and efficiently.

Innovative policies and solid information are only useful in the hands of capable managers, businesses, and communities. In each of the Seascapes, we have invested heavily in capacity building for the agencies and organizations that manage local and national marine protected areas. In all, 101 marine protected areas across the Seascapes have benefited from training in different aspects of marine protected areas management for government staff, local communities, and organizations.

4. Private sector engagement that promotes the increasing convergence of conservation and development objectives by linking major economic activities' viability and profitability with sustainable management.

So far most attention has been focused on the nature tourism sector, but increasingly Conservation International and our Seascapes partners are engaging other private industries and companies to develop innovative corporate conservation solutions.

5. Social and political support that increases the viability of marine conservation as an integral part of sustainable development and is important at all levels, from local marine managed area stakeholders up to national leaders, and the messages they convey in international arenas including conventions and policy fora.

Sustainable marine management ultimately depends on individuals and governments as committed marine resource stewards. Thus far, efforts to build a large constituency in favor of sustainable marine resource use have focused on local communities and political decision-makers with only some effort invested in influencing international agreements between countries.

6. Threatened species recovery that reverses declining population trends for threatened marine species.

Our ability to document the recovery of threatened species is influenced by several factors, including life history and ease of monitoring. Coral reef fish and sea turtles concentrate in specific locations, such as individual reefs and nesting beaches, which makes regular surveys feasible. We use these species as indicators of ecosystem health and reason that other marine species, more difficult to monitor, are likely benefiting from improved management.

7. Maintenance and restoration of critical habitats and ecosystems so that ecological processes and ecosystem services are sustained.

Abundant ecosystem services are only possible if we have healthy ecosystems. Although recovery of habitats takes from several years to decades, signs of ecosystem recovery such as increase in coral cover and recuperation of carnivorous fish populations have been documented in both anecdotal and peer-reviewed reports in all four Seascapes.

8. Human well-being benefits that improve the social, economic, and cultural well being of human communities that depend on marine resources and ecosystems.

Improved ocean management has many benefits for people. Reduced local conflicts over marine resources, better organization, and empowerment of local communities to actively manage marine areas and resources are some of the immediate benefits. Income from tourism and sustainable fisheries and enhanced food security may take longer to materialize but can be substantial over time. Already there are compelling examples of human well-being benefits emerging from the four Seascapes, including increased income from tourism and perceived increases in local fish catch.

9. Sustainable financing and market mechanisms with funding portfolios that are stable, diverse, and large enough to implement all priority activities.

The Seascapes were established with outside funding, but the long-term goal is to replace that funding with funds generated locally by fees for ecosystem services and income from sustainable uses of fisheries and other marine resources. User fees for diving and entry fees to protected areas, trust funds, conservation agreements, and increased local and national government allocations for marine management have been secured in all Seascapes, moving them toward the goal of full internal funding.

The time required to achieve success varies among essential elements. We are making progress on the legal framework, ecosystem-based management, and adequate capacity relatively rapidly in a matter of two to five years. Documenting behavior changes among citizens, politicians, and business leaders takes more time. Ecosystems take even longer to recover, and witnessing that recovery and the benefits to human well being from improved management takes even longer because of the lag between management action and ecosystem recovery. Still, we have already seen dramatic and surprisingly rapid change in all four Seascapes, with enthusiastic and growing support from local stakeholders and government agencies.

What We Have Learned

Build a strong team: All of the Seascapes' successes depend on strong partnerships that allow for complementary strengths, a common and shared vision, mobilization of more financial and human resources, building of long-term capacity, and ensuring conservation groups and governments share a common agenda.

Foster champions: Strong leadership among staff and local partners at the local and national levels can, with Seascape funding, make the difference between success and failure.

Good timing matters: Although it is critical to act quickly on time-sensitive opportunities, it's also crucial to know when to wait before advancing specific initiatives. A strong base is essential to avoid catalyzing political and business opposition that can overwhelm stakeholder support.

Stable funding makes risk-taking possible: Having committed and flexible long-term donor support allows the Seascape Approach to adapt to new opportunities and challenges, and allows teams to focus on delivering outcomes rather than continuous fundraising. Fewer opportunities need to be passed up due to lack of resources. Stable funding thus enables a level of experimentation and risk-taking that is necessary to try innovative approaches in the Seascapes.

Seascapes deliver: A thorough review of five approaches to large-scale marine management showed that Seascapes stood out for having delivered impressive results in a short time period. The authors attributed this success to the flexible nature of the funding and the effective mobilization of many partner organizations in the Seascapes (Bensted-Smith & Kirkman, 2010).

Remaining Challenges

Although it has been underway for centuries, the degradation of marine ecosystems has accelerated in most areas in recent decades. Achieving and sustaining ocean health and benefits for people at the Seascape level will take decades. Long-term commitment and investments are necessary to secure fully functional Seascapes. Conservation International has decided to commit to a small number of Seascapes, but to do so over the time span and scale required to achieve transformational change.

Progress across the nine essential elements has been uneven, in part because most conservation organizations have well-developed natural science expertise but only nascent financial and private-sector experience that is required for long-term sustainable solutions. The private sector needs to be more fully engaged in all Seascapes; this engagement represents both a challenge and a major opportunity. If businesses can align their practices and profits with sustainable behavior and local benefits, the Seascape Approach can move dramatically toward long-term sustainability.

For Seascapes to become sustainable, we need to increase our focus on effective governance of the Seascapes, placing decision making in the hands of local people and reducing their reliance on external funding and technical support. In this way, the Seascapes can become robust enough to influence dominant economic and social trends such as population growth, coastal development, marine fisheries, and new phenomena such as rapid aquaculture expansion, as well as make sure these take place using best environmental and social practices. This may include informing national development plans to direct economic and population growth to areas and in ways that minimize impacts on sensitive marine and coastal ecosystems. We must use Seascapes to catalyze development on a more sustainable path, toward a "green economy" that benefits its citizens while respecting the limits of its natural resources.

The extent to which climate change might compromise the Seascapes achievements remains unknown. Increased sea water temperature, ocean acidification, changes in ocean currents, sea level rise, and increased frequency and intensity of storm are highly likely to negatively affect sensitive species and habitats. Seascapes aim to maximize the resilience of ecosystems and human societies to these and other stressors basing plans on vulnerability assessments. Such assessments should make Seascapes better able to cope with climate change than regions with weak or nonexistent large-scale marine management.

	Abrolhos	Bird's Head	Eastern Tropical Pacific	Sulu–Sulawesi Seas
Enabling legal framework	Extractive reserves, a management category developed for terrestrial areas to allow co-management and sustainable use, have been successfully applied to three large marine areas in the Seascape	The *Bupati* (mayor) of Raja Ampat has banned manta ray and shark fishing as these charismatic species attract tourists who generate income and livelihoods for local communities. For similar reasons, the Bupati outlawed coastal mining and promotes ecotourism.	In Costa Rica, new management categories for marine areas have been created to allow for context-specific management needs. In Ecuador, a ban on manta ray fishing was put in place, and sharkfinning has been regulated Seascape-wide	The President of the Philippines issued a decree on biodiversity conservation after being inspired by scientific findings reported in the media highlighting the Verde Island Passage as the global center of marine shorefish diversity. Local governments have established dozens of marine protected areas.
Ecosystem-based management	Mangroves, nearshore, and offshore reefs are ecologically connected by commercially important fish species. Research surveys doubled the size of known reefs, the largest in the South Atlantic	A set of 17 research studies, ranging from genetic connectivity analyses to marine tenure mapping, informed the design of a network of 10 marine protected areas encompassing 36,000 km2	Migrations of sharks and sea turtles between coastal and oceanic marine protected areas demonstrate ecological connectivity across the Seascape.	Results from fish eggs and larval connectivity studies informed the design of marine protected area networks.
Adequate institutions & capacity	Workshops for the marine extractive reserve councils have greatly increased the capacity for informed decision-making. Training courses for marine protected area managers and students have improved their monitoring and management capacity. Training for local associations have improved their participation in marine protected area co-management.	Local leaders hired to manage marine protected areas have received technical training in management and have performed beyond expectations. Several of them are now participating in a campaign with RARE Conservation to build local pride in no-take marine reserves.	A new Ecuadorian Navy and Park Service vessel monitoring system for Galápagos, supported by WildAid, Conservation International, WWF, and others, has vastly increased surveillance efficiency and has facilitated high profile illegal fishing arrests in the marine reserve	A Trinational Committee for the Sulu–Sulawesi Seascape has been formalized and is operational. Capacity building efforts have resulted in a *Bantay Dagat* force of more than 1,000 municipal marine protected area and fisheries enforcement volunteers, now equipped with patrol boats and other equipment.
Private sector engagement	A local tourism company agreed to support the Canavieiras Extractive Reserve to ensure sustainable fisheries in their hotel surroundings	BP agreed to reroute their tankers from a huge natural gas facility to avoid sensitive coral reef areas around the Raja Ampat archipelago, in spite of significantly increased transportation costs.	Aviatur, the largest nature tourism operator in Colombia, has worked with Conservation International and partners to make operations in Gorgona National Nature Park more sustainable and more beneficial to the local community.	Energy company First Gen provided a landmark grant to First Philippine Conservation Incorporated for marine conservation in the Verde Island Passage.
Social & political support	Former President Lula of Brazil personally attended the creation of the Cassurubá Marine Extractive Reserve. The SOS Abrolhos Coalition brings together 23 non-governmental organizations to build support for sustainable management and to prevent destructive development projects.	The brightly painted and eye-catching outreach vessel Kalabia has visited each of the 103 communities in Raja Ampat. A customized interactive curriculum is taught to schoolchildren, and adults are invited to attend evening film sessions to learn about marine ecosystems and stewardship	The president's office has been actively involved in promoting expansion of marine conservation efforts in Colombia.	National government officials, four provincial governors, and ten mayors attended the 2nd Sulu–Sulawesi Seascape Conference and expressed their support for the Seascape. The community of Cagayancillo fully supports marine protected areas and has expanded the marine protected area network due to perceived increases in local fish catch.
Threatened species recovery	Research on the effect of no-take reserve areas shows increase in fish biomass of Endangered greenback parrotfish (*Scarus trispinosus*) and spillover from no-take reserves of economically important species such as the squared grouper (*Mycteroperca bonaci*) and yellowtail snapper (Francini-Filho & Moura, 2008).	In the Piai-Sayang Endangered green turtle (*Chelonia mydas*) rookery, an agreement with the local community employs villagers to patrol the nesting beach and has virtually eliminated sea turtle and egg poaching, with nesting increasing to over 1,000 nests per year.	Record nesting by vulnerable olive ridley turtles (*Lepidochelys olivacea*) has been recorded although improved management is only one contributing factor. Also, coral recovery across the Seascape since the last serious bleaching event suggests management is contributing to increased resilience.	Approximately one million Endangered green turtle (*Chelonia mydas*) eggs have been protected on Baguan Island. Abundance of reef fishes has increased in the Barangay Papaya marine protected area in the Verde Island Passage.
Maintenance & restoration of critical habitats & ecosystems	Mapping of critical habitats has informed marine protected area network expansion, including the protection of mangrove areas in Cassurubá that are important for the Abrolhos reef fauna.	n the 1,550 km2 Kawe marine protected area, all finfish are protected, and occasional collection of sea cucumber, top shell, and lobster by the community is allowed in less than 2.5% of the reefs. Dynamite fishing and sharkfinning have been eliminated, and observations suggest that bombed reefs are recovering, and juvenile blacktip reef sharks (*Carcharhinus melanopterus*) are increasing.	Monitoring shows that well-enforced marine protected areas display greater biomass of higher carnivorous fishes, lower densities of asteroids and urchins, and higher coral cover than less effectively enforced marine protected areas (Edgar et al., in press).	Marine protected area networks based on connectivity studies and life histories of focal species have been designed for Verde Islands Passage, Cagayan Ridge and Balabac Strait, and the Sea Turtle Corridor.
Human well-being	As many as 20,000 fishers and their families benefit from marine protected areas. Better community organization has allowed greater access to public services such as electricity and new housing. More sustainable fishing and increased tourism have generated opportunities for greater income and more diversified livelihoods.	The dive fee system in Raja Ampat generated nearly US$250,000 in 2010 alone for maternal health care in remote communities. At least seven villages in Raja Ampat are now deriving 20% or more of their total cash income from tourism.	Support to micro-business organization ARTURIS in Panama has helped the members make a better living from their small-scale businesses (95% have seen increased incomes) as well as created a very proactive constituency opposing destructive development projects.	Both in Cagayan Ridge and the Verde Island Passage, small-scale fishers have recorded an increase in fish catch and attribute this to marine protected areas and improved fisheries enforcement.
Sustainable financing & market mechanisms	A trust fund for all protected areas in the region is under development. Reduced reliance on philanthropic funding is secured by government agencies taking on monitoring responsibilities. Fisheries monitoring will be conducted by a government agency, and discussions are under way with other entities to continue socioeconomic and ecological monitoring.	The dive fee system in Raja Ampat captures direct financial benefits from the increase in dive tourism from 300 visitors in 2001 to 4,500 visitors in 2010. Another example of innovative financing was the Blue Auction hosted by Prince Albert II at the Monaco Oceanographic Museum, where bidders competed for naming rights to newly found species, raising US$2 million for the Bird's Head Seascape.	Malpelo Fauna and Flora Sanctuary in Colombia now has a trust fund that, in collaboration with the navy, pays for permanent boat patrols. In another World Heritage Site, Coiba in Panama, the income from higher visitor and user fees is used to fund improved management of the site.	Local governments are allocating increasing resources for marine protected area management and fisheries enforcement, with over US$270,000 contributed in 2010.

Going Global

In 2011 the four Seascapes made up less than 1% of the global ocean, but their influence was growing. For them to have a global impact, we must scale up the Seascapes approach through policies and by helping others to replicate and adopt the methodology.

Already there are encouraging signs that the Seascapes Approach is gaining wider acceptance. The Coral Triangle Initiative for Coral Reefs, Fisheries, and Food Security is a six-country agreement governing the most diverse ocean region on the planet, where over 150 million people depend on ocean resources for survival. One of five goals of the Coral Triangle Initiative is the designation and effective management of priority Seascapes. The Philippines is moving forward with a South China Sea Seascape, and ideas for additional Seascapes, declared and promoted by individual or multiple governments, are gaining political traction and momentum.

Similarly, fifteen heads of state of countries in the western and central Pacific announced the Pacific Oceanscape in August 2010, envisioning a secure future for Pacific island nations based on ocean conservation and management, strong leadership, and regional cooperation. Although not explicitly mentioning Seascapes, the designers of the Pacific Oceanscape benefited from the Seascapes experience.

The Eastern Tropical Pacific Seascape, the Coral Triangle Initiative, and the Pacific Oceanscape were recognized as models for conservation and collaboration in the United Nations General Assembly's Coral Reef and Oceans and the Law of the Sea resolutions passed in New York in December 2010. This is evidence that the Seascape Approach and its successes are inspiring decision makers at the global level.

PREVIOUS PAGE: Wide-ranging ocean connectivity and global-scale issues like climate change, which is already causing coral bleaching in many shallow areas, as can be seen here on Lissenung Island, Papua New Guinea—along with ocean acidification, pollution, unsustainable fishing, and other pressures—mean that marine management must target large areas, from tens of thousands to millions of square kilometers, to be effective. **Photograph by Jürgen Freund/ iLCP**

LEFT: Perhaps nowhere is the shaping hand of evolution on an odd assemblage of fauna more evident than in the Galápagos. Endemic penguins (the Galápagos penguin, *Spheniscus mendiculus*) and fur seals (*Arctocephalus galapagoensis*), originating from coasts bathed by Antarctic waters, dart with Galápagos sea lions (*Zalophus wollebaeki*), like these seen on the island of Española whose ancestors originated from North America, through coral reefs teeming with a mix of colorful fish with affinities throughout the Pacific. **Photograph by Tim Laman/ iLCP**

Beyond any nation's jurisdiction, the high seas cover almost half of the planet's surface and produce ten million tons of fish each year. This is where ocean governance and management remain the weakest, far from the coasts and outside the controls of national governments. Conservation International is exploring how the Seascape experience and its nine essential elements can be adapted and applied to the high seas, a final frontier for the Seascapes Approach.

The oceans are the largest habitat on earth, and they demand our commitment on a global scale. Merely the name Seascape won't be enough, and no one country, organization, or agency can solve the ocean crisis alone. What will be necessary to manage our oceans—for the survival of people and all life on Earth—will be commitment on an international scale, across boundaries of expertise and ideologies, directing adequate resources to effectively address threats to ocean health. Only through a shared ambitious vision of restored ocean health aggressively pursued through joint actions at the Seascape level—and by sharing our experiences and learning from them as we collaboratively implement Seascapes—will we be able to achieve ocean health at a global scale. This endeavor calls for a transformation of the relationship between people and the oceans and will lay the building blocks for a new future, both for the unique biodiversity of the largest biome on Earth and for people around the world.

RIGHT: Coral reef in Komodo National Park, Komodo, Indonesia. The reefs in Komodo are among the richest in the world and home to over 1,000 types of fish, nearly 400 varieties of coral, 70 kinds of sponges, and several types of whales, sharks, turtles, and dolphins.
Photograph by Michael Patrick O'Neill

FOLLOWING SPREAD: Green sea turtles (*Chelonia mydas*), like this one photographed off Mabul Island, Sabah, in Malaysian Borneo, migrate long distances between feeding grounds and hatching beaches. **Photograph by Stewart Westmorland**

SEASCAPES

EASTERN TROPICAL PACIFIC SEASCAPE

Scott Henderson, Fabio Arjona, Xavier Chalén, María Claudia Diazgranados, Arturo Dominici-Arosemena, Graham Edgar, Ginny Farmer, Keith Lawrence, Fernando Ortiz, Marco Quesada, Ana Maria Rodriguez, Michael Rothschild, Luís Suárez, and Sebastian Troëng

Tucked in the elbow that connects Central and South America, the Eastern Tropical Pacific Seascape (ETPS) sits in a geological crucible and the crossroads of five marine currents. Spanning the national waters, coasts, and islands of Costa Rica, Panama, Colombia, and Ecuador, the ETPS measures 2 million square kilometers (more than 770,000 sq mi)—nearly five times the size of the state of California. This seascape is bisected by shipping lanes extending from the Panama Canal. The lanes were dug through the juncture of two tectonic plates that collided four million years ago, closing off the Pacific and Atlantic Oceans (Kirby et al., 2008). Tectonic collisions also formed the two submarine ridges that mark the boundaries of the ETPS: the Cocos Ridge running across the north and the Carnegie Ridge between Galápagos Islands and the Ecuadoran coast to the south.

Intense geological activity past and present has also produced the array of volcanic features around the Galápagos Islands at the Seascape's western end. "Black smokers"—deep-sea hydrothermal vents—lie in rifts where the seafloor is ripped apart by tectonic plates slowly drifting in opposite directions. Above water, the highest of the Galápagos Islands, Isabela, soars 1,700 meters above the Pacific. On this largest of the islands, ten-kilometer-wide calderas are crisscrossed by ancient trails of giant tortoises (*Chelonoidis nigra*) and punctuated with active fumaroles, fissures in the Earth's crusts that emit steam.

For over ten million years (Christie et al., 1992), converging currents have assembled one of the world's richest and most biologically unique ecosystems. This convergence of currents mixes species carried thousands of kilometers away from their home ranges and concentrates nomadic, open-ocean species.

At the northern edge of the ETPS lies the mobile open-ocean gyre known as the Costa Rica Dome, where rich waters attract major aggregations of the world's largest creature, the blue whale (*Balaenoptera musculus*). Warm waters flow southward from the bay called the Panama Bight, producing over ten meters of annual rainfall along Colombia's Chocó Coast. Some thousand kilometers to the south, the Peruvian current's cold waters flow northward along one of the world's driest deserts, the Sechura. These currents veer westward off the Ecuadoran coast, and are bounded on both sides by easterly flowing countercurrents that deliver potential colonizing species to the ETPS from the waters of the biologically distinct central Pacific.

Rounding out this current milieu, the cold, deep Equatorial Undercurrent flows east, colliding with the western margin of the Galápagos platform and shunting cold, nutrient-rich waters to the surface. Over the centuries, crews of becalmed pirate vessels have referred to this Galápagos hideout as the "Enchanted Islands," after the unpredictable way boats would drift when caught in the mix of currents.

Although seasonal climate variations are generally mild, the region sits at the epicenter of El Niño events. In the ETPS El Niño causes much warmer oceans and dramatically increased rainfall, especially in the southern and western parts of the ETPS. The rain and warmth provides ideal growing conditions for plants, which produces a windfall of food for many land-based animals. On the other hand, in the ocean upwelling drops drastically, nutrient levels plummet, and primary productivity virtually shuts down, producing mass die-back of seabirds, marine mammals, and other species, and high sea temperatures produce mass coral bleaching and mortality.

Strong El Niño years are generally followed by La Niña years when sea temperatures and rainfall drops and very strong upwelling returns to inject nutrients back into the system and drive ecosystem recovery. These sharply contrasting events are a motor of evolution. Marine populations are strongly culled by El Niño, but La Niña rewards survivors with bounteous conditions to rebuild depleted populations built on stronger individuals. Had Charles Darwin spent any time underwater he would have witnessed the same pattern that inspired his revolutionary theory of evolution through natural selection. High island endemism, the strong north-south gradients of temperature and rainfall, and the diversity of coastal habitats combine to account for the Seascape's high species diversity.

Perhaps nowhere is the shaping hand of evolution on an odd assemblage of fauna more evident than in the Galápagos. Endemic penguins (the Galápagos penguin, *Spheniscus mendiculus*) and fur seals (*Arctocephalus galapagoensis*), originating from coasts bathed by Antarctic waters, dart with Galápagos sea lions (*Zalophus wollebaeki*) whose ancestors originated from North America, through coral reefs teeming with a mix of colorful fish with affinities throughout the Pacific.

Although its biodiversity is high and faunal uniqueness exceptional, the Seascape's most outstanding biological feature may be its sheer biomass and concentration of migratory pelagic species, many of which are rare or absent elsewhere. Following food supplies driven by seasonal shifts in wind and upwellings, whales, tuna, sharks, turtles, and seabirds migrate back and forth through the Seascape between breeding and feeding areas, making it the marine equivalent of the Serengeti.

UNESCO has recognized the Seascape's outstanding marine and coastal natural beauty and biodiversity by designating a remarkable seven World Natural Heritage Sites within the ETPS. These World Heritage Sites and other sites of great natural beauty support a thriving ecotourism industry that, in the case of Costa Rica, is the nation's principle source of foreign revenue. The economies of local communities have seen a steady rise in incomes from scuba diving, catch-and-release sport fishing, whale watching, observation of wildlife such as sea turtles, and visits to coastal reefs, beaches, and mangroves.

Highly productive waters and diverse marine habitats support valuable coastal and pelagic fisheries. Many coastal communities in all four ETPS countries depend primarily on fish for protein. Offshore commercial fisheries, in particular associated with yellowfin and skipjack tuna (*Katsuronus pelanis*) and the common dolphinfish or mahi-mahi (*Coryphaena hippurus*), contribute significantly to national incomes through the sale of fresh fish. Canning and the production of fishmeal create thousands of additional jobs. Over the last two decades the tuna fleet of Ecuador has become the largest in the Eastern Pacific, dwarfing the US fleet's catch by a factor of fifteen (IATTC, 2008).

The ETPS provides additional ecosystem services beyond its fisheries. Extensive coastal reefs and vast mangrove forests buffer the impacts of recurrent storms and rarer tsunamis. All four ETPS countries have coastal wetlands recognized for their outstanding importance by the Ramsar Convention on Wetlands, an international treaty signed in Iran in 1971. Along with marine habitats, wetlands serve as "blue carbon" sinks that reduce the accumulation of the greenhouse gases that fuel climate change (Pidgeon, 2010).

The ETPS' privileged location, stunning beauty, and bounteous waters also create challenges. The greatest of these are the impacts of overfishing, fishing practices that damage fragile habitats, and the impact of nonselective methods on non-target species—otherwise known as bycatch. Most coastal fisheries have been overfished as both local communities and commercial operations target the most accessible fishing grounds to meet demand, which has increased globally from 9.9 kg per capita in the 1960s to 16.4 kg by 2005 (FAO, 2005). As a result, high-value species, including predators such as snapper, grouper, and sharks, and "ecosystem engineer" species such as lobster and sea cucumbers, are seriously depleted. The loss of these ecosystem-regulating species sets off a cascade of effects that ultimately reduces jobs, incomes, and food supplies and drives fishermen into protected areas, the last repositories of healthy fish populations. Displaced fishermen from the Ecuadoran mainland drove the establishment—and subsequent collapse—of the lucrative but short-lived Galápagos sea cucumber fishery (Hearn, 2008).

Large, high-tech purse seining vessels equipped with sophisticated sonar to detect fish around a growing number of free-floating Fish Aggregating Devices are remarkably effective at locating and then scooping up entire schools of fish. These methods have led to reductions in bigeye tuna populations (*Thunnus obesus*), due in part to excessive capture within breeding areas west of the Galápagos. Industrial long-line vessels, each of which deploys thousands of hooks on monofilament lines extending over one hundred kilometers, unintentionally snare sharks and turtles. Of particular concern are drastic reductions in sea turtle populations, such as the Eastern Pacific population of the Critically Endangered leatherback (*Dermochelys coriacea*). This species hangs on the brink of extinction, with only a few hundred breeding individuals nesting on the beaches of Costa Rica and Panama. Bycatch on long-lines affects shark populations, especially given the surge in shark finning spurred by rising affluence in Asia. In 2009, the IUCN listed the iconic and once common scalloped hammerhead (*Sphyrna lewini*), depicted on the national park logos for Galápagos, Cocos Island, and Malpelo, as Endangered on its Red List of Threatened Species (Baum et al., 2010).

Bottom-trawling for shrimp, especially near the grounds where turtles feed and nest, has resulted in high turtle bycatch in Costa Rica and has affected sensitive reefs both there and in Panama. High bycatch and discard of non-target species have brought commercial fishing trawlers into serious conflict with coastal fishing communities in Ecuador.

Unregulated coastal tourism and shrimp aquaculture development in Costa Rica, Panama, and Ecuador exacerbates fisheries' impacts by damaging turtle nesting grounds and mangrove areas that serve as nursery grounds for many other species. Pollution and garbage from coastal cities and shipping lanes, and chemicals and sediments that make their way to the sea from inland agriculture and mining areas, threaten marine species and degrade their habitats.

Although national governments, development agencies, local communities, and conservationists often promote ecotourism as a benign alternative to fishing, ecotourism is not always the panacea it is made out to be. Unmanaged visitation can degrade sensitive habitats, such as

Following food supplies driven by seasonal shifts in wind and upwellings, whales, tuna, sharks, turtles, and seabirds migrate back and forth through the Seascape between breeding and feeding areas, making it the marine equivalent of the Serengeti

RIGHT: A male hawksbill turtle (*Eretmochelys imbricata*) courts a female in the Cocos Island National Park, Costa Rica, Eastern Pacific Tropical Seascape.
Photograph by Octavio Aburto/ iLCP

RIGHT: A view of a volcanic crater, Isabela Island, Galápagos Islands. Many volcanoes are topped by a caldera, a large circular depression derived from the original crater.
Photograph by Frans Lanting/ iLCP

RIGHT: A bigeye thresher shark (*Alopias superciliosus*), caught by fishermen of the Santa Rosa Fishing Village. The village has the largest fish market for artisanal fishermen. Santa Elena Peninsula, Manabi Province, Ecuador.
Photograph by Pete Oxford/ iLCP

LEFT: The oceanic whitetip shark (*Carcharhinus longimanus*) like this one photographed off Cocos Island, Costa Rica, in the Eastern Pacific Tropical Seascape, is a large pelagic shark inhabiting tropical and warm temperate seas.
Photograph by Octavio Aburto/ iLCP

coral reefs damaged by careless divers and boat anchors. Without proper supervision, the most well-meaning ecotourists can disrupt sea turtles and seabirds during egg laying and breeding and inadvertently introduce nonnative invasive species and pathogens—an especially serious threat on isolated offshore islands. Tourism also fuels rapid coastal development and immigration into sensitive areas, which puts greater demands on local marine environments to produce food for more people and absorb the wastes of growing coastal populations.

Global climate change is an overarching threat that is likely to amplify other threats. Species that are especially vulnerable include those with small, threatened, or limited range populations (including sea turtles, mangroves, the Galápagos flightless cormorant, and the Galápagos fur seal) and those sensitive to high temperatures, including corals. Increase in the frequency and intensity of El Niño events, possibly linked to climate change, have already forced over fifty Galápagos species onto the IUCN Red List, including nine species now thought to be extinct: the Galápagos damselfish (*Azurina eupalama*), the 24-rayed sunstar (*Heliaster solaris*), Galápagos stringweed (*Bifurcaria galapagensis*), and six other macroalgal species (*Dictyota galapagensis, Spatoglossum schmittii, Desmarestia tropica, Phycodrina elegans, Gracilaria skottsbergii,* and *Galaxaura barbata*) (Edgar et al., 2010).

Establishing a regional network of well-managed Marine Protected Areas (MPAs) that protects all main habitat types within the ETPS and includes especially vulnerable species, including those of commercial interest to allow fish stocks to recover, is a top conservation priority.

Since 2004, Conservation International's Eastern Tropical Pacific Seascape Initiative has contributed to the creation of fifteen new MPAs. These include fully protected national parks and marine reserves, as well as multiple-use marine management areas that complement conservation goals with improved fisheries production, especially for local communities that participate in management. Colombia, Costa Rica, and Panama have also significantly expanded six other MPAs. In total, well over 15,000 square kilometers of ocean have been placed under targeted management.

Creating these new MPAs took strong investment in policy and science and the development of dozens of partnerships with local and national authorities, nongovernmental organizations, and research organizations. All four ETPS countries— Costa Rica, Panama, Colombia, and Ecuador—expanded their legislative frameworks to facilitate and clarify the process for creating MPAs, especially those that respond to the social and ecological conditions particular to each location. Dozens of research expeditions have generated vastly improved natural and social science information to inform and evaluate management strategies. MigraMar, a research collaboration among organizations based in the ETPS, used sophisticated beacons affixed to scalloped hammerhead sharks (*Sphyrna lewini*) to track their movements from island to island across the Seascape (Hearn et al., 2010). These results underscore the need for coordinated international management. Additional research, especially into the value of ecosystem services, is required to justify conservation investments and clarify the benefits that improved marine management provides for local communities and national economies.

To ensure MPA designations do not result in "paper parks," between 2005 and 2011 the ETPS Initiative has strengthened the skills of MPA staff to effectively manage resources and instructed tourism operators and fishermen in the implementation of best practices to reduce environmental impacts. Effective enforcement is a central element to any functional MPA. In a revolutionary new approach to enforcement, the Galápagos National Park and Ecuador's Navy implemented a state-of-the art Vessel Monitoring System in 2008 to nearly eliminate the threat of industrial fishing in the Galápagos Marine Reserve. Encouragingly, a recent comprehensive regional study demonstrated that MPAs are producing the desired results: MPAs with improved management have healthier fish populations, fewer ecological impacts of overfishing, and higher coral cover (Edgar et al., in press).

Networks of well-managed MPAs must complement more effective management of national waters. Many species move freely out of MPAs into the open ocean, where they are vulnerable to the range of threats noted above. To address this problem, the ETPS Initiative has supported the creation of National Action Plans for turtles, sharks, and priority habitats, including corals. In Ecuador, legislators have passed regulations to strictly manage bottom trawling, restricting bottom-trawling vessels to areas where they can do the least damage, and have banned all fishing that targets sharks and manta rays.

To effectively turn the historical tide driving marine degradation for decades, the ETPS Initiative must scale up site-level efforts, coordinate efforts regionally, and make them financially sustainable. Through supporting important regional conventions, including the Southern Pacific Permanent Commission, and promoting regional networks of partner organizations specializing in shark and turtle conservation, tourism management, communications, and MPA management, the ETPS Initiative promotes information exchange between sites and the provision of high-quality information at national and regional decision-making forums. In an example of sustainable financing, following years of virtually no funding for its management, the Malpelo Fauna and Flora Sanctuary in Colombia now has a US$5 million trust fund to cover its core management costs in perpetuity.

Ultimately, the key challenge to improving marine management in the ETPS requires transitioning from economic development paradigms that rely on drawing down natural capital and diminishing ecosystem services. Our collective challenge is to develop "green economies" that generate revenues through the sustainable use of resources and provide incentives for the private sector and local communities to become better stewards of marine resources.

UPPER RIGHT: **Eastern Tropical Pacific Seascape marine protected area network.** Within this globally significant marine protected area network, many management categories govern different types and intensities of human use.

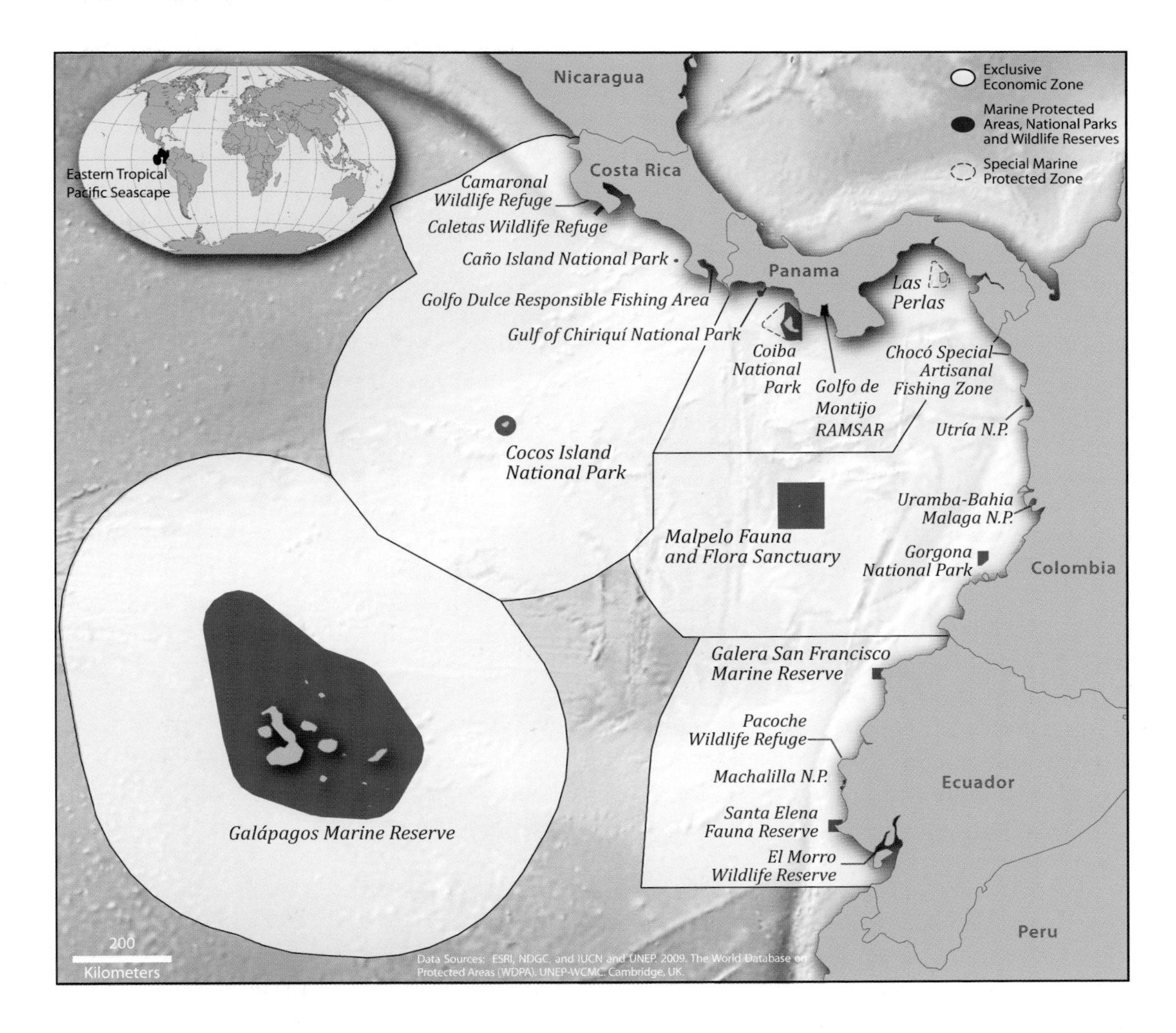

LOWER RIGHT: **Vessel monitoring system within the Galápagos Marine Reserve.** Enforcement using a vessel monitoring system is proving effective, keeping industrial fishing vessels outside the reserve while allowing them to operate close to the reserve's borders where fishing is best.

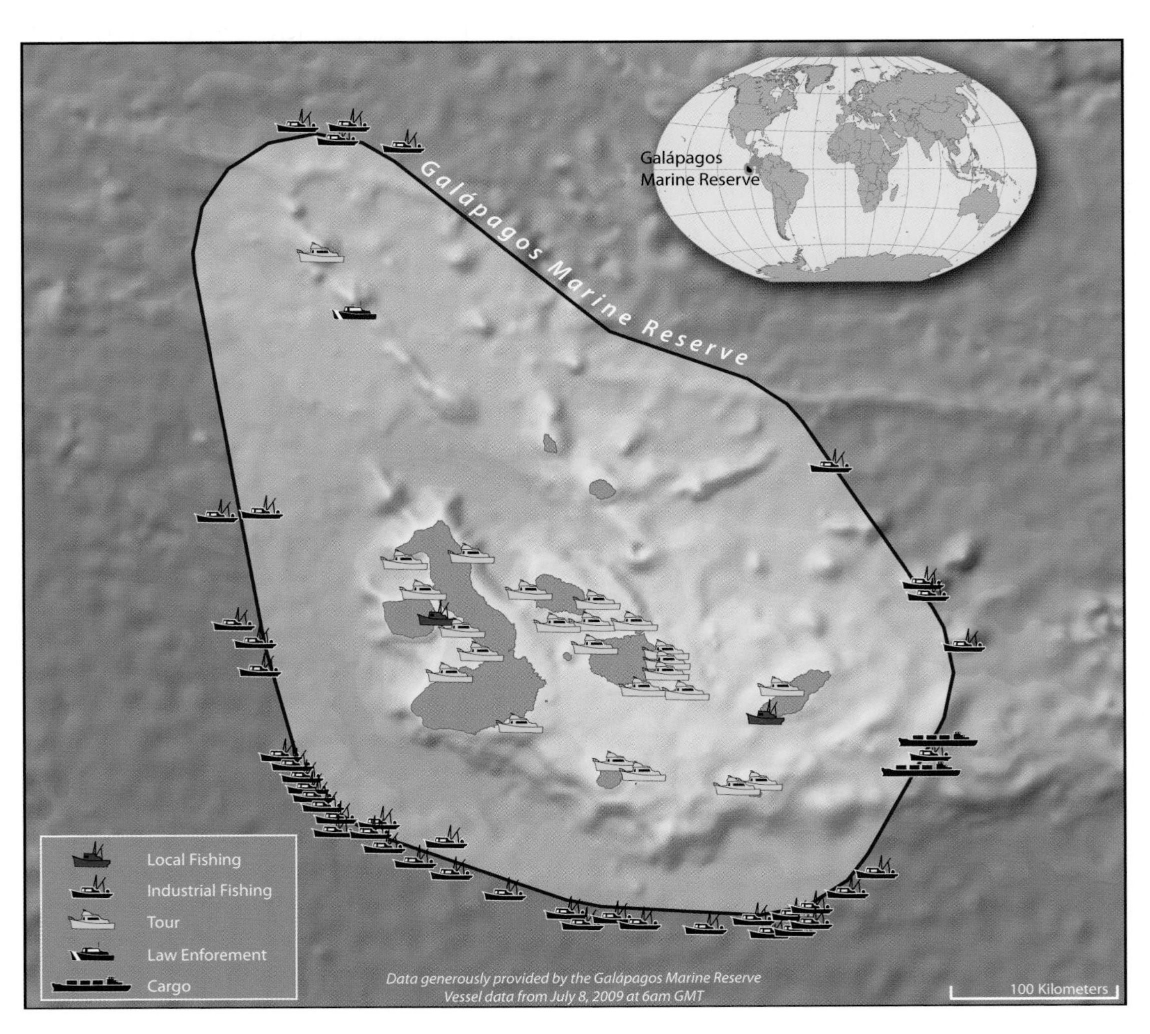

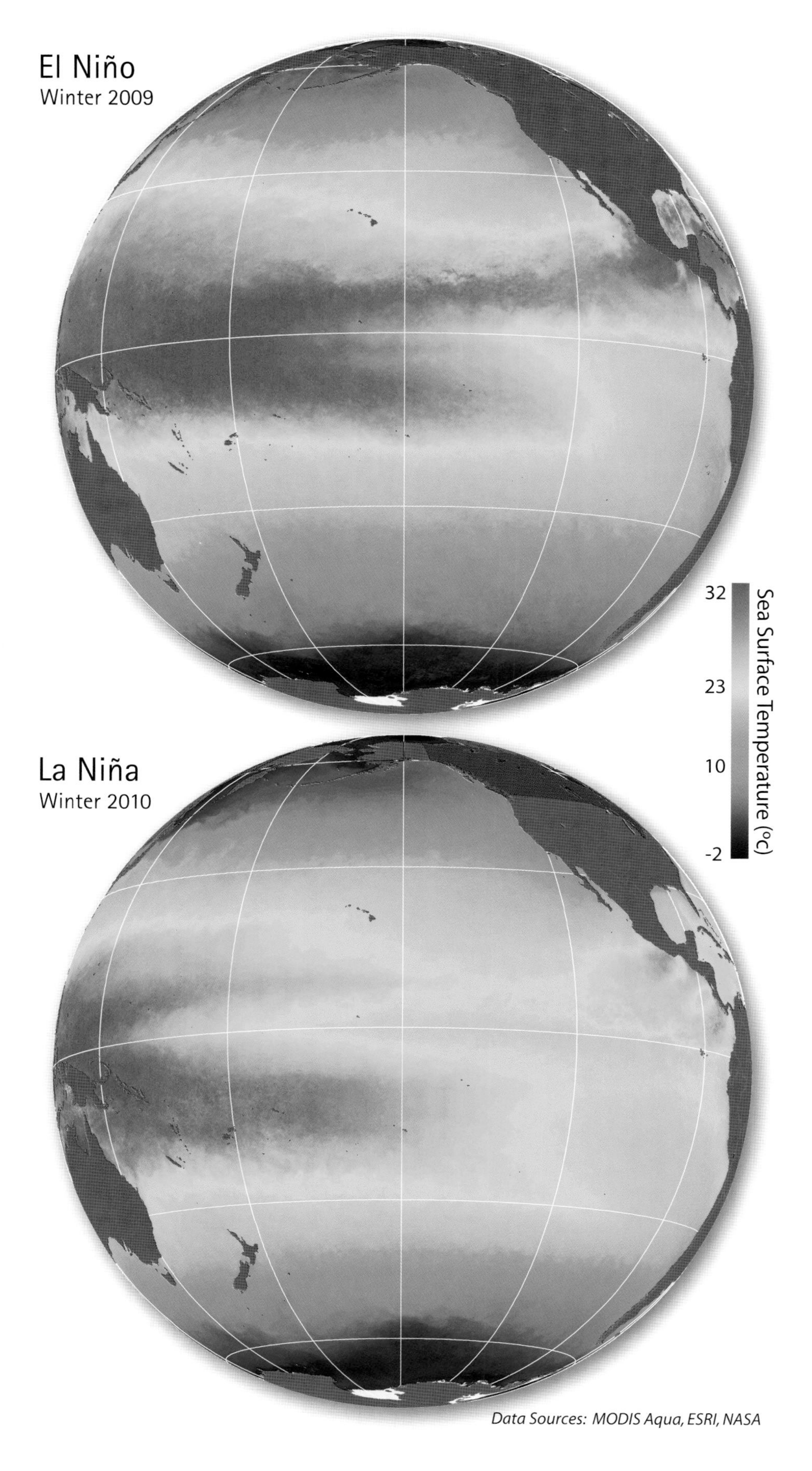

ABOVE: Dramatic changes in sea surface temperature between El Niño and La Niña conditions. The changes of the El Niño/La Nina Southern Oscillation have major effects on ocean species and ecosystems.

RIGHT: The Eastern Tropical Pacific Seascape's privileged location, stunning beauty, remarkable wildlife—like this marine iguana (*Amblyrynchus cristatus*) photographed in Fernandina Island, Galapagos, Ecuador—and its bounteous waters create many conservation challenges. The greatest of these are the impacts of overfishing, unregulated tourism, immigration pressure, and, increasingly, climate change.
Photograph by Tui De Roy/ Roving Tortoise Photos/ iLCP

THE CORAL TRIANGLE

Mark Erdmann

Covering a mere 1.6% of the oceanic area of the planet, the Coral Triangle contains over 35% of the world's coral reef habitat and is home to more marine plant and animal species than any other area of similar size on the planet (Spalding et al., 2001). Unlike most of the seascapes highlighted in this book, the Coral Triangle is not bounded by currents and coastlines and other oceanographic features. Rather, it is defined by its biodiversity, with its boundaries drawn around those reefs that are home to 500 or more species of hard coral (Green and Mous, 2004). More precisely, of the 141 coral ecoregions defined globally by Veron et al. (2009) based on their biogeographic similarity and patterns of endemism, sixteen contain 500 or more hard coral species and thus constitute the Coral Triangle.

The Coral Triangle encompasses all or part of six countries, including the Philippines, Malaysia, Indonesia, Timor-Leste, Papua New Guinea, and the Solomon Islands. While the northern, southern, and eastern boundaries of the region are well defined, ongoing taxonomic surveys in the neighboring South China Sea Coral Ecoregion (Devantier and Turak, 2009) may soon broach the 500-species mark for hard corals, thereby extending the boundaries of the Coral Triangle westward to include all of the island of Borneo, including Brunei Darussalam.

The Coral Triangle region sits at a tectonic and oceanographic crossroads, which is undoubtedly one of the factors responsible for its superlative marine biodiversity. Its complex shorelines and wildly varying bathymetry (it is not uncommon for the ocean to reach depths of 3,000 meters or more within a kilometer of the coast) are the result of a dynamic and often violent tectonic history, with numerous plate edges rubbing against one another and island arcs constantly shearing off and colliding over the past fifty million years (Hall, 1998). The island archipelagos of the Coral Triangle also straddle the Indian and Pacific Oceans, and thereby are home to species unique to each. Moreover, this position at a great ocean crossroads means the reefs here are constantly exposed to and fed by plankton-rich currents that commonly reach speeds of one meter per second, with the so-called Indonesian Throughflow providing the main pathway through which a mind-boggling twenty million cubic meters of seawater moves every *second* between the Pacific and Indian Oceans (Gordon and Fine, 1996).

Though the term "Coral Triangle" has only recently entered the vernacular, scientists have noted the marine biogeographic patterns that define it for nearly a century (Hoeksema, 2007). In charting the distributions of a wide variety of marine taxa, Ekman (1934, 1953) and Briggs (1974) conclusively showed that almost all groups reached their maximum diversity within the area they dubbed the "Indo-Malayan Triangle" or the "East Indies Triangle." Ongoing taxonomic work (aided by intensive scuba surveys) over the past thirty years has allowed the mapping and overlay of individual species distributions, confirming this pattern repeatedly for most marine plant and animal groups investigated.

With the hard corals, for example, at least 605 species (over 75% of the world's known taxa) are found in the Coral Triangle (Veron et al., 2009). The pattern of maximum diversity in this region also holds true when specific families of corals are examined individually, as shown by surveys of staghorn corals in the family Acroporidae (Wallace, 1997) and mushroom corals in the family Fungiidae (Hoeksema, 2007).

Similarly, over 2,700 species (37% of the world's total) of coral reef fishes thrive in the region (Allen, 2007). Groups as diverse as sea slugs and other mollusks (Gosliner, 2002; Wells, 2002); mantis shrimps, order Stomatopoda (Erdmann, 2007); seagrasses, order Alismatales (Spalding et al., 2003); and mangroves (Groombridge and Jenkins, 2002) all display the same pattern of maximum species diversity within the Coral Triangle. Moreover, as scientists begin to synthesize data from molecular studies of marine organisms, they are finding the Coral Triangle boasts very high genetic diversity *within* species as well (Carpenter et al., 2011). Many groups include a wealth of so-called cryptic species that look remarkably similar but are actually descended from genetically distinct lineages (Barber et al., 2000; DeBoer et al., 2009). As we learn more about species at the molecular level, the diversity with the Coral Triangle may climb yet higher.

The Coral Triangle also provides feeding, breeding, and calving grounds for an outstanding diversity of dolphins and whales, including blue whales (*Balaenoptera musculus*) and sperm whales (*Physeter macrocephalus*). It is the setting for much of the action in Herman Melville's epic tale Moby Dick, and Yankee whalers targeted the large sperm whale populations of the area throughout the 1800s.

Though biogeographers broadly concur with the abovementioned pattern of maximum marine biodiversity in the Coral Triangle, they have long debated the evolutionary processes that have generated this pattern (Briggs, 1974; Randall, 1998; Hoeksema, 2007; Halas and Winterbottom, 2009). Many have noted that the area represents a center of overlap of Indian and Pacific ocean biotas, while others postulate that the prevailing ocean currents tend to disperse marine species that evolved elsewhere (e.g., the central Pacific) toward the Coral Triangle, making it a "center of species accumulation." Others still—Briggs (1974, 2005) chief among them—argue vociferously that the region is in fact a "center of origin," with active speciation occurring to this day.

Though each of these explanations likely contributes to the unparalleled diversity of the Coral Triangle, the surprising level of local endemism (e.g., Allen and Erdmann, 2009) and presence of multiple concordant genetic breaks between populations of a number of marine species in the region clearly suggest that active speciation here is ongoing, making the area an even higher priority for conservation efforts (Barber et al., 2006; Briggs, 2005). There is no shortage of proximal mechanisms to explain this. High habitat diversity, complex shorelines and circulation patterns, a hyperactive tectonic history, and the presence of numerous deep sea basins that virtually became isolated marine lakes during periods of greatly lowered sea level in the past (Voris, 2000) have all provided a fertile substrate for speciation and make this region an evolutionary cauldron (McManus, 1985).

Whatever the reason for its peerless marine biodiversity, no one can argue the tremendous importance of the ecosystem goods and services provided by the marine ecosystems of the Coral Triangle. Of the roughly 363 million people that live in this region, over 120 million are directly dependent on its coastal and marine resources for livelihoods and food security (Coral Triangle Secretariat, 2008). In Indonesia alone, over 70% of the population depends on fish as their main source of protein. Across the Coral Triangle, the total value of coral reef fisheries alone is estimated at US$2.4 billion annually (Burke et al., 2002). Included within this is nearly US$800 million per year of live reef food fish exports to China and over US$100 million per year in aquarium fish exports to the United States, Europe, and elsewhere (Coral Triangle Secretariat, 2008). Not included within this figure is the important contribution of the reefs and other near-shore environments as spawning grounds and nurseries for the largest tuna fishery in the world—also a multibillion-dollar industry.

However, food security is only one of the primary services provided by the marine ecosystems of the Coral Triangle. The coral reefs of the region in particular are the basis for a rapidly expanding industry in marine tourism, which plays an increasingly important role in the economies of the six Coral Triangle countries, including remote Timor-Leste and the Solomon Islands. Though a regionwide economic valuation of this sector has not yet been made, tourism to the neighboring Great Barrier Reef of Australia is estimated to be worth up to US$1.6 billion annually (Carr and Mendelsohn, 2003).

Covering a mere 1.6% of the oceanic area of the planet, the Coral Triangle contains over 35% of the world's coral reef habitat and is home to more marine plant and animal species than any other area of similar size on the planet

Each of the three main coastal ecosystems in the region—coral reefs, seagrass beds, and mangrove forests—plays a crucial role in protecting coastlines. Though most of the Coral Triangle is not regularly exposed to hurricanes, the coasts are nonetheless subject to intense wave energy during monsoon storms, and the region's active tectonics make tsunamis relatively common, occurring on average once every two years over the past two decades.

Those same mangrove forests, which typically thrive in estuaries, also provide another critical ecosystem service by filtering water—all the more important in a region where even large cities rarely have even primary sewage treatment. Healthy mangrove forests can also slow river outflows and act as giant settling ponds, dramatically decreasing the amount of suspended silt and sediment that would otherwise be deposited directly onto fringing coral reefs where coastal rivers empty into the ocean.

It is ironic that the Coral Triangle's reefs and related marine ecosystems, unquestionably the most biodiverse and among the most economically valuable in the world, are also among the most endangered. Burke et al. (2002) considered over 80% of the coral reefs in the region to be at risk, due to threats that vary widely from country to country.

One of the most pervasive threats in the region is destructive fishing practices that range from blast fishing (using explosives to kill and collect fish), to cyanide fishing (using cyanide solution to stun lobster, grouper, and aquarium fishes for easy collection and eventual live export), to trawling and *muro-ami*—a net-fishing technique in which a line of divers uses weighted "scare-lines" or pipes to pound the reef surface and drive fish into a large net (Erdmann et al., 2002). Each of these techniques destroys the reef framework, the structure of which may take decades to recover.

More widespread is the problem of overfishing in general. Southeast Asian coral reefs are among the most intensively fished on the planet, particularly in the heavily populated areas of the Philippines, Malaysia, and central Indonesia. Moreover, fisheries management policies in the region are generally woefully deficient, and governments seem loathe to admit that they cannot continue to wring increasing yields from overexploited demersal and pelagic fisheries (Mous et al., 2005).

Though less of a problem in the sparsely populated eastern reaches of the Coral Triangle, marine pollution and excessive nutrient loading (*eutrophication*) as a result of untreated wastewater from urban areas entering the ocean is a growing concern. Similarly, poor coastal development practices that denude steep slopes and allow construction to clear away coastal vegetation buffers lead directly to erosion and heavy

LEFT: These gem-like islands of uplifted coralline limestone are uninhabited. The limestone (known as karst) islands lie northwest of Waigeo in West Papua, Indonesia. **Photograph by Tim Laman/ iLCP**

LEFT: A bigfin reef squid (*Sepioteuthis lessoniana*) in Malaysia. This large squid is often seen on coral reefs and seagrass beds. It is found throughout the tropical Indo-Pacific, from Hawaii to the Red Sea.
Photograph by David Fleetman/ Oceanwide Images

LEFT: The great barracuda (*Sphyraena barracuda*), like this one seen here swimming with teira batfish (*Platax teira*), photographed in Kimbe Bay, West New Britain, is a curious, fearsome-looking, usually solitary predator common to reefs and shallows in many oceans.
Photograph by Jürgen Freund/ iLCP

RIGHT: A small brittle starfish, class Ophiuroidea, appears to rest on a larger, bright red starfish.
Photograph by Tim Laman/ iLCP

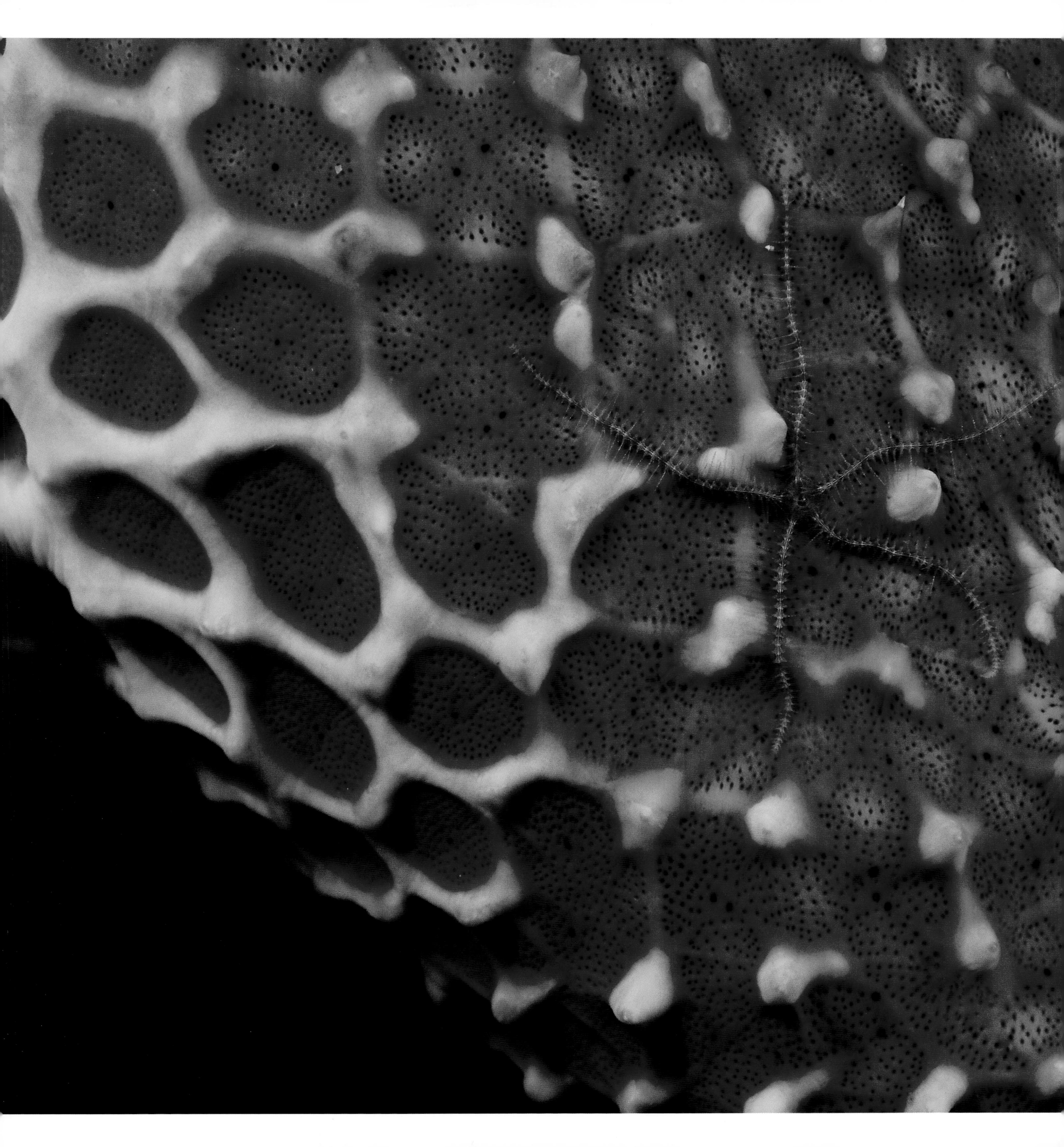

sedimentation into the marine environment (Burke et al., 2002). Throughout the region, disposal of solid waste at sea, in particular plastics, is a tremendous problem. It is difficult to find a beach that has not been sullied by the ubiquitous floating plastic, and many seabirds, turtles, whales, and dolphins suffer from entanglement or direct consumption of this flotsam.

The skyrocketing demand for energy and raw materials in Asia is driving a major push by governments in the Coral Triangle to increase offshore drilling for oil and gas reserves (with its attendant risk of spills), while also opening coastal ore deposits that were previously considered uneconomical to mining. Sedimentation from coastal strip mining frequently smothers reefs and near-shore ecosystems, but a more recent trend in the region may potentially pose an even greater threat: submarine tailings disposal, whereby mining waste is piped into the ocean and disposed of at depths below 200 meters. Though advocates claim the tailings sink harmlessly into the abyss, strong currents and upwellings ubiquitous in the Coral Triangle most certainly redistribute these finely ground sediments broadly, thus introducing a host of heavy metals into local food chains.

Sedimentation from coastal strip mining frequently smothers reefs and near-shore ecosystems, but a more recent trend in the region may potentially pose an even greater threat: submarine tailings disposal, whereby mining waste is piped into the ocean and disposed of at depths below 200 meters

As with all of the world's ocean regions, climate change also poses a significant threat to the Coral Triangle in the form of sea-level rise, ocean acidification, and coral bleaching (Hoegh-Guldberg et al., 2009; McLeod et al., 2010). Evidence for changes already underway and predicted long-term impacts in the region remain patchy, with some reefs and coastal ecosystems expected to show strong resilience, and others likely to succumb completely.

Marine resource management has a long history in the Coral Triangle, ranging from centuries-old traditions of seasonal harvest closures to more modern concepts of integrated coastal zone management, marine protected areas, and now ecosystem-based management of fisheries. Indeed, many of the approaches to managing marine resources introduced over the past three decades were first tested and refined in this region, with the Philippines in particular having served as a pilot site and early adopter of many international marine management initiatives.

Summarizing these management initiatives across the Coral Triangle in a succinct manner is nonetheless a difficult task. As with its extreme marine biological diversity, the six countries of the Coral Triangle feature hundreds of separate cultures and tens of thousands of different islands. Major differences exist among these countries and cultures in terms of political structure, the degree to which authority to manage natural resources is decentralized, and the capacity of local nongovernmental organizations (NGOs) to advocate for and monitor sustainable use of marine resources. Many of these cultures and governments have historically viewed the ocean as a commons, while others have a strong tradition of marine tenure, whereby families or clans "own" individual reefs and bays. They also vary widely in their human population density and the degree of marine resource exploitation (Schuttenberg and Bizot, 2002). These major differences also manifest themselves in the widely varying approaches to marine resource management and conservation in each of the six nations.

The Philippines, for example, with its highly decentralized governance and relatively dense coastal populations, has tended toward community-based approaches to marine management, including the development of hundreds of small community marine reserves (Christie et al., 2002). Malaysia, with more centralized authority, has instead developed a system of marine national parks with a more command-and-control approach to management. Indonesia has experimented with both ends of this spectrum of top-down central government control of marine management to fully community-based initiatives, and is now seemingly focused on a mid-spectrum approach that is perhaps best exemplified in the Papuan Bird's Head Seascape. This initiative combines a network of larger marine protected areas, based on strong ecosystem science and including large no-take areas, with a strong focus on training local communities and government officials to effectively manage them (Agostini, 2009).

The Melanesian peoples of Papua New Guinea (PNG) and the Solomon islands have relied on traditional marine resource management for centuries; nonetheless, a dedicated marine tourism private sector and several conservation nongovernmental organizations have been working with local communities and the government to formally gazette networks of marine protected areas in such key areas as Kimbe Bay in PNG (Green and Lokani, 2004).

The nation known as Timor-Leste (formerly East Timor) is both the smallest and youngest country in the Coral Triangle. Newly independent since 2002, it is only beginning to develop its approach to managing its rich marine resources. The government of Timor-Leste is making big strides, however, having recently developed the nation's first MPA, the Nino Konis Santana Marine Park (Edyvane et al., 2009), and prioritizing marine tourism as a leading green economic sector.

Despite this wide range of approaches to management of their marine resources, the six countries of the Coral Triangle are now formally committed to working together to share and build upon lessons learned. In 2007, Indonesian President Susilio Bambang Yudhoyono invited his counterparts from the five other Coral Triangle countries to launch the Coral

ABOVE: The waters off of Bali, Indonesia, are home to this otherworldly creature, a peacock mantis shrimp (*Odontodactylus scyllarus*). The shrimp feeds by smashing open its prey until it can feed on its tissue. **Photograph by Tim Laman/ iLCP**

Triangle Initiative on Coral Reefs, Fisheries and Food Security (CTI-CFF). Since launching this ambitious endeavor, governments, universities, NGOs, and international aid agencies have worked together to develop a Regional Plan of Action that commits to the following five actions: designating priority seascapes and effectively managing them; fully applying the ecosystem approach to fisheries management; establishing and effectively managing networks of marine protected areas; achieving measures to adapt to climate change; and improving the status of threatened marine species (Coral Triangle Secretariat, 2008).

Implementing these commitments will require a massive mobilization of political will and human and financial resources. Fortunately, the CTI has significant political clout (having been launched directly by the heads-of-state of the six Coral Triangle countries), and the past several years have witnessed a tremendous increase in both local and global awareness of the importance of the Coral Triangle and the challenges now facing it. There is much to be done, but at stake is nothing less than the global epicenter of marine biodiversity.

THE PATAGONIAN SEA

Claudio Campagna, María Victoria Zavattieri, and Valeria Falabella

What is the Patagonian Sea? It is not the southwest Atlantic, the "Argentine Sea," or the Patagonian Large Marine Ecosystem, though it integrates and expands all of these. The Patagonian Sea is a new ocean, one defined by the diversity of life it supports, rather than by any geographic boundary, national jurisdiction, or fishing zone.

Three prominent physical features characterize this vast oceanscape: the shallow continental shelf off Patagonia, the abrupt continental slope, and the broad abyss of the Argentine Basin. Oceans are dominated by quasi-sterile environments, low biomass areas that are the marine equivalent of deserts. Exceptions are the shallow waters nurtured by the sun, where upwellings or mixing currents create the fertile conditions that sustain life in abundant splendor.

The Patagonian Shelf is one such area. The largest submerged plain in the Southern Hemisphere, it covers one million square kilometers to a depth of one hundred meters. The bottom slopes gently toward the open ocean at a rate of about one meter of descent for every thousand meters from shore, until it reaches the eastern edge and drops off steeply. The western edge is bound by the coast of Argentina, a 4,000-km line, relatively poor in such physiographical features as islands, peninsulas, or fiords.

The few abrupt breaks in this uneventful coast occur near the continental border of the oceanscape. Circulation of the ocean waters around the Valdés Península and the islands of Golfo San Jorge affect the distribution of wildlife. Wind is also a prominent feature here, defining water circulation and productivity. The action of wind on the surface produces currents that vertically mix the water column. At the macroscale, the cold Malvinas and the warm Brazil currents form the functional backbone of an oceanic area the size of the Mediterranean Sea (Acha et al., 2004).

The Malvinas Current, rich in plankton, krill, and other nutrients, circulates in a northerly direction along the western edge of the Argentine Basin. The nutrient-poor Brazil Current enters the Patagonian Sea from the north and contacts its counterpart in the Brazil–Malvinas Confluence Zone, whose location varies, according to season, between 30° and 46° S. The Confluence represents an intense mixing of warm subtropical and cool sub-Antarctic waters. Over a surface area of a few hundred thousand square kilometers, these conditions allow for a great flourishing of forage fish and other prey.

The combined physical and functional features of these coastal and open-ocean interfaces, where heat meets cold and low-salt meets high-salt, shape the structure of food webs in the water column, at the ocean surface, and along the seabed and coastline. The distribution of colonial species of marine birds and mammals, for example, is tightly tied to frontal areas that function as well-provisioned supermarkets in a largely empty ocean. Plankton concentration can be three times more abundant along such fronts than in other areas of the already fertile shelf. But the highest life-supporting region occurs along the outer edge of the shelf: the Patagonian Shelf breakfront. Along 1,500 km (from 38° to 52° S) chlorophyll can reach concentrations of 20 mg/m3. This productivity provides ecological services of global importance, as large quantities of carbon dioxide are removed from the atmosphere, mitigating the effects of climate change.

Oceanfronts in the Patagonian Sea are relatively stable and predictable, a function of the geology of the ocean floor. The contours and features of the ocean floor—called bathymetry—force circulation in certain directions (Acha et al., 2004). In other oceans, regions of upwelling arise from the interaction of atmospheric and oceanographic variables—forces much less constant than the physical anatomy of the Patagonia Sea floor. Bathymetry-dependent fronts remain predictable over time and space. Having a reliable seasonal source of abundant food powerfully shapes the foraging behavior of top predators (Falabella et al., 2009).

Like other ecosystems in the temperate oceans, the Patagonian Sea supports a considerable diversity of resident species and visitors (Croxall and Wood, 2002). What distinguishes it is the striking abundance of food, an extraordinarily high biomass that supports the overall structure of the food web (Campagna et al., 2007). About 1,400 species of zooplankton have been described for the waters of the Brazil and Malvinas currents. A full inventory of invertebrate biodiversity has yet to be accomplished and will no doubt yield surprising results. Vertebrate species account for at least 700 described species. Bony fishes are the most common (400 species), followed by cartilaginous fishes (sharks, skates, and chimaeras; 122), marine and coastal birds (83), marine mammals (47 out of a total of 129 in the world), and marine turtles (five of the seven extant species).

At least one quarter of the bony fish of the southwest Atlantic are endemic (Foro, 2008). Among marine and coastal birds, the Olrog's Gull (*Larus atlanticus*) and two species of steamer ducks, the White-headed (*Tachyeres leucocephalus*) and the Flying (*Tachyeres patachonicus*), are

PRECEDING SPREAD: No place on the planet contains more marine species than the Coral Triangle, a region that extends from central Indonesia to Papua New Guinea and the Solomon Islands northward to the Philippines. The Coral Triangle has 605 species of zooxanthellate corals, which amounts to 76% of the world's species complement. This one was photographed off Sipadan Island, Sabah, and Malaysian Borneo.
Photograph by Stuart Westmorland

endemic to the Patagonian oceanscape. Four dolphin species are either endemic or have very restricted distribution outside Patagonia: the La Plata (*Pontoporia blainvillei*), Peale's (*Lagenorhynchus australis*), Chilean (*Cephalorhynchus eutropia*), and Commerson's dolphin (*Cephalorhynchus commersonii*).

Among bony fishes, two species with high abundance are the Argentine anchovy (*Engraulis anchoita*) and the Falkland sprat (*Sprattus fuegensis*). Together with a few squid species, they form the critical components of a food chain that sustains charismatic wildlife such as albatrosses and penguins, whales, dolphins, sea lions, and elephant seals.

Compared to the oceans of the northern hemisphere, intensively exploited and polluted since early times (Foro, 2008; Halpern et al., 2008), the Patagonian Sea remained a relatively well-preserved secret until the 1980s. Then the word spread from adventurous travelers, and that brought Patagonia's beauty to the attention of avid tourists. A few thousand visitors to the Patagonian Península Valdés in the early 1990s had increased to 330,000 by 2009.

Also about two decades ago, this ocean was discovered by the ocean's most rapacious new predators, the highly efficient factory fisheries of China, Japan, and the European Union (especially Spain). The resources of the Patagonian Sea have been extracted to satisfy the markets of the developed nations of Europe, Asia, and North America. Today, far from being pristine, this once-distant ocean is exposed to a variety of threats. Most serious are the impact of introduced species, chronic oil pollution, unsustainable and illegal fishing, overfishing, discard as bycatch of fishes and dozens of species of invertebrates, and the entanglement of seabirds, marine turtles, and marine mammals in fishing gear (Foro, 2008).

Several regional and international fisheries are at risk of collapse due to overfishing, especially the fishery for Argentine hake (*Merluccius hubbsi*), for decades the most important Argentine fishing fleet (Foro, 2008). Between 1993 and 2004, declared landings for this species were well above the maximum allowed catches. The actual landings were doubtless even higher. Between 1987 and 2009, overfishing caused the biomass of breeding adults to fall by 70%. Excess fishing capacity, government subsidies, and haphazard enforcement all encourage the practice of overfishing. As happens in many overfished grounds, between 1989 and 2003, caught fish for those species of choice were smaller, and the industry began to turn its attention to new species. In the Common Fishing Zone between Argentina and Uruguay, fewer and fewer carnivorous bottom fish are caught, while there has been an increase in the fishing of those fishes that occupy other niches in the food web, such as detrivores, herbivores, and omnivores. As a result, the whole food web is thrown out of balance.

Bottom trawling dominates coastal and deep sea fishing in Argentina, and the bycatch of benthic invertebrates is discarded by the ton. Birds, turtles, and marine mammals are also captured accidentally by trawlers and long-line fishing, threatening populations and entire species. The human footprint in the Patagonian Sea so far has threatened sixty-five species with extinction, according to the International Union for the Conservation of Nature. Albatrosses and marine turtles are at serious risk of global extinction and local extirpation due to pressure from fisheries. At least thirty species of sharks and rays face local extinction from similar pressures.

The economic value of the ecological services provided by this still-healthy system can only be estimated, but it is clear that market costs do not reflect the environmental impact of the consumed products (Boersma et al., 2004). Reliable information on bycatch and biodiversity is essential for solving the overfishing crises, yet regional cooperative research programs aimed at alleviating the impact of overfishing and bycatch on biodiversity do not exist. Management is not informed by modern understanding of ecosystems, and regional fishing organizations are dysfunctional. Fisheries are managed species by species, and quotas often fluctuate in response to economic and political demands rather than to demands of environmental sustainability. The conflict between Britain and Argentina over the Malvinas (Falkland) Islands has hampered regional and international cooperation. Efforts to control nonnative species and prevent new introductions remain weak.

However, there is still time to enact solutions to counter all these threats, as no extinctions have yet been reported for the Patagonian Sea. Important coastal protected areas recently have been created, such as the Parque Interjurisdiccional Marino Costero Patagonia Austral, located along one of the most physically diverse stretches of coastline. The proportion of the open ocean under protection thus far is negligible, and very far from the goal. Far from the coast and out of sight, pelagic environments remain underexplored and largely ignored. Yet, expected targets could be reached by creating a few open-ocean protected and special management areas. The small open-ocean Burdwood Bank special management area for biodiversity is an underwater seamount 136 miles from the tip of Argentina. Rich in hard and soft corals, it is an important feeding and breeding ground for albatross, penguins, whales, and sea lions as well as southern blue whiting (*Micromesistius australis*) and Fuegian sardines (*Sprattus fuegensis*). In 2008 the government of Argentina set all 1,787 sq km apart as a marine protected

The Patagonian Sea remained a relatively well-preserved secret until the 1980s. Then the word spread from adventurous travelers, and that brought Patagonia's beauty to the attention of avid tourists

RIGHT: An orca (*Orcinus orca*) purposely beaches itself to capture a southern sea lion (*Otaria byronia*) pup in the shallow water. **Photograph by Theo Allofs/ iLCP**

RIGHT: The San Rafael glacier ends its long, icy journey in the shoreline of Patagonia, Chile. **Photograph by Daniel Beltrá/ Greenpeace/ iLCP**

RIGHT: Two southern right whales (*Eubalaena australis*) off the coast of Patagonia. This species formerly occurred in very large numbers in the Southern Hemisphere, but whaling during the last century seriously depleted its numbers. They are now starting to recover. **Photograph by Howard Hall/ Howard Hall Productions**

LEFT: Black-browed albatross, (*Thalassarche melanophrys*) like all other albatrosses, are long-winged seabirds uniquely adapted to extremely long-distance sea flights. They generally only come to land during breeding season when they will rear only one chick. In this image, the sun sets over the Patagonian Sea as ten thousand nesting pairs of black-browed albatrosses settle in for the hot summer night.
Photograph by Art Wolfe/ Art Wolfe Stock/ iLCP

The biodiversity crisis that could bring about the collapse and extinction of certain marine populations clearly is upon us

area. This represents an important first step in a promising direction.

The advent of new technology in the form of satellite tracking is providing new data on which to base conservation priorities. Using satellite tracking, scientists have identified the principal foraging areas of seventeen species of pelagic birds, mammals, and marine turtles (Falabella et al., 2009). Data suggest that special management is urgently required for the waters adjacent to the Malvinas (Falkland), Isla de los Estados (Staten), and Diego Ramírez islands. Areas crucial to the successful reproduction of top predators include the waters off the Valdés Península as far as Golfo San Jorge, the shelf-slope at the latitude of the Gulf of San Jorge, the outflow of the Río de la Plata, and the eastern portion of the Burdwood Bank. The Patagonian Sea's most productive front, along the slope of the Patagonian Shelf, offers opportunities to create mobile protected areas and areas under both exclusive economic zone (EEZ) and international jurisdiction. Mobile parks, for example, would adapt to the seasonal circulation of waters that causes changes in the location of priority areas for biodiversity. Transboundary parks may also serve to prevent unreported and illegal fisheries in a few pockets of the shallow shelf that lie beyond national jurisdiction.

The current situation of the seas of the world, under even greater threat as a result of climate change and its attendant acidification, demands immediate action. The biological diversity and functionality of the world's ecosystems are of extraordinary importance for the future of humankind. However, the biodiversity crisis that could bring about the collapse and extinction of certain marine populations clearly is upon us. An integrated ecosystem management approach is required to avert such collapse in the Patagonian Sea. Detailed data exist for implementing such an approach. A network of marine areas, managed with biodiversity is mind, is sorely needed. Such a network would incorporate those open ocean environments whose function is most affected by heavily populated coastal areas. Political will, regional cooperation, international dialogue, and thorough research will be necessary to make such a network a success.

RIGHT: **The Patagonia Sea.** This region supports many marine species including seals, whales, and seabirds. The marine protected area network cover some but not all the significant marine areas in the region.

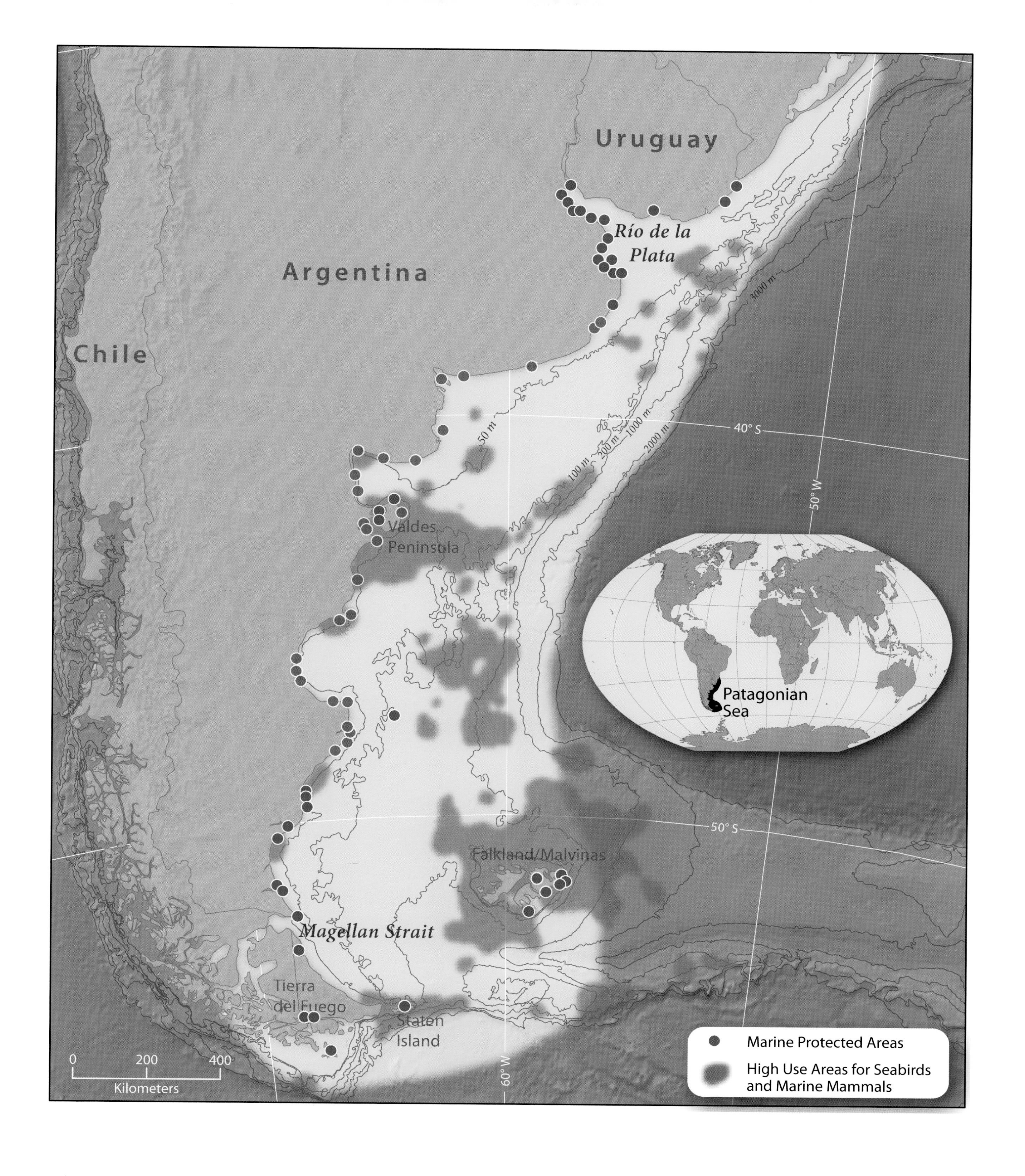
Uruguay
Río de la Plata
Argentina
Chile
3000 m
40° S
50 m
100 m
200 m
1000 m
2000 m
50° W
Valdes Peninsula
Patagonian Sea
50° S
Falkland/Malvinas
Magellan Strait
Tierra del Fuego
Staten Island
60° W
0
200
400
Kilometers
Marine Protected Areas
High Use Areas for Seabirds and Marine Mammals

THE POLAR OCEANS

Carin J. Ashjian

Covered during winter or year-round by sea ice and subject to dramatic cycles in air temperature and light, Arctic and Antarctic marine environments are the most extreme and variable on earth. Air temperatures can range from -40° to -50°C up to 60°C, while light cycles vary between total darkness during midwinter and 24 hours of daylight in midsummer. Sea ice in many locations is seasonal while other regions harbor what may be the last vestiges of multiyear sea ice.

Geographically, the north and south polar regions are a contrast in morphology. The Antarctic is an ice-covered continent, with massive ice sheets that coat the underlying land mass, while the Arctic is an ocean basin, surrounded by continents. Despite these differences, the biology of both regions is similar in that each is exquisitely attuned to the seasonality in light and sea ice. Sea ice also provides an important substrate for life forms ranging from the smallest microbe to invertebrates to marine mammals. Because of the food web's dependence on sea ice, these regions and the biological communities within them are vulnerable to the consequences of ongoing climate change. In particular, changes in the extent and timing of seasonal sea ice formation and melt, in ocean temperature and currents, and in the persistence of perennial or multiyear ice, may dramatically affect multiple components of the polar marine ecosystems.

The Arctic is further distinguished from the Antarctic by the long-term presence of communities of indigenous peoples who also have developed traditional lifestyles that are adapted to the severity and seasonality of the environment. Many aspects of these lifestyles are dependent on marine resources and the marine environment for subsistence food (fish, seabirds, and marine mammals) and for transportation both during winter, over sea ice, and during summer using boats. With twentieth and twenty-first century transportation of food and manufactured goods into Arctic communities and with access to global communications, indigenous lifestyles have diversified. Yet the lives of the first peoples of the Arctic remain dependent on marine resources in some part for subsistence and in great part as an integral part of the culture.

The Arctic marine environment also is important to commercial interests of the world economy, including fishing, exploitation of oil and gas, tourism, and international marine shipping.

The Antarctic, by contrast, is home to no indigenous peoples and, under the Antarctic Treaty, is protected from most commercial interests such as oil and gas exploration and development. Some commercial fishing and hunting does occur, however; much of that is strictly regulated through the Commission for the Conservation of Antarctic Marine Living Resources (Kock et al., 2007). Tourism and scientific research bring a number of people to the Antarctic each year, with approximately thirty countries establishing permanent research stations along the coast.

Defining the Antarctic and Arctic regions geographically can be difficult. One simple definition is that each is composed of regions of latitude greater than that of the Arctic (66°33'N) or the Antarctic (66°33'S) Circles. However, this definition excludes several key regions that lie geographically outside of each yet exhibit ecosystem characteristics, especially the presence of seasonal sea ice, that are distinctly polar. In practical terms, then, the polar regions could be defined as those that regularly experience seasonal sea ice. Using that definition, the Arctic includes the Arctic basins and marginal shelf seas surrounding them, the Canadian Archipelago, Baffin Bay, portions of Hudson Bay, and the Bering, Barents, Greenland, Iceland, and Norwegian Seas. According to the Antarctic Treaty, the Antarctic includes all of the continent and islands, ice shelves, and seas south of 60°S, a boundary that coincides approximately with the northward extent of sea ice in austral winter (Smith and Comiso, 2008).

The Arctic Ocean contains two major basins deeper than 3,000 meters. The Eurasian and Amerasian Basins are separated by the shallower, mid-ocean Lomonosov Ridge and are surrounded by the large, shallow shelf seas of adjacent North America, Greenland, and Eurasia (Jakobsson, 2002, 2004). A number of large rivers drain into the Arctic Ocean, particularly along the coast of Siberia. Limited connection to the outside oceans occurs via three main routes (MacDonald et al., 2004). The most significant lies at the northern end of the Atlantic Ocean, where broad currents flow to the north through the Norwegian and Barents Seas, bringing warm, salty water from the Atlantic into the colder, fresher Arctic. Cold water also exits the Arctic along the east coast of Greenland. Water from the Bering Sea enters the Arctic through the Bering Strait between Alaska and Russia, with some reverse flow occurring usually during winter. Water also exits the Arctic through the myriad of channels in the Canadian Archipelago. Both of these latter are much lower in magnitude than is seen between the Atlantic and the Arctic.

The Antarctic is a continent, with ocean surrounding it. Collectively, the waters surrounding Antarctica to as far north as 60°S are considered the Southern Ocean, with the boundary between polar and subpolar waters known as the Polar Front (Carmack, 1990). The largest and perhaps most important ocean current in the world, the Antarctic Circumpolar Current (ACC), is a river of ocean that flows from west to east and surrounds the Antarctic continent. The ACC is deep and massive; its circulation, temperature, and condition influence all other ocean currents and the climate of Earth generally. Deep, nutrient-rich water from this current upwells episodically onto the shelves, supporting high production and rich ecosystems. Inshore of the Antarctic Circumpolar Current lie a series of Antarctic seas, including the Amundsen, Bellingshausen, Lazarev, Ross, and Weddell Seas. Much of the continental shelf surrounding Antarctica is quite narrow, although the shelves of the Weddell and Ross Seas are broad and deep. One of the prominent features is the Antarctic Peninsula that extends northward toward the southern tip of South America.

Both the Arctic and Antarctic are characterized by the presence of sea ice. In the Arctic, seasonal sea ice extends to the south through the northern Bering Sea, the Barents Sea, the Norwegian and Greenland Seas, and Baffin Bay in winter and retreats back into the Arctic Basin and Canadian Archipelago during summer. The Arctic Basin contains multiyear ice as well, which remains intact throughout the summer and is much thicker than first-year ice because of repeated seasons of freezing. Seasonal sea ice surrounds the Antarctic continent in winter as well, extending quite far from the shoreline in the Ross and Weddell Seas and extending north to approximately 60°S. Much of the Antarctic sea ice melts during the summer so there is little multiyear ice.

The known (or described) diversity of organisms in the polar regions is somewhat less than in temperate and tropical regions, yet there are still an impressive number of marine species found in each region. Each polar region is characterized by an iconic animal: the polar bear (*Ursus maritimus*) in the Arctic and the penguin (family Spheniscidae) in the Antarctic. Despite their prominence, these icons each represent only a small piece of an intricate and fascinating ecosystem that is dependent on the seasonal variation in light and sea ice and, for some animals, on sea ice itself.

Polar marine ecosystems are distinguished by having relatively short food chains, with few links from the primary producers (phytoplankton and ice algae) to the marine mammals and birds at the top of the food chain

Polar marine ecosystems are distinguished by having relatively short food chains, with few links from the primary producers (phytoplankton and ice algae) to the marine mammals and birds at the top of the food chain. In a number of instances, there can be as few as three links in that chain, such as phytoplankton to zooplankton to baleen whale. Primary production occurs through growth of phytoplankton, seaweeds or macroalgae in coastal regions, and ice algae that grow in and under the sea ice. Some species of ice algae, such as *Melosira arctica* in the Arctic, can grow to significant size, suspended from the sea ice to lengths of several meters (Melnikov, 1997). Other ice algae are composed of shorter chains or solitary cells in or on the sea ice and lend a "dirty" appearance to the underside of sea ice. With increased light to the bottom of the sea ice and to the upper ocean each spring, a veritable explosion of life ensues. Light drives growth of the phytoplankton and of the ice algae. The edge of retreating sea ice, or the marginal ice zone, is particularly active as the spring sunlight reaches newly exposed ocean. Numerous microscopic planktonic animals respond to the sudden availability of food, with life cycles timed to coincide with the spring renewal or bloom. Large diatoms dominate the phytoplankton during the spring bloom in both regions, with the community composition shifting to smaller nanoplankton and picoplankton later in the summer. In the Ross Sea, Antarctica, the colonial haptophyte alga *Phaeocystis antarctica* can dominate even in spring (Smith et al., 2007).

Overall, Antarctic ecosystems are the more productive of the two polar regions (Arrigo et al., 2008a; Pabi et al., 2008), although total production varies both regionally and interannually (Smith and Comiso, 2008). Elevated production in Antarctic regions is sustained in part by the upwelling of nutrient-rich water from depths along the shelf break around the continent. These elevated levels of primary production largely support relatively high abundances of pelagic organisms that in turn sustain the whales, penguins, seabirds, and seals at the top of the food chain.

The Arctic Ocean, by contrast, has low primary production due to the presence of perennial sea ice at many locations and nutrient limitation in the upper water column. Access to nutrients becomes limited as nutrient-rich deep water becomes segregated from the upper water column by a permanent density gradient. In warmer oceans, storms mix the upper and lower water columns, distributing nutrients. But in the Arctic the density gradient keeps the nutrients out of the upper water column. Because of the

LEFT: The reason this block of multiyear ice photographed in Antarctica looks green is because it serves as habitat for ice algae, a general term used to describe all the various types of algal communities found in sea ice. These ice algal communities play a key role in primary production and a critical part of the food chain in both the Arctic and Antarctica. **Photograph by Maria Stenzel/ National Geographic Stock**

LEFT: Amphipods are the dominant fauna at the underside of Arctic sea ice and the foundation of the food chain in this seascape. Here we see an amphipod encapsulated in ice, Nunavut, Canada. **Photograph by Paul Nicklen/ National Geographic Stock/ iLCP**

LEFT: A scientist working under the sea ice suctions tiny amphipods from an ice floe in Canada Basin, Arctic Ocean. **Photograph by Paul Nicklen/ National Geographic Stock/ iLCP**

RIGHT: A group of crabeater seals (*Lobodon carcinophagus*) surfaces to breathe through a fast ice lead, or channel, in the Weddel Sea, Antarctica. **Photograph by Tui De Roy/ Roving Tortoise Photos/ iLCP**

RIGHT: The albedo effect, or the percentage of incoming radiation reflected on the sea ice surface, was grossly underestimated by scientists factoring in sea ice surface reflectivity change. As ice disappears, its white reflective surface changes to a dark blue surface, which absorbs a much larger percentage of radiation, hence accelerating the melting process. **Photograph by Chris Linder/ iLCP**

RIGHT: An Adelie penguin (*Pygoscelis adeliae*) waves its wings over its chicks, Antarctic Peninsula. **Photograph by Art Wolfe/ Art Wolfe Stock/ iLCP**

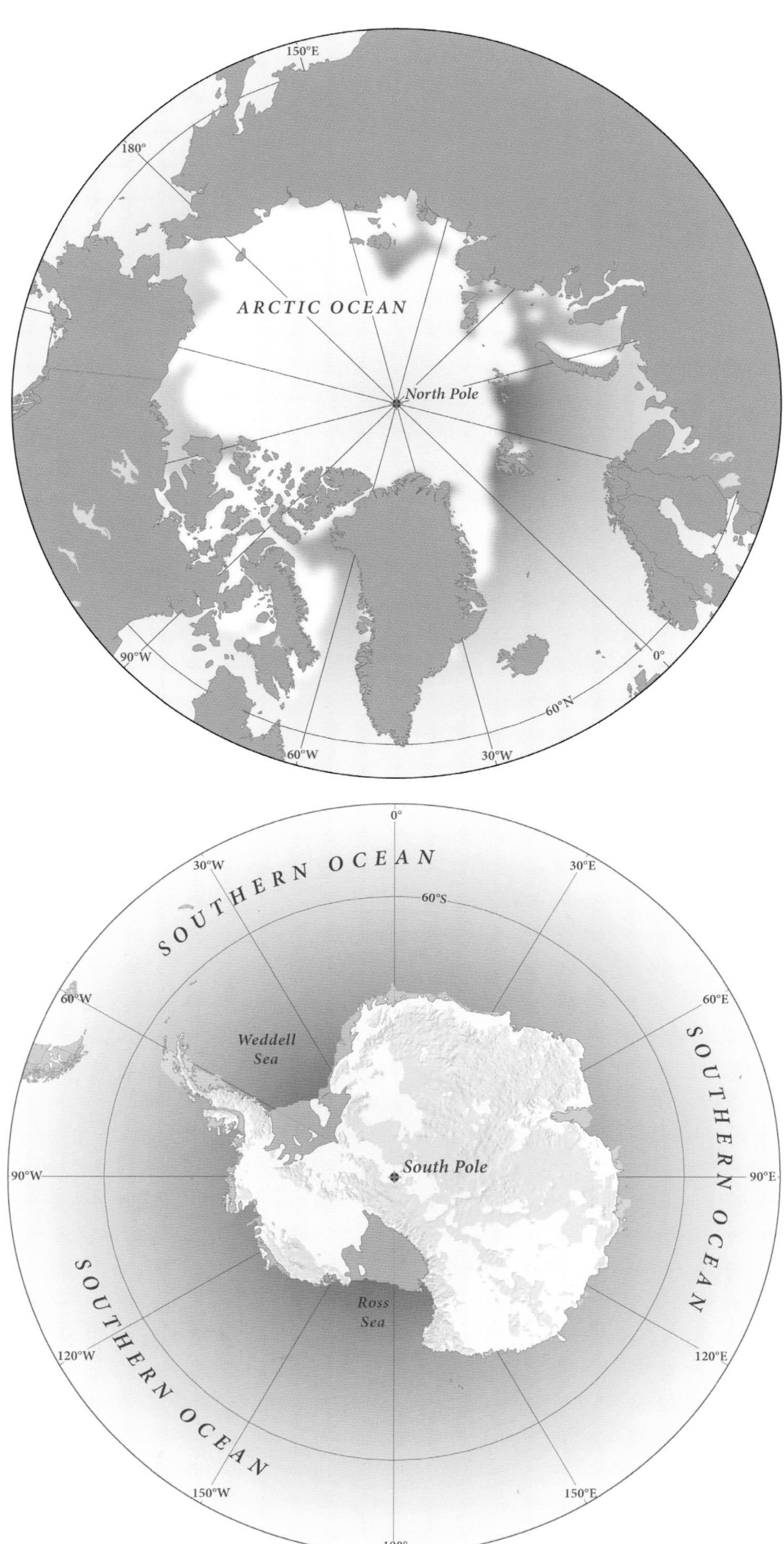

lower primary production, numbers of pelagic organisms are quite low in the Arctic Ocean. Arctic marginal seas, however, can receive significant inputs of nutrients from outside the Arctic, as happens through the Bering Strait in the western Arctic or from the inflow of Atlantic water in the eastern Arctic, and from rivers. As a consequence, production in some Arctic marginal seas can be quite high.

In the Antarctic, a single animal, the euphausiid *Euphausia superba*, also known as the Antarctic krill, is central or key to the food chain (Marr, 1962; Smith and Schnack-Schiel, 1990). This shrimp-like crustacean member of the zooplankton consumes phytoplankton and microzooplankton, can grow to be 60 mm in length, and is a critical prey item for crabeater seals (*Lobodon carcinophagus*), penguins, fish, marine birds, and baleen whales, as well as other zooplankton including jellyfish and squid. Krill are often found in massive swarms or schools, providing high concentrations of easily captured prey for their predators, particularly the baleen whales that must find such dense patches in order to efficiently filter sufficient prey. The success of krill populations is correlated with the presence of sea ice, with low abundances of krill in regions, and years with a low winter sea ice extent. Larval stages of krill are dependent on sea ice for food during overwintering (Atkinson et al., 2004). The krill follow two- to four-year life cycles, so survival of the larval stages is critically important for development to the adult stages and for recruitment success. The tight dependence of krill on sea ice is further demonstrated by the replacement of krill by salps, gelatinous chain-forming filter feeders, in oceanic waters when sea ice is absent during the previous winter (Loeb et al., 1997; Atkinson et al., 2004).

The Atlantic Sector of the Antarctic in particular is a region with abundant krill, although the animals are found in shelf water all around the Antarctic (Atkinson et al., 2008). Krill are preyed upon directly by penguins, Antarctic fur

ABOVE: **The Polar Oceans.** These seas at the extreme north and south of the planet support unique constellations of organisms above, below, and even within their ice.

seals (*Arctocephalus gazella*) and crabeater seals, fish, squid, baleen whales, and seabirds such as petrels (family Procellariidae) and southern polar skuas (*Catharacta maccormicki*). Some of these are in turn prey for larger mammals, such as the leopard seals (*Hydrurga leptonyx*) that feed on penguins, Weddell and Ross seals (*Leptonychotes weddellii* and *Ommatophoca rossii*) and toothed whales that feed on squid and fish, and the killer whale (*Orcinus orca*). The extent to which krill and other pelagic animals consume phytoplankton in the water column affects the supply of food to the benthic community, and, as a result, the numbers and biomass of benthic animals.

Some of the most visible Antarctic animals are dependent on sea ice. Of the eight penguin species found in Antarctica, two are ice-obligate, the Adélie, *Pygoscelis adeliae*, and the Emperor, *Aptenodytes forsteri*. The other six penguin species are ice-tolerant (Forcada and Trathan, 2009). For marine mammals, the Antarctic minke whale (*Balaenoptera bonaerensis*) and four seals (crabeater, Ross, Weddell, and leopard) are permanent residents of the pack ice. Other mammals found seasonally during the summer ice-free months include the large baleen whales (see caption) and elephant and fur seals (Ainley and DeMaster, 1990). Krill are fished commercially by a number of countries including Poland, Korea, Japan, and Ukraine, with the catch primarily going to fishmeal, although some countries market krill for human consumption. Fisheries quotas are regulated by the Convention for the Conservation of Antarctic Marine Living Resources.

Although several species of euphausiids are endemic to Arctic marginal seas and fjords, a different crustacean, the copepod, is much more important overall to Arctic food webs. One genus of copepod, *Calanus*, is particularly important. *Calanus* copepods follow a multiyear life history dependent on Arctic seasonality. Adults reproduce in spring, either before the spring bloom, using their fat reserves, or coincident with the algal bloom. In early fall, the copepods migrate to deep water to overwinter, using fat stored during the summer to maintain a reduced metabolism and to sustain them until the spring bloom the following year.

Copepods provide food for larger zooplankton, Arctic cod and other fish, as well as seabirds and cetaceans. The Arctic cod sustain ice seals that in turn are prey for the polar bear. The extent to which zooplankton including large copepods consume phytoplankton in the Antarctic water column will determine the supply of food to the sea floor and the abundance of benthic organisms. For example, most phytoplankton is consumed in the water column of the southern Bering and Barents Seas, supporting high pelagic productivity of such commercially important fishes as pollock (Bering) and cod (Barents). By contrast, in the northern Bering and Chukchi Seas, a greater proportion of phytoplankton reaches the sea floor and in the benthic communities we find a high and varied biomass, with much lower abundances of pelagic fishes.

Four Arctic marine mammals are ice-dependent: ice seals (ringed, *Phoca hispida*, and bearded, *Erignathus barbatus*) that pup and den on the ice, walrus that use the ice as a resting platform, and polar bears that access ice seals from the sea ice (Moore and Huntington, 2008). Other marine mammals are ice-associated, adapted to life in seasonally ice-covered waters but not critically dependent on sea ice itself, including the beluga, narwhal, and bowhead whales (*Delphinapterus leucus*, *Monodon monoceros*, and *B. mysticetus*), and the harp, hooded, ribbon, and spotted seals (*Pagophilus groenlandicus*, *Cystophora cristata*, *Histriophoca fasciata*, and *Phoca largha*).

Because they are so finely tuned to the environmental extremes of polar seasonality and because many ecosystem members depend on seasonal and perennial sea ice as a substrate or habitat, polar ecosystems are particu-

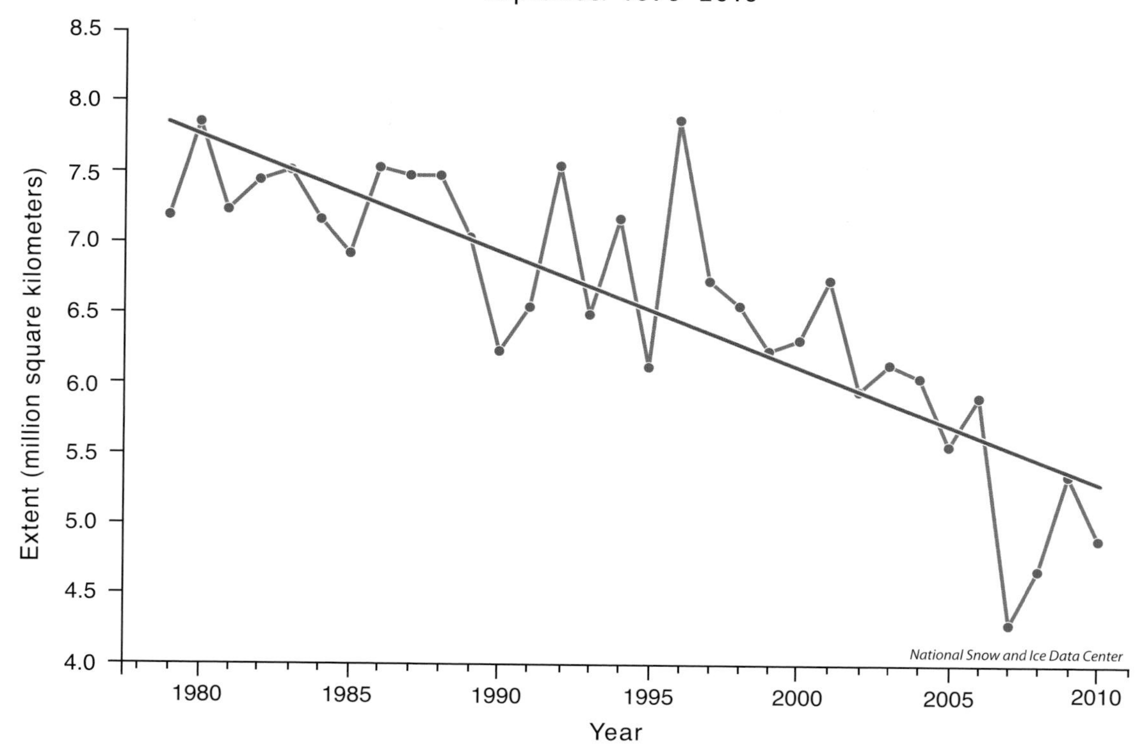

ABOVE: **Arctic sea ice extent.** Arctic sea ice is melting as a result of climate change. The loss of sea ice is also allowing an exchange of species between the Pacific and Atlantic oceans.

larly vulnerable to ongoing climate change and accompanying changes in the extent and timing of seasonal sea ice. Species respond to climate change by contracting or expanding their ranges or with changes in abundance, in the timing of their life histories, and in their behavior. Detecting these responses to climate change can be difficult because we lack long-term records for many populations and constituent species of polar ecosystems. Yet scientists have recorded responses to global warming and changes in sea ice across multiple trophic levels, primarily in regions experiencing the greatest environmental change such as the Western Arctic and the Antarctic Peninsula.

A dramatic decline in the extent of Arctic sea ice starting in the 1980s and continuing to the present has been observed using satellites, with losses particularly in the Western Arctic, along the coast of Siberia, and through the Canadian Archipelago. This decline results in much thinner sea ice in those regions in winter, since the ice reforms each year and does not build on multiyear ice that has survived the summer months (Maslanik et al., 2007). Stroeve and colleagues have suggested that summer sea ice may be virtually gone in the Arctic by 2030 (Stroeve et al., 2008). In contrast to the Arctic, overall sea ice area has not changed to as great a degree in recent years in the Antarctic (Ducklow et al., 2007; Smith and Comiso, 2008; Mayewski et al., 2009). However, ocean warming and a regional reduction in sea ice have occurred along the Antarctic Peninsula (Meredith and King, 2005; Mayewski et al., 2009; Ducklow et al., 2007).

Primary productivity in the open waters of the central Arctic has increased during the last decade in tandem with increases in ice-free seas during summer (Arrigo et al., 2008b). In the Western Arctic, where sea ice has declined most precipitously, the effects of retreating sea ice have been observed on both prominent marine mammals as well as the larger ecosystem. Benthic amphipod abundances decreased in the northern Bering Sea, accompanied by sea ice reduction and air and water temperature increases, shifting an important foraging location of gray whales that feed on these amphipods to the southern Chukchi Sea (Grebmeier et al., 2006). Higher up the food web, ice-dependent marine mammals experience changes in sea ice extent as a loss of habitat (Laidre et al., 2008). Mass haul-outs of walrus along the Alaskan coast of the Chukchi Sea have recurred in that region with the loss of summer sea ice that is the pinniped's haul-out platform. In 2004, several drowned polar bears were observed from aerial surveys in the Beaufort Sea. They had apparently succumbed to high seas during a storm over the then ice-free Chukchi Sea (Monnett and Gleason, 2006). Reductions in condition, survival, and recruitment of polar bears have been observed in years when sea ice is low (Stirling et al., 1999; Regehr et al., 2007, 2010; Rode et al., 2010), since polar bears feed primarily on ice-associated ring and bearded seals.

Climate change is driving many Arctic species northward. Copepods of Pacific origin have been observed in the Chukchi Sea and Arctic basin during summer months (Hopcroft et al., 2010, and references therein). Whether these individuals survive is not known; however, successful recruitment of expatriate populations could modify the structure of Arctic ecosystems.

In Antarctica, most ecological responses to changing climate have been observed on the Antarctic Peninsula, where water temperature has risen and sea ice is retreating. Chlorophyll concentration has decreased on the northern and increased on the southern shelves of the western Antarctic Peninsula, with increased proportions of large diatoms in the southern regions (Montes-Hugo et al., 2009). Long-term records on krill abundance in the southwest Atlantic sector of Antarctica, including the Peninsula, demonstrate a thirty-year decline associated with increased water temperature and decreased sea ice (Atkinson et al., 2008). Adélie penguins and other birds along the western Antarctic Peninsula also have declined, coincident with the long-term decrease in the krill on which they prey (Fraser et al., 1992; Moline et al., 2008; Nicol et al., 2008; Forcada and Trathan, 2009). Further to the north, declines in the births of fur seal pups have coincided with low availability of krill (Forcada et al., 2005). As the availability of krill declines, whales such as the southern right whale may experience negative impacts as well.

Both polar regions are vulnerable also to direct anthropogenic impacts, particularly those associated with ongoing climate change and the new opportunities afforded by reduced sea ice cover and increased access to commercially important species and resources that come with open water. In the Arctic, ecosystems are vulnerable to disturbance and, potentially, pollution associated with increased commerce and shipping, exploration and exploitation of marine hydrocarbon resources, and tourism. At present, fishing in the Arctic remains limited to marginal seas such as the Bering, Norwegian, and Barents. In the future, seas such as the Chukchi that in the past experienced much greater ice cover may become exploited, requiring responsible management and stewardship. Indigenous peoples in the Arctic also are a part of the marine ecosystem, and their subsistence needs have to be balanced with the needs of the larger global society. Antarctic ecosystems, while vulnerable to climate change, at present may be less vulnerable to human impacts because of the Antarctic treaty. Even though the continent has no indigenous human population, Antarctic fisheries still require careful management, particularly in the face of ongoing climate change (Kock et al., 2007). Environmental pressures exerted by tourism and the limited human settlements at Antarctic research stations also require continued vigilance. Polar regions have long captured the imagination and passion of scientists, adventurers, students, and the global human community. Protecting and conserving these unique and strangely fragile seas is a responsibility common to all citizens of this Earth.

RIGHT: A young caribou herder from the Nenets ethic group, Kánin Peninsula, Russia. In addition to caribou meat, the Nenet's diet depends on fish from the White and Barents Seas.
Photograph by Staffan Widstrand/ Wild Wonders of Europe/ iLCP

FOLLOWING SPREAD: Atlantic walruses (*Odobenus rosmarus*) from Russia in Svalbard, Norway. **Photograph Paul Nicklen/ National Geographic Stock/ iLCP**

THE MEDITERRANEAN SEA

Enric Sala

The Mediterranean Sea ("the sea in the middle of the Earth") is a microcosm of the world's ocean. Twenty-two countries surround its 2.5 million square kilometers, and throughout history its waters have suffered the strongest human pressure of all the world's oceans. For many people, the magic of the Mediterranean lies in its culture and humanized nature—a sea made to man's measure—not in the ecosystem itself. However, it is the marine ecosystem that has attracted people to its shores and supported them for thousands of years, allowing that culture to flourish.

The Mediterranean Sea is connected to the Atlantic through the Gibraltar Strait on the west, and to the Black Sea and the Sea of Marmara through the Dardanelles Strait on the northeast. The average depth of the Mediterranean is 1,500 m, and its deepest point is the Calypso Deep in the Ionian Sea at 5,267 m. Compared to the global oceanic average depth of 4,000 m, the Mediterranean is relatively shallow, although it is the deepest enclosed sea on the planet.

To understand the current Mediterranean biome, we must first understand the history of this geologically active area. The Mediterranean was formed by the convergence of the Eurasian and African continental plates. The initial point of contact occurred between the Iberian Peninsula and the northern coast of West Africa. Africa rotated counterclockwise, joining the Arabian Peninsula with Eurasia and closing the Mediterranean Basin. Because of its virtually enclosed nature, the Mediterranean is evaporating faster than it is being replaced by the water cycle. The Mediterranean loses three times more water from evaporation than it receives from the discharge of rivers and from rainfall. Without the water flowing in from the Atlantic, the Mediterranean would dry up.

It has already happened once. Six million years ago, the European and African continental plates collided and closed the Strait of Gibraltar, separating the Mediterranean from the Atlantic Ocean. After becoming a closed sea, the Mediterranean all but evaporated in less than 2,000 years, except for some hypersaline lakes. Given these "dead sea" conditions, most marine life in the Mediterranean disappeared. As the water evaporated, salt was left behind, forming huge deposits that reached a thickness of about 2,000 m. Some 5.3 million years ago, an earthquake caused the collapse of the Gibraltar threshold, releasing a massive cascade of Atlantic seawater into the empty Mediterranean basin—a volume of water three times that of the Amazon River. Within two years, the Mediterranean was refilled (García-Castellanos et al., 2009).

The Atlantic floodwaters carried with them the ancestors of the species found in the Mediterranean today. About 17,000 species have been described from the Mediterranean Sea, and this is clearly an underestimate (Coll et al., 2010). A long tradition of marine science and a wealth of taxonomists and natural history students in the Mediterranean means that larger plant and animal taxa are relatively well described, although we are only starting to discover the diversity of microbes in the sea, which might boost the number of known species from the hundreds of thousands to hundreds of millions. Twenty percent of the known marine species (other than microbes) are found only in the Mediterranean; among some groups, such as sponges, these endemics account for a remarkable 48% of the total number of species.

Biodiversity in the Mediterranean is generally greater in the western basin (Coll et al., 2010), where strictly Mediterranean species mix with Atlantic species because of the influence of the flow of Atlantic water through the Gibraltar Strait. However, the flow of species through the strait is composed mostly of shallow water species, because Atlantic water flows near the surface. This explains why Mediterranean deep-sea fauna is species-poor compared to the Atlantic: The desiccation of the Mediterranean meant a late start for colonization of deep fauna, and the shallow sill at the Gibraltar Strait may pose a considerable barrier for the dispersal of adults and larvae of deep-sea fauna.

Mediterranean flora and fauna inhabit a rich diversity of habitats, including salt marshes, coastal lagoons, sandy beaches (which can include vegetated sand dunes), rocky reefs, sandy bottoms (with extensive seagrass beds, from the surface to about 40 m depth in some locales), muddy bottoms, seamounts, deep canyons, hydrothermal vents, cold seeps, and open waters. Distinct biological communities characterize each habitat. Within habitats, distinct communities also replace each other with depth, in a well-known zonation. Rocky reefs, for instance, exhibit dozens of distinct communities, each in a fringe so narrow it can be observed by scuba divers. Large benthic algae dominate near the surface, where light is stronger, and sessile animals (mostly suspension feeders, which eat small organisms such as plankton) replace benthic algae with increasing depth (Zabala and Ballesteros, 1989). Some algal assemblages can harbor up to 120 species in an area the size of a dinner plate (Ballesteros, 1992)—which makes the Mediterranean the sea with the greatest biodiversity of algae at a microscale.

The Mediterranean marine biome has changed throughout history because of human impacts, many more dramatic than changes due to environmental variability (Sala, 2004). The major impact since antiquity has been fishing; over succeeding centuries coastal development, habitat destruction, pollution, introduced species, and global warming have further decimated Mediterranean marine life.

Large marine animals used to be abundant in the Mediterranean. After centuries of exploitation, the Mediterranean monk seal, sea turtles, sharks, Atlantic bluefin tuna, and other large animals have now declined to historically low levels. The monk seal (*Monachus monachus*) has been hunted since the Stone Age (Johnson and Lavigne, 1999); now fewer than five hundred individuals remain in isolated populations, mostly in Greece, Turkey, and the coast of Western Sahara. Sea turtles once nested on sandy beaches throughout the Mediterranean; today nesting beaches are limited to a few locations in Libya, Tunisia, and the Eastern Mediterranean. Dolphins and whales are still common in some locales, but their abundance also has declined dramatically.

The Atlantic bluefin tuna (*Thunnus thynnus*) is probably the most striking example of overexploitation. A seemingly insatiable appetite for the species—mostly from Japan—has resulted in industrial fishing at unsustainable levels, driving the species to its current endangered status (McKenzie et al., 2009). Overfishing has reduced shark biomass by up to 99% (Ferretti et al., 2008), and many other species of commercial interest have been depleted to functional and commercial extinction; though they have not totally disappeared, their abundance is so low that they cannot fulfill their former ecological roles. Such pervasive overfishing is exacerbated by the fact that government regulation of fisheries in the Mediterranean Sea is poor. Despite the existence of international agreements and treaties, enforcement is weak, and both legal and illegal fishing continue to deplete Mediterranean marine resources. Traditional fisheries management has clearly not worked.

Humans have exploited more than the large, oceangoing megafauna such as tuna and whales. Invertebrates such as the large limpet, *Patella ferruginea*, have been overfished to the brink of extinction to satisfy local appetites throughout the Mediterranean. The precious red coral, *Corallium rubrum*, has been exploited since antiquity. Although red coral is not likely to go extinct in the short term, large red coral colonies have been extirpated from most of the shallow waters of the Mediterranean (Garrabou and Harmelin, 2002). During ancient times, red coral was found at the depth of a few meters in the western Mediterranean. Because of overexploitation, its distribution has been restricted to depths below 60 m. Only a few protected areas and deep reefs that have not yet been discovered by coral divers still support significant populations.

Invasive species place significant stress on Mediterranean marine life. With the opening of the Suez Canal in 1869, invaders began to trickle in from the Red Sea. Since then, other species have moved in from the Atlantic or were introduced through aquaculture, aquaria, or the ballast water of ships. At present there are some six hundred alien species in the Mediterranean (CIESM 2011). Some of these aliens remain in low abundance and have no conspicuous effects on the native communities, but others can have disastrous effects at the ecosystem level. The epitome of invasive is the green alga *Caulerpa taxifolia*, which in the 1980s and 1990s expanded from its original introduction point in Monaco, smothering all benthic communities and dramatically reducing the complexity of the ecosystem (Boudouresque et al., 1995). The spread of invasives, many of them tropical species, seems to be facilitated by the warming of Mediterranean waters. Warming events have also caused mass die-offs of many shallow-water species, including sponges, red coral, and sea fans (Perez et al., 2000). Warming is also affecting the biomass and productivity of deep-sea communities.

The Mediterranean Sea is a microcosm of the world's ocean. Twenty-two countries surround its 2.5 million square kilometers, and throughout history its waters have suffered the strongest human pressure of all the world's oceans

Although most of the central Mediterranean (Balearic Islands, Corsica, Sardinia) and the eastern Mediterranean can have crystal clear waters, pollution is a serious problem around big cities, harbors, and industrial areas. In the Adriatic, organic pollution may be causing yearly mucilage explosions, concomitant with low-oxygen events at the sea floor.

Before the Roman period, development along the coastline had already begun to reshape the Mediterranean. Logging upstream sent a heavy load of sediment down to the sea, while pollution caused the decline of important coastal habitats, including salt marshes, seagrass beds, oyster reefs, and algal forests. Humans since have encroached on critical breeding grounds for sea turtles, monk seals, and seabirds, and development continues to speed habitat loss.

The interaction of all these human impacts has led to unintended and unpredictable effects, including increasingly frequent and widespread

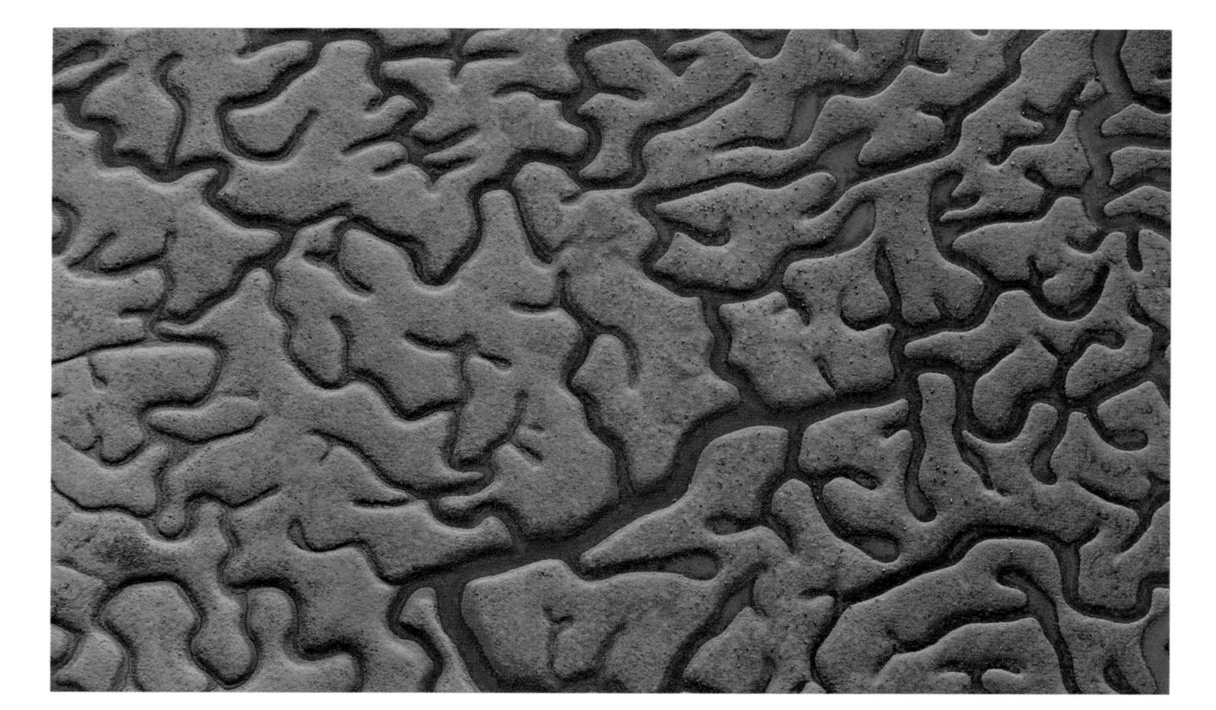

LEFT: Marshes in Bahíade Cádiz Natural Park, Cádiz, Andalusia, Spain. **Photograph by Diego Lopez Alvarez/ Wild Wonders of Europe**

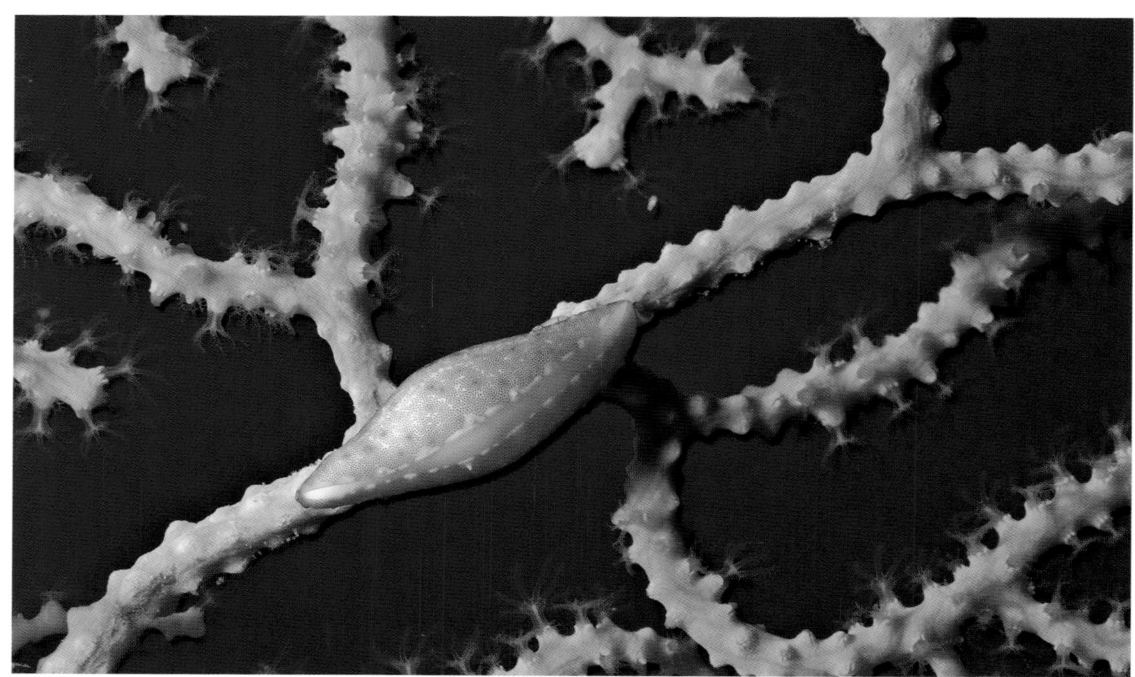

LEFT: A keys simnia (*Neosimnia spelta*) on a yellow gorgonian (*Eunicella cavolini*). This highly carnivorous and often parasitic snail is a common denizen in shallow ecosystems. Larvotto Marine Reserve, Monaco, Mediterranean Sea. **Photograph by Franco Banfi/ Wild Wonders of Europe**

LEFT: A little blenny looks for predators from a hole in the rock - Medes Islands Marine Reserve, Mediterranean Sea, Spain. **Photograph by Enric Sala**

RIGHT: Short-snouted seahorse (*Hippocampus hippocampus*), Gozo, Maltese Islands. **Photograph by Slovin Zankl/ Wild Wonders of Europe**

RIGHT: The region of the Camargue in the Mediterranean coast of France has many marshes, swamps, and coastal lagoons, like this one photographed near the town of Saintes-Maries-de-la-Mer. **Photograph by Theo Allofs/ iLCP**

RIGHT: Canal with drought patterns near Etang du Fangassier, Camargue, France. **Photograph by Theo Allofs/ iLCP**

blooms of such jellyfish as *Pelagia noctiluca* (Licandro et al., 2010). What used to be a healthy sea full of marine "monsters"—large fish, sharks, turtles, and sea mammals—has been emptied to satisfy human appetites. Our greed for fish and other resources, and the money they command, has turned the Mediterranean into a sea increasingly dominated by microbes and jellyfish.

Because of its virtually enclosed nature, the Mediterranean is evaporating faster than it is being replaced by the water cycle. The Mediterranean loses three times more water from evaporation than it receives from the discharge of rivers and from rainfall

The Mediterranean is under siege. While the human threats to the biome are serious, there are some small success stories that, if scaled up, could reverse the trend of degradation. No-take areas—marine reserves where fishing is prohibited—are the best example. After a decade, fish biomass in these reserves can be more than five times larger than in unprotected sites nearby (Guidetti and Sala, 2007). Wonderful success stories of marine reserves include the Scandola Nature Reserve in Corsica, the Tavolara Marine Reserve in Sardinia, and the Medes Islands Marine Reserve in Catalonia. Outside the reserve, the landscape is empty of large fish, and sea urchins often become so abundant that they overgraze the bottom-dwelling algae, turning a once lush algal forest into a barren. Within the reserves, by contrast, a diver can wonder at the sight of large fish such as groupers, corvina, and sea bass. In some reserves, groupers live more than forty years, reaching 120 cm in length—a far cry from the virtual absence of groupers larger than 20 cm in most Mediterranean locales.

It is not just the marine life within reserves that recovers. After some years the biomass spills over into nearby areas, enhancing local fisheries. For instance, between 4% and 7% of spiny lobsters in the Columbretes Marine Reserve disperse to nearby unprotected areas, benefiting fishermen (Goñi et al., 2010). Also, the spectacle of large fish in Mediterranean reserves contributes more to the economy than fishing. The Medes Islands no-take area is less than one square kilometer in size, but it generates 6 million in tourist revenue from diving, snorkeling, and glass-bottom boats—twenty times more revenue than fishing—and many more jobs (Merino et al., 2009).

These reserves are time machines that allow us to catch a glimpse of what the Mediterranean was like hundreds of years ago. Sharks and monk seals are so critically endangered it will be difficult for their populations to recover, but we have a chance to restore much of the richness of the Mediterranean—and develop a sustainable economy—if we scale up these few-and-far-between success stories. However, less than 2% of the Mediterranean lies within marine protected areas with management programs, and less than one-tenth of 1% is fully protected from fishing. The Mediterranean conserves a fascinating culture and history, but much remains to be done to restore the biological richness upon which that culture and history grew.

LEFT: A school of wrasses forages on invertebrates among brown algae at the Cabrera National Park, Mediterranean Sea, Spain.
Photograph by Enric Sala

THE CENTRAL PACIFIC OCEAN

Sue Miller Taei, Michael Donoghue, Gregory S. Stone, and William Wrigley, Jr.

Like jewels in a crown, the more than 10,000 islands found in the Pacific Islands region are set in an ocean area of nearly forty million square kilometers, an area that covers about 10% of the Earth's surface. Comprising the ethnogeographic groupings of Micronesia ("small islands"), Melanesia ("black islands"), and Polynesia ("many islands"), the region lies at the heart of the Pacific Ocean, our planet's largest geographic feature.

Pacific Island peoples rely on the ocean, its biodiversity, and the ecosystem services it provides for their well-being and security. More than 50% of Pacific Islanders—more than 7.5 million people—live within thirty kilometers of the coast. The ocean and coasts also provide the greatest opportunities for regional and national economic development, notably through tuna fishing and tourism. The region holds the world's largest remaining stocks of tuna, providing more than 30% of the world's landings of tuna (*Thunnus* spp.) and related pelagic species (Gillett and Langley, 2007). The waters of the region also contain globally important stocks of sharks (superorder Euselachii), billfish (families Istiophoridae and Xiphiidae), and other large, pelagic species, including dolphins and whales (order Cetacea), dugongs (family Dugongidae), and turtles (order Testudines).

Coral reefs and associated habitats such as lagoons, seagrass, and mangroves dominate the coastal marine environs of the central Pacific. With more than 66,000 square kilometers of coral reefs, the region is home to more than a quarter of the planet's coral reef habitat, much of it in significantly better condition than reefs closer to major population centers (Burke et al., 2011). Fringing and barrier reefs are commonly associated with high islands, with New Caledonia's double barrier reef, at more than 1,500 kilometers, being the world's third largest barrier reef after Australia's Great Barrier Reef and the Mesoamerican Barrier Reef off the coast of Mexico and Honduras. In Polynesia and Micronesia, reefs often develop as part of atoll formation or as fringing reefs surrounding volcanic highlands, combining to form extensive coral reef-based archipelagos. Many of these reef systems, such as the Phoenix Islands in Kiribati, are among the most pristine remaining in the world today.

Terrestrial biodiversity of islands in the region is characterized by high species endemism with many species of plants, invertebrates, and birds found nowhere else in the world. Including Australia and New Zealand, the Oceania region contains six globally recognized hotspots for terrestrial biodiversity and a major wilderness area in Papua New Guinea. The Polynesia-Micronesia Biodiversity Hotspot alone has 564 threatened species. Regrettably, more species extinctions are recorded from this one Hotspot than from any other.

Pacific Island nations are often referred to as "small island developing states," depicting them as isolated both from the wider world and each other. This view, based almost entirely on their tiny landmasses, is most often promulgated by those from outside the region. It does not reflect a Pacific Islander view. Rather, the peoples of Pacific Island States and Territories see themselves as "Large Ocean States," with more than 98% of the 38.5 million square kilometers of the Earth's surface over which these states have direct influence consisting of ocean. The region has also been called "Oceania," perhaps a more fitting name, as it emphasizes the vastness of the ocean rather than the tiny area of the islands. Epeli Hau'ofa, a Tongan who lived and worked across the region, perfectly describes this oceanic identity:

Oceania is vast, Oceania is expanding, Oceania is hospitable and generous, Oceania is humanity rising from the depths of brine and regions of fire deeper still, Oceania is us. We are the sea, we are the ocean, we must wake up to this ancient truth . . .

—*Our Sea of Islands*, Epeli Hau'ofa, 2008

Throughout the central Pacific, marine and terrestrial biodiversity as represented by species number decreases eastward and toward higher latitudes. However, the proportion of unique species, both marine and terrestrial, increases as you move eastward. Both trends are the consequence of evolution over millions of years of isolation from continental landmasses.

Most of the land across the region is held in some form of customary tenure and heavily relied upon for small-scale agriculture and subsistence use. Despite the rules and regulations often set in the capitals of many island states, coastal tenure is also managed largely by communities following traditions that are centuries old. This benefits both people and the environment, with the dependence on marine resources and the need to ensure their security reflected in many community rules of access and use. However, in recent decades customary tenure has also become a weakness, as communities and their resources are targeted and influenced by outsiders, particularly with the increasing need for cash income wanted by communities to purchase material goods.

Despite the relative health of Pacific Island ecosystems, the region has more rare, endangered, and threatened species than anywhere else on Earth. More than 50% of the region's biodiversity is listed as At Risk (Pippard, 2009). As we have seen with other seascapes in this book, environmental threats in the region include habitat loss and degradation, overexploitation, invasive species, pollution, and, increasingly, impacts from climate change. These threats vary widely in impact and, except for climate change, are generally correlated with human occupation of islands.

Overexploitation of resources, both marine and terrestrial, is a common theme. The story of Oceania's humpback whales (*Megaptera novaeangliae*) illustrates this well and is both sobering and inspirational. Hunted originally by the sailing vessels of the nineteenth century, Oceania's humpback whales suffered catastrophic decline during the twentieth century. Intensive illegal whaling by the former Soviet Union on the summer feeding grounds in the Antarctic Ocean in the 1950s and 1960s came to light in the 1990s, due to the bravery of individual Soviet citizens who kept the real catch records safe until changes in political regimes allowed the true facts to emerge. The devastation wrought on Oceania's humpbacks was almost complete—an initial population of around 40,000 was reduced to a few hundred. However, key countries like Tonga offered protection to these creatures even before the global whaling moratorium in 1986. Over the last twenty-five years, conservation of whales in the region, including the creation of national sanctuaries and supporting international conservation measures, has fostered a slow recovery, and today, Tonga enjoys a multimillion-dollar tourism industry centered on humpback whale watching (SPREP, 2010, Ocean Voices).

The devastation wrought on Oceania's humpbacks was almost complete—an initial population of around 40,000 was reduced to a few hundred. However, key countries like Tonga offered protection to these creatures even before the global whaling moratorium in 1986

Despite these successes at addressing localized threats, the increasing and overwhelming impacts of climate change offer a new set of challenges on a scale not before seen. Both the radiative (warming, sea level rise) and pollutant (acidification) impacts of increasing levels of carbon dioxide in the atmosphere threaten the way of life in Oceania. Pacific Islanders did not create climate change, but lacking significant international action on mitigation, climate change threatens the very existence of some Pacific Island states, including Tuvalu, Tokelau, and Kiribati.

What has been done, and what needs to be done? Over the last thirty years, significant and growing conservation efforts—at village to global scale—have been undertaken in and by the region. The region united to lead the United Nations ban on drift-net fishing in 1992. At a village level, the growing network of Locally Managed Marine Areas in countries such as Fiji has empowered local people, benefiting biodiversity and livelihoods, and also has inspired a growing effort in community-based conservation in many other Pacific Island states. Samoa has shown leadership by establishing village- and district-based community-based marine protected areas (MPAs), as well as uniting to support their recovery after the severe environmental and humanitarian disaster of the Samoa tsunami of September 2009. After the failure of the International Whaling Commission to establish a South Pacific Whale Sanctuary, many Pacific Island countries and territories took action, declaring more than eighteen million square kilometers of their exclusive economic zones (EEZs) as whale sanctuaries. States in the region are used to working together for collective regional benefit, as exemplified by the Micronesia Challenge, a commitment by Palau, the Federated States of Micronesia, Marshall Islands, Guam, and Mariana Islands to conserve not less than 20% of their terrestrial areas and 30% of their nearshore marine areas by 2020. Further, Kiribati has received global attention by establishing the world's second largest marine protected area, the Phoenix Islands Protected Area, affectionately known as PIPA. In 2010, Kiribati succeeded in having PIPA inscribed on UNESCO's list of World Heritage sites (UNESCO, 2010). Today, at more than 400,000 square kilometers and an average depth more than 4,000 meters, PIPA is the world's largest and deepest World Heritage site.

Conservation International has partnered with many countries, nongovernmental organizations, and communities in the region to sup-

LEFT: A swift-moving school of bannerfish (*Heniochus diphreutes*) photographed in the Fijian archipelago. Their banded pattern may seem to make them conspicuous, but when they move quickly as a group, it may be confusing and make it harder for a predator to target an individual. **Photograph by Tim Laman/ iLCP**

LEFT: A golden damselfish (*Amblyglyphidodon aureus*) photographed against a background of red coral and crinoids. Namena Island, Fiji. **Photograph by Tim Laman/ iLCP**

LEFT: A burrowing crab in a hard coral. The pink glow around the edge suggests an irritation that is revealed through fluorescence photography.
Photograph by Keith Ellenbogen/ iLCP

RIGHT: Giant clams (*Tridacna gigas*) in the Phoenix Islands in Kiribati, Polynesia. **Photograph by Paul Nicklen/ National Geographic Stock/ iLCP**

RIGHT: Staghorn coral (*Acropora cervicornis*) in the Fiji Reef that has been recently bleached. Coral bleaching happens for many reasons, and its effects can be devastating on coral communities. **Photograph by Tim Laman/ iLCP**

RIGHT: A beautiful reef scene with soft and hard corals, anthias, and golden damselfish (*Amblyglyphidodon aureus*) in the shallow waters off the Fijian Islands.
Photograph by Tim Laman/ iLCP

port such initiatives as the PIPA, the Micronesia Challenge, and the Coral Triangle Initiative. In the view of many conservationists, including those from Conservation International and the Pacific Leaders Forum, such laudable efforts are still insufficient. The conservation gains made over the last twenty years are dwarfed by the increasing scale of threats and an often-unsustainable development agenda.

In 2009, Kiribati President Anote Tong issued a call to Pacific Forum Leaders to design a new ocean conservation agenda (Pacific Islands Forum Secretariat, 2009). Less than one year later, the region's intergovernmental agencies, supported by NGOs including Conservation International, had researched and designed the Framework for a Pacific Oceanscape (Pratt and Govan, 2010). Meeting in Vanuatu in August 2010, members of the Pacific Forum Leaders formally recognized fundamental truths and the need to work together as stewards of Oceania by adopting the Framework for the Pacific Oceanscape. In their words:

"In our Pacific Islands Ocean Region, the ocean unites and divides, connects and separates, sustains and threatens our very survival. For all those who venture within this, the world's largest ocean, and have made it their home, the ocean influences every aspect of life. It has done so for millennia. (Pacific Islands Forum Secretariat, 2010)."

The initiative has quickly moved toward implementation. The Pacific Oceanscape aims to secure the future for Pacific Island Countries and Territories based on sustainable development, management, and conservation of the Pacific. The Framework addresses rights and responsibilities, good ocean governance, conservation management, climate change, and the need to work collaboratively to foster ocean stewardship at local, national, and regional scales. The Pacific Oceanscape is the largest single integrated ocean conservation and management initiative undertaken by any group of countries.

The Pacific Oceanscape recognizes that no single country in a region can by itself protect its own slice of the ocean. The very nature of the ocean means collaboration and cooperation and unity are fundamental requisites for success. By recognizing the Pacific Oceanscape as a management tool, the countries and territories of the region can offer a united voice to the world to call for change in how we view and use the ocean. Change is needed to ensure the survival of Pacific Island people in the face of global environmental and climate change. Change is needed to recognize that wise management of this part of the ocean, more than one third of the Earth's surface area, will benefit not only Pacific Island peoples but also all humankind. Change in perspective is needed to realize that these island nations are not small, and that they carry a huge responsibility of ocean stewardship for the benefit and survival of all people, everywhere. The adoption of the Pacific Oceanscape heralds this change.

RIGHT: Spike-like breathing roots (*pneumatophores*) of *Sonneratia* mangrove trees exposed at low tide. **Photograph by Tim Laman/ iLCP**

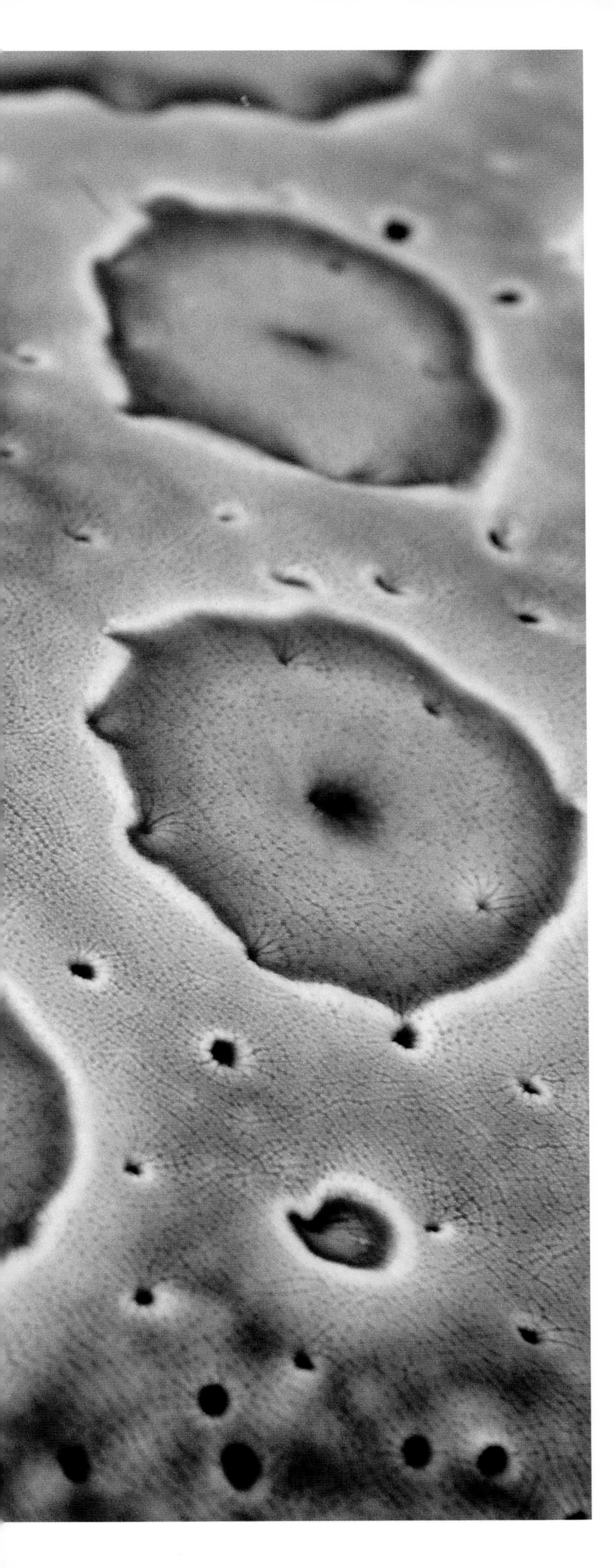

LEFT: An emperor shrimp (*Periclimenes imperator*) rests on a sea cucumber (*echinoderm*) in the shallow waters off the island of Kostrae in the Federated States of Micronesia.
Photograph by Tim Laman/ iLCP

THE WESTERN INDIAN OCEAN

David Obura

Unlike the Atlantic and Pacific, the Indian Ocean is bounded to the north by the landmass of Asia. This has resulted in distinct features of climate and oceanography, such as the seasonal monsoons (Schott, 2009), which have defined not only the biology of this ocean and the climate of the surrounding continents, but its human history as well. Northern monsoon currents and winds brought traders from Asia during one half of the year, and southern monsoons powered their return home, establishing a mix of cultures that still defines the varied peoples of the region.

The South Equatorial Current flows from east to west just south of the equator, drawing water from the Pacific Ocean through gaps among the islands of Indonesia. On its path westward it flows into and around the Chagos Archipelago, over a submerged mountain range that also bears the Maldives and Lakshadweep Islands, and thence to the banks and islands on the Mascarene Plateau and mid-ocean shoals.

Encountering the landmass of Madagascar, the current splits north and south, with the northern current accelerating around the tip of Madagascar as it continues westward. Research over the last decade has shown that this acceleration may initiate a complex series of eddies, both clockwise and counterclockwise around the Comoro Islands in the center of the northern Mozambique Channel. Once formed, these eddies follow the channel southward, meandering between Madagascar and Mozambique, and may move east or west across the channel, and even return northward (de Ruijter et al., 2002). At the southern end of Madagascar, the eddies merge with the current flowing down the east coast of Madagascar, forming the fast and narrow Agulhas Current that hugs the South African coast. Part of the South Equatorial Current reaches Africa at the coast of Tanzania, deflecting northward as the East African Coastal Current. With the advent of the monsoon season, this current returns water eastward, back into the central part of the Indian Ocean.

Until the end of the twentieth century, taxonomists had done relatively little biodiversity work in the western Indian Ocean, with particularly large gaps in sampling along the African coast and parts of Madagascar. Charles Darwin passed briefly through the Indian Ocean on the *Beagle* in May 1836, visiting Rodrigues and Mauritius. By the late twentieth century (Rosen, 1971; Sheppard, 1987; Veron, 2000), diversity maps of coral reef species showed higher diversity around the islands of the central Indian Ocean (Seychelles, Madagascar) than along the African coast, and that this diversity was an extension or outpost of the high-diversity region in the Indo-Malayan region now known as the Coral Triangle (see Erdmann, this volume).

Research in the western Indian Ocean has been plagued by the low level of investment in biodiversity work throughout the region. Individual programs and researchers have been unable to sample many sites on a regional scale. At the same time, differences in methodology, effort, and taxonomy make it difficult to pool results into coherent, broader findings. Richmond (2001) compiled species numbers for a comprehensive swath of marine invertebrates and vertebrates, yet he concluded that even this represented minimum numbers for many taxa.

In 2002, I began compiling a biogeographic data set on scleractinian reef corals (Obura, unpublished data). A decade later, the data set is beginning to reveal new diversity patterns in the western Indian Ocean and suggest hypotheses for their origins. Taking advantage of different expeditions and opportunities to sample remote corners of the western Indian Ocean, including Conservation International's Rapid Assessment Program surveys of northern Madagascar, eighteen sites have been surveyed in the western Indian Ocean and the Red Sea. This approach compensates for two of the biggest problems facing species inventories conducted across broad geographic scales and over multiple years: sampling effort and taxonomic consistency.

These new biodiversity patterns are challenging our previous understanding of the biogeography of the Indo-Pacific. The northern Mozambique Channel appears to be a highly diverse core region, covering some 7° of latitude from 8° to 15° S and 10° of longitude from 40° to 50° E, an area of some 420,000 sq km. Lower-diversity islands that lie upstream of this region in the central Indian Ocean may serve as stepping stones for species along the path of the South Equatorial Current. To the north and south of this core region lie peripheral regions with varying oceanographic characteristics that receive larvae and genetic material from the core and may return material to the core through recirculating gyres (as happens in the Seychelles) or may serve as sinks for genetic material (as in southern Mozambique, southern Madagascar, and South Africa).

Work over the last decade has focused on identifying the evolutionary mechanisms behind this core region of diversity in the western Indian Ocean. Some mechanisms were active in the past, over the long geological history of the western Indian Ocean, while others are active today.

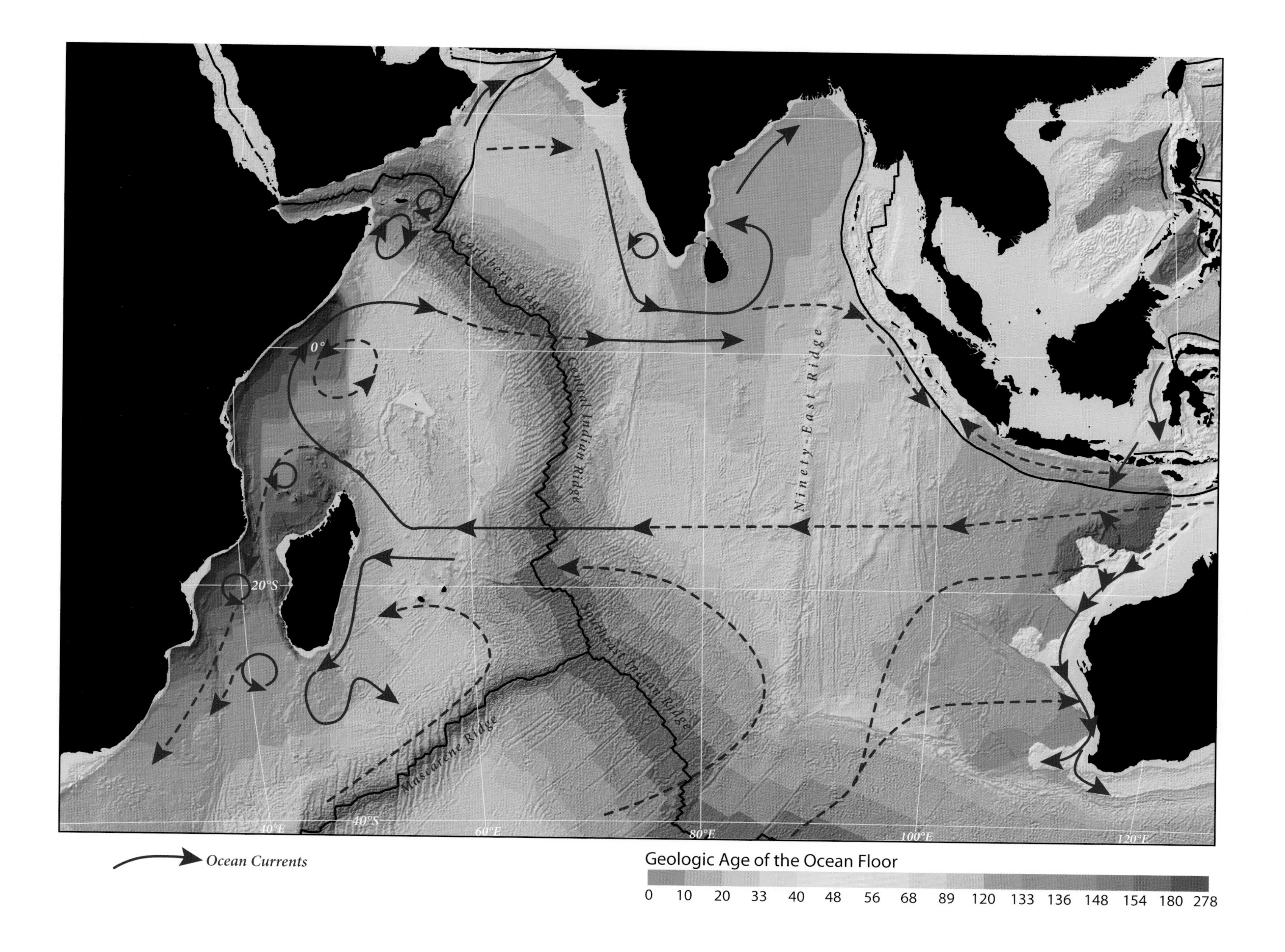

The recently discovered eddies dominating flow in the Mozambique Channel (de Ruijter, 2002) suggest a mechanism that may underlie the current concentration of biodiversity in the core region. Eddies retain water within the system and serve to concentrate larvae, enabling high levels recruitment and retention of species over ecological time of decades to hundreds of years, and perhaps over evolutionary time of millions of years. Outside of the core region, where linear currents flow up the East African coast or down to South Africa, diversity declines as species drop off the conveyor belt for many reasons, such as river barriers. Furthermore, because eddies may be clockwise or counterclockwise, and move in all directions within the Mozambique Channel, transport of genetic material and species may occur in all directions within the channel, maintaining a single large assemblage of species.

The geological history of the Indian Ocean also provides clues to present levels of diversity. The configuration of the Mozambique Channel appears to have remained nearly unchanged for the last one hundred million years, and the relatively steep continental coastlines mean shallow marine habitats would have been relatively

ABOVE: The Indian Ocean. Mid-ocean spreading centers on the ocean floor, highlighted in red, are geologically active centers where magma emerges from the earth's mantle and cools to form new crust.

RIGHT: A bronze whaler shark (*Carcharhinus brachyurus*) gorges on the Southern African pilchard (*Sardinops sagax*). The sardine run of southern Africa occurs from May through July, when billions of sardines spawn in the cool waters of the Agulhas Bank and move northward along the east coast of South Africa. **Photograph by Thomas P. Peschak/ iLCP**

RIGHT: A hermit crab (*Pagurus armatus*) makes its way down a white sandy beach on the island of Aride, a sanctuary for wildlife and seabirds, in the Seychelles archipelago.
Photograph by Cristina Goettsch Mittermeier/ iLCP

RIGHT: A fisherman carries the carcass of a hammerhead shark (*Sphyrna lewini*) caught with a hand line in Inhassoro, Mozambique. This type of low-impact artisanal fishery is common throughout the coast of East Africa.
Photograph by Jeff Rotman/ Jeff Rotman Photography

LEFT: Two fishermen assess their afternoon catch. A handful of small fish is what they get for their work. Morondava, Western Madagascar.
Photograph by Cristina Goettsch Mittermeier/ iLCP

stable even through sea level fluctuations of several hundreds of meters. This represents a long and stable geological "lifetime" that allows species to be maintained over time.

The configuration of the rest of the Indian Ocean has changed considerably, however. Australia and India split off from Madagascar and migrated east and north between 90 and 40 million years ago, and the Tethys Sea narrowed and finally closed between fifteen and five million years ago. The movement of these landmasses profoundly influenced the currents in the Indian Ocean as well as the exchange of species between the stable region of the northern Mozambique Channel and the less stable regions of the Indian, Pacific, and the Atlantic Oceans. Old monospecific genera of corals—corals that are the sole species in a given genus—offer tantalizing clues to past species events. For instance, blister coral, *Horastrea indica*; crisp pillow coral, *Anomastrea irregularis*; and African pillow coral, *Siderastrea savignyana*, may be evidence of evolutionary processes in ancient times that have led to what may now be the second-highest center of diversity for shallow marine organisms in the world.

Biodiversity is increasingly recognized as the foundation for natural resources and ecosystem services that are useful to people (McNeely et al., 2009). People throughout the world, especially in developing countries such as those surrounding the western Indian Ocean, derive their primary sustenance directly from the environment in the form of crops or wild-caught food, materials for shelter, fuel, and clothing, and medicines. As in the history of other regions, the peoples of the western Indian Ocean have been driven by environmental and ecological possibilities: The monsoon winds enabled trade between the Middle East and East Africa, the calm reef lagoons drew predominantly terrestrial tribes to the shore to practice subsistence fishing, and the settlers on remote oceanic islands planted coconuts and other crops, mirroring the plantation culture that also developed in the remote Pacific.

Population and poverty drive all ecological threats in the Indian Ocean. The Asian shores of the Indian Ocean hold some of the most populous and densely settled countries on the planet. By contrast, the western Indian Ocean is bounded by some of the poorest countries in Africa, with rapidly growing populations

In the modern global economy, growing population pressure is threatening to exhaust natural resources before they have been studied and understood. With the biogeographic patterns and origins of the western Indian Ocean still poorly understood, the patterns of diversity revealed by reef-building corals suggest a similarly vast, as yet unknown diversity among other groups of marine invertebrates, vertebrates, plants, and microbes. The biota of the Western Indian Ocean may hold a genetic diversity unique on the planet. They await our discovery.

Population and poverty drive all ecological threats in the Indian Ocean. The Asian shores of the Indian Ocean hold some of the most populous and densely settled countries on the planet. By contrast, the western Indian Ocean is bounded by some of the poorest countries in Africa, with rapidly growing populations. In both regions people want, and have the right, to increase their standard of living, which means higher consumption rates of resources from a limited planet and ocean. Combined, these factors are causing an exponential growth in pressures on the resources of the Indian Ocean. The globalized economy and better transport of marine products to local, national, and international markets have led to overexploitation of marine species. As subsistence fishers abandon artisanal fishing methods, increasing numbers of men and unemployed youth go to work for commercial fisheries, eroding a culture in which fishers grew up in coastal communities with intimate knowledge of the sea and its limits. As local resources are depleted, migrant fishers follow fish across porous maritime borders, leading to conflict with local fishers. By the 1980s, demand in Asia for sea cucumbers and shark fins—products that are easily dried, stored, and brought to market with little infrastructure—had already driven local fisheries to depletion in many remote parts of the western Indian Ocean. Coastal development in countries with expanding economies and rapidly growing cities can lead to high levels of erosion and water pollution, as seen in Mombasa, Dar es Salaam, and Maputo.

Like the rest of the planet, the Indian Ocean is being affected by climate change. In 1998, positive El Niño Southern Oscillation and Indian Ocean Dipole (the Indian Ocean's equivalent of the Pacific Ocean's El Niño–La Niña) cycles coincided with the warmest year on record, resulting in mass bleaching and die-off of corals in the Indian Ocean (Wilkinson et al., 1999). This coral bleaching demonstrated to the world that climate change was indeed underway and was capable of wreaking biological havoc. Corals serve as an indicator for what may happen to other species groups and ecosystems. Scientists estimate that sometime between 2020 and 2080 climate change will make many parts of the Indian Ocean too warm to support corals (Sheppard, 2003; Donner, 2009). If those predictions come to pass, it is unlikely that reef-building corals will go extinct en masse, but they will likely not be able to form the hard skeletons necessary to build reefs, and reef ecosystems may vanish from regions where they have thrived for millions of years. The loss of reefs will have serious consequences for the many species that depend on them as a habitat, causing a cascade of biodiversity loss as reef systems simplify. Further, as the ecosystem services provided by reefs decline, the increasingly heavily populated coastal societies dependent on reefs and marine resources will have to adapt to the changing climate and its consequences (Adger et al., 2005).

Immediate action must be taken to expand and improve management of the marine environment, and limit the extraction of fish and other resources from the sea if we are to halt and reverse biodiversity loss. Some of the first marine protected areas in the world were established in the western Indian Ocean in Kenya, in Malindi and Watamu in 1968, which later received Biosphere Reserve status from the United Nations Environment Programme. However this early awareness of the value of protecting marine environments in the region has focused on small "Save the Bay" actions, rather than the larger scale government and intergovernmental policy changes that are needed to achieve conservation on a regional scale. The transboundary nature of fish and other marine resources has long posed an additional challenge, complicating efforts to manage resources effectively.

Nevertheless, intergovernmental processes in the region are growing stronger under such conventions as the Convention on Biological Diversity and all ten countries of the western Indian Ocean ratifying the Nairobi Convention, which commits them to joint protection of the marine environment (Nairobi Convention, 2010). The nongovernment sector and civil society organizations are similarly engaged with both local conservation organizations and regional planners.

Countries of the western Indian Ocean are minor contributors to greenhouse gas emissions, but highly vulnerable to climate change (IPCC, 2007). They therefore tend to feel powerless to mitigate the impacts of climate change. Nevertheless, governments and nongovernmental organizations are beginning to recognize the value of adapting to climate change. For example, they are beginning to invest in new and improved crop varieties to cope with changing rainfall patterns, and in climate forecasting systems to be better prepared for change. In this regard, research on reef-building corals and their vulnerability to climate change is showing we can take action and buy time for corals—helping them to resist the increasing temperatures they will experience and/or to recover more quickly following bleaching and mortality.

If this core region of high biodiversity in the western Indian Ocean is the tropical ocean's second hotspot for biodiversity, it ranks high as a conservation priority, particularly for the countries and continents surrounding the western and northern Indian Oceans. The currents and configuration of the northern Mozambique Channel are critical for maintaining high levels of biodiversity, as well as high recruitment and replenishment of species within the region. Currents lead out from this region to all other parts of the Indian Ocean—southward from Madagascar and Mozambique to South Africa, and northward to Kenya, the Seychelles, the northern Indian Ocean, and thence to the Red Sea and Indian subcontinent. This may make the region a key source of larvae in the short term, and of genetic diversity in the long term. As human population and climate threats further degrade marine ecosystems, punching holes and widening gaps between the few natural or artificial refuges in marine protected areas, the resilience of the entire ecosystem may break down. A core source region can help peripheral regions survive threats as long as it remains intact. If it also degrades, however, a cascade of downstream effects will likely ensue. Developing an effective regional management plan for this newly recognized core region of high biodiversity should be a conservation priority.

THE ABROLHOS SEASCAPE

Guilherme F. Dutra, Rodrigo Leão de Moura, and Les Kaufman

Meaning "open your eyes!" in Portuguese, Abrolhos was named by sailors aboard the first European ships to navigate these waters. Those mariners saw, and sometimes crashed upon, massive reefs shaped like giant mushrooms 25 m high and 5 m wide (Leão et al., 2003). These strange structures, called reefal pinnacles, exist only in this isolated coralline outpost of the South Atlantic. They are the only reefs in the world whose backbones are built by a group of "living fossil" corals that live today only in Brazil. One of these is the genus *Mussismillia*, a relict of the Neogene, up to 2.6 million years ago. Living in this otherworldly environment is a host of marine creatures equally unique to Abrolhos, species born of isolation from their nearest relatives in the Caribbean, or descendants of species that branched off in the evolutionary past. Although these pinnacles are the most prominent structural features in the region, they are but one small piece of a complex puzzle of habitats and little-known species found here, some yet to be scientifically described.

Located on the eastern Brazilian coast, the Abrolhos Seascape extends from the Jequitinhonha River estuary in the state of Bahia to the Doce River mouth in the state of Espírito Santo. This diverse seascape includes a large extension of the Brazilian shelf—the Royal Charlotte and Abrolhos banks and two isolated seamounts, Rodger and Minerva. On the west, the Abrolhos Seascape comprises a group of estuaries and coastal habitats, such as mangroves and *restinga* forests (tropical moist broadleaf forest found in Brazil, part of the Atlantic Forest biome). Parts of these habitats are included in the present marine protected areas (MPA) network, including the Abrolhos Marine National Park (882.49 sq km), and three Extractive Reserves: Marinha do Corumbau (895.25 sq km), Canavieiras (1006.45 sq km), and Cassurubá (1006.87 sq km).

As we better understand all the ways in which marine communities are connected, our view of the Abrolhos Seascape and our understanding of its geographical boundaries are evolving. Recent surveys to the east, along the vast chain of nine seamounts and two oceanic islands, Trindade and Martin Vaz, are demonstrating the importance of biological connections with this area. Evidence of such species richness may result in the eastward expansion of the seascape another 650 miles.

Abrolhos harbors the highest marine biodiversity in the southern Atlantic (Werner et al., 2000; Dutra et al., 2006). It owes its extreme richness in both species and habitats to the huge area of shallow water covering a myriad of hard- and soft-bottom habitats. The list of superlatives includes the South Atlantic's largest and richest coral reefs, greatest variety of reef types (e.g. mushroom-shaped reefs, platform reefs, and fringe reefs), as well as reefs thriving in the ocean's mesophotic or twilight zone between 30 m and 150 m. In its shallows, Abrolhos has extensive beds of seagrass and calcareous algae. Along the shoreline, mangroves and estuaries harbor their flora and fauna, providing important nursery sites for many reef species. In the mesophotic zone and in deeper waters can be found paleochannels and other remarkable formations, such as the *buracas*—large depressions in the shelf plain (20 to 40 meters deep and 70 to 150 meters wide).

The Abrolhos Seascape is also dense with iconic species. Brain corals, especially the *Mussismilia* genus mentioned above, are among the most important reef builders in the region. Large populations of reef and coastal fishes are also present, nearly 20% of these endemic from Brazil (Moura, 2003). Abrolhos is an important feeding habitat for the green turtle (*Chelonia mydas*) and the hawksbill (*Eretmochelys imbricata*), and holds nesting sites for the leatherback turtle (*Dermochelys coriacea*) and the loggerhead (*Caretta caretta*). The area is also of special importance for the Southern Hemisphere populations of the humpback whale (Megaptera novaeangliae). Estimates based on aerial surveys conducted between 2001 and 2008 place the Southwestern Atlantic breeding stock at 9,300 individuals, most of them concentrated in Abrolhos (Andriolo et al., 2010; Wedekin et al., 2010), where they mate, give birth, and nurse calves between July and November.

Marine biodiversity provides a variety of ecosystem services, such as seafood, recreation (including tourism), cultural and aesthetic maintenance, coastal protection, carbon sequestration, and nutrient dispersal and cycling—all of special importance for the communities living along the coast. Abrolhos is the most important area for fisheries in northeast Brazil. Nearly 20,000 fishermen depend on these ecosystem services, as marine resources are their major income source, as well as often the main protein source for their families. The engagement of the coastal fishing populations under co-management regimes—such as in the Deliberative Councils of the Extractive Reserves, where traditional knowledge is taken into consideration together with scientific knowledge in management decisions—is a much-needed step to maintain the flow of these services from one generation to the next.

If the Abrolhos shallows have been full of recent surprises—a highly commercial variety of snapper was recently discovered to be a species new to science (Moura & Lindeman, 2007)—then its depths are a whole new universe. Recent studies have demonstrated the eastern part of the Abrolhos is dominated by calcareous algae banks and mesophotic reefs. These calcareous algae banks, together with seagrass beds and mangroves forests, are known as major carbon sinks, mitigating the effects of greenhouse gas release into the atmosphere. Initiatives to develop adaptation strategies to climate change are also in place, including research on coral bleaching, disease, and susceptibility to identify areas that must be protected to make the system more resilient along time. Key to these adaptation strategies will be a better understanding of the deleterious effects on marine ecosystems from ongoing ocean acidification.

Despite its global importance, the Abrolhos ecosystem is seriously threatened. Coastal reefs are severely overfished and subjected to high sedimentation rates due to poor land management in coastal watersheds. These same watersheds include important segments of the Mata Atlântica, the Atlantic rainforest, itself a threatened ecosystem that would once have shielded marine communities from harmful runoff. Marine communities have already been dramatically altered, and in many areas a few harmful algae species have now dominated reefs that were until recently covered by living corals. Overfishing has forced many vessels to seek their catch farther offshore, and fishing now threatens the outer arch of coral pinnacles as well as deeper reefs on the middle and outer shelf. The existing marine protected areas are doing all they can to sustain ocean and human health, and with them the region's fisheries. Meanwhile, enforcement and prosecution of illegal fishing are still insufficient, due to the small political will for improving these activities. The future of Abrolhos and the welfare of its peoples hang by a thread.

The historical deforestation of the Atlantic Forest—reduced to 11.4% to 16% of its original cover, especially during the last century (Ribeiro et al., 2009)—and recent dredging of navigation channels, have contributed to increased sedimentation rates and led to an unprecedented decline in coastal reef health. Sedimentation, sewage, and temperature anomalies are triggering a region-wide coral decline due to pathogens. If corals continue to die at the current rate, about 40% of the cover of the region's main reef builder, M. braziliensis, will be lost by 2060 (Francini-Filho et al., 2008).

In 2003 the Brazilian government was intending to offer large areas of the Abrolhos Bank for oil and gas exploitation. A comprehensive technical report and a national media campaign led by the recently created SOS Abrolhos Coalition (composed by Conservation International and a small group of NGO partners), followed by a governmental discussion of the development policies for the region, changed the scenario (Marchioro et al., 2005). The government decided to exclude the Abrolhos area from the auction. However, as of 2011 no formal agreement has been implemented, and protection of coral reefs under the legal framework for the region's zoning remains precarious.

Large shrimp farms were also proposed in sensitive estuaries and mangrove areas. In the Cassurubá estuary—which concentrates near 95% of the mangroves of the Abrolhos Bank—developers proposed to build the largest shrimp farm in Brazil. Again, CI and the SOS Abrolhos Coalition—at this point composed of twenty-three nongovernmental organizations (NGOs)—worked in partnership with local communities to prevent this highly incompatible development project from moving forward. The estuary and surrounding marine areas since have been protected by the Cassurubá Extractive Reserve, which places the region in a co-management regime with local communities. Meanwhile, in the northernmost of Abrolhos, near the Canavieiras Extractive Reserve, shrimp farms remain in operation, forcing a trade-off between short-term shrimp production and the long-term health of this estuary.

Formal scientific knowledge of the marine biodiversity of the Abrolhos began with visits by Charles Darwin in 1832 and Charles Frederick Hartt in 1870. Jacques Laborel made important contributions to coral taxonomy in the 1960s. In the 1970s and early 1980s, research and data compilation from the universities of São Paulo (Museu de Zoologia), Rio de Janeiro (Museu Nacional), and Bahia contributed to the creation of the Abrolhos Marine National Park in 1983, the first marine park in Brazil. In 1998 an initiative by local communities, supported by the Brazilian government and CI, resulted in the creation of the first co-management protected area in the region, the Corumbau Marine Extractive Reserve, gazetted in 2000. In the same year, CI and a group of Brazilian academic partners led a Rapid Marine Biodiversity Assessment in the Abrolhos Bank. The revelation of nearly 1,300 species from six focal taxa revealed Abrolhos as an important conservation priority for Brazil and the world (Dutra et al., 2006).

By 2000, CI and its academic partners had begun to monitor the effects and effectiveness of marine managed areas for biodiversity conservation and fisheries. Results have demonstrated

Abrolhos harbors the highest marine biodiversity in the southern Atlantic. It owes its extreme richness in both species and habitats to the huge area of shallow water covering a myriad of hard—and soft-bottom habitats

RIGHT: An artisanal fisherman drags a homemade net over the beach to catch crabs. Abrolhos National Park, Brazil.
Photograph by Cristina Goettsch Mittermeier/ iLCP

RIGHT: A reef parrotfish (*Sparisoma amplum*) wraps itself in mucus to rest for the night. Abrolhos Marine Reserve, Brazil.
Photograph by Luciano Candisani/ iLCP

RIGHT: A chelonian sea turtle (*Chelonia mydas*) rests on the sandy, grassy sea bottom in the Marine National Park of Abrolhos.
Photograph by Paul Nicklen/ iLCP

LEFT: A diver explores a large brain coral in the the Marine National Park of Abrolhos. This park's hot and crystalline water, varying between 24C and 28C degrees, hides a great diversity of species of the Brazilian fauna and flora, some of them rare and endemic.
Photograph by Paul Nicklen/ iLCP

representative increase in fish biomass inside, and spillover effects of economically important species from no-take zones (Francini-Filho and Moura, 2008a, 2008b). These results helped shape national policies, showing that conservation goals were compatible with fisheries management. The findings were also influential in the successful campaign to expand the network of marine protected areas in Abrolhos.

From 2005, larger-scale studies have focused on the functionality of the Abrolhos system. These include the Marine Management Area Science Program, the Pro-Abrolhos, Fisheries Monitoring Program, and Rede Abrolhos. Scientists in these programs are mapping marine habitats, studying biodiversity distribution at a regional scale, and investigating the biological connectivity and life cycles of key ecologically and economically important species. They are monitoring fisheries landings and the distribution of the regional fleets, determining the effects and effectiveness of marine zoning, as well as conducting social and economic surveys. All of this information is informing and driving the present conservation efforts, including the creation of Cassurubá Extractive Reserve in 2009, and an ongoing systematic conservation planning process aiming to expand the Abrolhos MPA Network.

The scale of conservation efforts is steadily changing in Abrolhos. From protected areas created to preserve emblematic natural places for tourism and research (e.g., Abrolhos National Park), conservation efforts have now graduated to fisheries co-management areas along the coast (Corumbau, Canavieiras, and Cassurubá Extractive Reserves). Furthermore, these local efforts have now been united under a broader Seascape vision. Abrolhos is now recognized within Brazilian society and in wider international circles as a priority for conservation in the world's oceans.

Despite its global importance, the Abrolhos ecosystem is seriously threatened. Coastal reefs are severely overfished and subjected to high sedimentation rates due to poor land management in coastal watersheds

To ensure a secure future for Abrolhos, we must confront a complex challenge. We must build a workable model for maintaining functional ecosystem services and improving the lives of the people in the region. Concrete field models for monitoring, protecting, and providing sustainable use of natural resources, managed by strong governance mechanisms, are the key tools needed to meet this challenge. Their creation will be the focus of much of the conservation efforts in the coming years.

LEFT: A mother humpback whale (*Megaptera novaeangliae*) and her young calf rest in the Abrolhos Marine National Park, off the coast of Bahia, Brazil. **Photograph by Luciano Candisani/ iLCP**

THE GULF OF CALIFORNIA (SEA OF CORTÉS)

Octavio Aburto-Oropeza and Cristina Goettsch Mittermeier

One hundred and thirty million years ago, what we now know as the Peninsula of Baja California began drifting away from mainland Mexico. As the two land masses separated, they created a large interior sea. Five million years ago, the mouth of this sea began to open, allowing the cold waters coming from the North Pole (now known as the California Current) to mix in with the warm waters coming from the tropics (the Equatorial Current). This mixing bowl created one of the most productive seas in the world: the Gulf of California, or Sea of Cortés, named after the famous Spanish conquistador.

The geology of the region is extremely complex, and numerous islands have broken off from the peninsula and the mainland as a consequence of the rift processes. Some of these isolated lands are also the product of rising land along the numerous faults, while others have formed after recent volcanic activity. Over 900 islands, islets, and emergent rocks have been identified in the Gulf's waters, making it one of the world's largest island archipelagos.

Wind-induced upwellings, tidal mixing, water exchange between the Gulf and the Pacific Ocean, and nutrient input from rivers are some of the oceanographic features responsible for the amazing richness of ecosystems and biodiversity of the Gulf (Alvarez-Borrego, 2010). In the winter months, the northwesterly winds fertilize the eastern Gulf, while during the summer, winds nourish the peninsula's coast. Spring tides and tidal action also produce a vigorous stirring of the water column down to 500 meters, bringing cold, nutrient-rich water to the surface. Some permanent offshore sites benefit from year-round upwellings. At these sites, low surface temperatures and high concentrations of dissolved inorganic carbon (carbon dioxide, bicarbonate, and carbonate) important for living organisms, trigger high concentrations of production in the form of beautiful, planktonic forms like diatoms and dinnoflagelates. Together, these oceanographic processes produce and sustain incredible volumes of life unrivaled worldwide, including sardines, anchovies, and herrings that together are called "forage fish."

Forage fish are small species that sustain larger predators higher up in the marine food chain (Alder et al., 2008). These forage fish comprise around ten species in the Gulf of California, forming immense shoals that move along coastlines and migrate across pelagic waters as they efficiently filter plankton. Although they are fast-growing and prolific, their abundance is influenced by the ocean's ever-changing conditions. Despite their small size, they number in the millions, and they feed all the top predator fish, seabirds, and marine mammals. Sea lions, fin whales, and dolphins are some of the species that take advantage of these fish. Their abundance is what makes it possible for this sea to be home of the highest concentration of cetacean diversity in the world (thirty-four species), with 61% of the baleen whales and 33% of the toothed whales species worldwide (Urbán, 2010).

Almost all seabirds depend on sardines and anchovies as their primary food items. An astonishing number of seagulls and terns synchronize their breeding seasons with the bursts of forage fish. When these pelagic fish reach shallow rocky reefs, other species join the feast. Groupers, snappers, and jacks congregate in rocky points and seamounts in one of the most incredible feeding frenzies in the underwater world. With this eruption of productivity, new life is infused into the reefs as reef fish take advantage of the season of plenty to form spawning aggregations and replenish their populations. Forage fish are just a small fraction of the 900 species of fish recorded in these Gulf waters. Most have a tropical ancestry, but a significant number come from temperate areas, and nearly 10% of the species are endemic to this region (Hastings et al., 2010).

Forage fish also reach reefs at depths of 400 meters, where sit-and-wait predators such as grouper and bass lurk. But these dark deep reefs are home to another, bigger predator: the Humboldt squid (*Dosidicus gigas*). These squids can reach 2.5 meters in length, traveling in large schools of up to 1,200 individuals. Because sharks, which are their main predator, have been fished out, these invertebrates have become one of the most important predators in the region, staging frenetic attacks on the schools of sardines and anchovies.

Squids aren't the only invertebrates that benefit from the abundance of forage fish. When fish die or when the feces of animals that feed on them reach the ocean floor, an alternate life-generating cycle begins. Flatworms, sea cucumbers, sea stars, brittle stars, sea urchins, and lobsters are some of the scavengers or detrivores that feed on this stream of organic matter raining down from above. From the surface waters to the great depths of this sea, over 4,900 species of marine invertebrates (Brusca and Hendrickx, 2010), are linked throughout the food web. Most of these species inhabit bottom habitats in the continental shelf, and hundreds of them inhabit the estuaries and mangroves lagoons along the coast.

Like no other region in the world, the

Gulf of California supports a remarkable and singular diversity of species. From rhodoliths—purple-pink spheres of seaweed the size of golf balls—to the largest animal that ever lived on Earth, the blue whale, the Gulf's rich waters are home to more than 8,000 marine species. Overall, marine macroinvertebrate diversity is exceptionally high: 4,916 named species, with new taxa being described at the rate of thirty to forty species every year. More importantly, while levels of endemicity average 16%, they can reach as high as 80% in groups like the Brachiopoda, commonly known as lampshells. Of the 900 Gulf fish species, 87% are represented by tropical species, and this productive sea also attracts five of the world's seven sea turtle species. Finally, with 170 sea bird species and 34 marine mammals, the Gulf of California represents one of the most important biodiversity hot spots on the planet.

The marine biodiversity in the Sea of Cortés is connected by the constant flow of forage fish and is sustained by the geology and the oceanography of the region. From the surface to the ocean floor, from sandy bottoms to rocky reefs, from the water column to the shore, everything is coupled in cycles of abundance and scarcity (Ezcurra, 1998) brought about by climatic oscillations. Cold La Niña years are the main cause of the aridity of the land, but they also bring larger upwellings of nutrient-rich waters to the surface that increase the food for forage fish and, in turn, for the entire food web. In these years the ocean subsidizes the land ecosystems, giving food for birds, mammals, reptiles, and insects directly through fish or indirectly by algae or invertebrates that reach beaches and coastal areas.

However, variations in the Earth's flow of air weaken the wind patterns and alter oceanic currents, causing warm oceanic waters to accumulate in the southern and central parts of the Gulf. During these El Niño years, ocean currents slow down and warm up, trapping nutrients in cold water far below the sea surface and halting the production of plankton. There is no food for sardines or anchovies, nor for the rest of the food web. The sea becomes a desert, and large marine animals migrate to other regions, seabirds' offspring die, reef fish recruitment plummets, and squid disappear. But when the seas are warm, the land is soaked with abundant rainfall, a result of the atmospheric condensation that induces rains. Rainfall brings nutrients from the upper parts of the Sierras, and when this runoff reaches coastal ecosystems there is an explosion of productivity in estuaries and mangrove lagoons. Now, with the cycle inverted, the land subsidizes the ocean, allowing juveniles of many species to grow faster and seek refuge inside the wetlands. Months later, this productivity in the form of shrimp, blue crabs, and fish is exported and serves as an energy refill for reefs, seamounts, and sandy bottoms.

Land and sea work together and complement one another to maintain the region's rich ecosystems. More importantly, these land–sea cycles, as well as their effects on natural resources, are predictable. The magnitude of the sardine and anchovy fisheries can be predicted a couple of years in advance (Velarde et al., 2004). For some mangrove-dependent species, the magnitude of their fisheries can be predicted four years in advance, and in the case of some fisheries of species with cold year affinities, predictions can be made seven years in advance. While this information is relatively new and hasn't been used in management efforts, understanding how these abundance–scarcity cycles work is vital for natural resource administration. By following and monitoring these cycles, the damage to wildlife populations and their habitats can be reduced or minimized to guarantee the preservation of the Gulf's biodiversity. The knowledge is there. We just need political will to implement and enforce regulations.

It is now well known that overfishing and destruction of critical habitats, such as mangroves, is threatening the marine biodiversity of the Gulf—sharks, large groupers, and marine mammals have become threatened, and some are even endangered. This overexploitation has transformed several areas of the Gulf, with negative impacts on the ecosystems' resiliency and on local and regional economies.

Until now, economic growth of coastal communities in the Gulf has been achieved through the exploitation of its natural resources. The "sardine" fishery has been one of these economic engines. Far from being sustainable, it has collapsed several times, resulting in serious economic crises and the loss of thousands of jobs. Quite shockingly, over 50% of this fishery's landings are used to make fishmeal and fish oil for aquaculture, poultry farms, and other uses. Why are valuable natural resources wasted in this manner? It is time to change the approach used by the fisheries administration (Erisman et al., 2011); it is time to protect high-productivity habitats and safeguard the connectors, such as forage fish, that transfer nutrients and energy between them.

Over 900 islands, islets, and emergent rocks have been identified in the Gulf's waters, making it one of the world's largest island archipelagos

Eighty-five percent of Mexican fisheries are at their maximum sustainable level. Now more than ever, the Gulf of California needs a serious agenda for the implementation of no-take marine reserves. Almost ten years ago, a network of these areas was proposed for the region (Sala et al., 2002); it would have protected 37% of the most abundant marine habitats, 85% of black coral beds and seamounts, 89% of mangrove forests, and 100% of the fish-spawning aggregation sites known at that time. Unfortunately, that proposal gained little support from regional policymakers. Today, attempts to sustain the "world's aquarium" (sensu Jacques Cousteau) are falling short, since less than 1% of its marine waters are protected from extractive activities.

Nevertheless, there is an outlier among the

RIGHT: Blue whale (*Balaenoptera musculus*) feeding, showing the grooves on its gular, or throat, pouch. This, the largest animal on our planet, is considered endangered. Gulf of California, Mexico. **Photograph by Hiroya Minakuchi/ National Geographic Stock/ iLCP**

RIGHT: A group of giant barrel cactus (*Ferocactus digetii*), a species that is endemic to a handful of islands in the Gulf of California. Catalina Island, Loreto Bay National Park, Mexico. **Photograph by Ralph Lee Hopkins/ iLCP**

RIGHT: An aerial photograph of the Colorado River's estuary system that drains into the Gulf of California. By the time the Colorado River reaches the Upper Gulf of California, it basically runs dry. **Photograph by Art Wolfe/ Art Wolfe Stock/ iLCP**

LEFT: Brown pelicans (*Pelecanus occidentalis*) gather around an artisanal fishing boat in Magdalena Bay, Gulf of California. **Photograph by Octavio Aburto/ iLCP**

degraded marine areas in the Gulf of California: Cabo Pulmo. Located near the Southern end of the Baja California Peninsula, it was designated as a national park in 1995 through the desire of a few local families to protect it as a no-take area. At 71 sq km, Cabo Pulmo is one of the smallest marine protected areas in Mexico, yet it has recovered its top predator species, has more ecological linkages and more species and complete ecosystems than any other area in the Gulf.

Eighty-five percent of Mexican fisheries are at their maximum sustainable level. The Gulf of California needs a serious agenda for the implementation of no-take marine reserves

The high densities and large sizes of fish inside the park generate almost three times more production than any other reef in the entire Gulf. The spillover from this production is equal to twenty-five tons of fish that are exported from the area every year and are available for fishing outside the reserve. These economic benefits are the result of the healthy marine ecosystems, which speaks of the community's success in resource management.

More than half of the reefs in the Gulf of California show signs of overexploitation. In this bleak scenario, Cabo Pulmo is a refreshing success story of local conservation; but more importantly, it is the example that contradicts the belief that coastal development cannot be achieved without the overexploitation of natural resources. We must communicate the success of Cabo Pulmo simply because we need to replicate this success all over the region and we need to do it fast. Time is running out for the Gulf of California.

RIGHT: An enormous school of Munk's devil ray (*Mobula munkiana*) migrates through the Gulf of California. **Photograph by Florian Schulz/ iLCP**

FOLLOWING SPREAD: A school of cow-nosed eagle rays (*Rhinoptera bonasus*) glides through the clear waters around the Bocas del Toro Islands, Panama. **Photograph by Art Wolfe/ iLCP**

FOLLOWING SPREAD: A male clownfish (*Amphiprion ocellaris*) guards and tends his clutch of eggs in Anilao, Philippines, an area within the Coral Triangle rich in marine biodiversity.
Photograph by David Doubilet/ iLCP

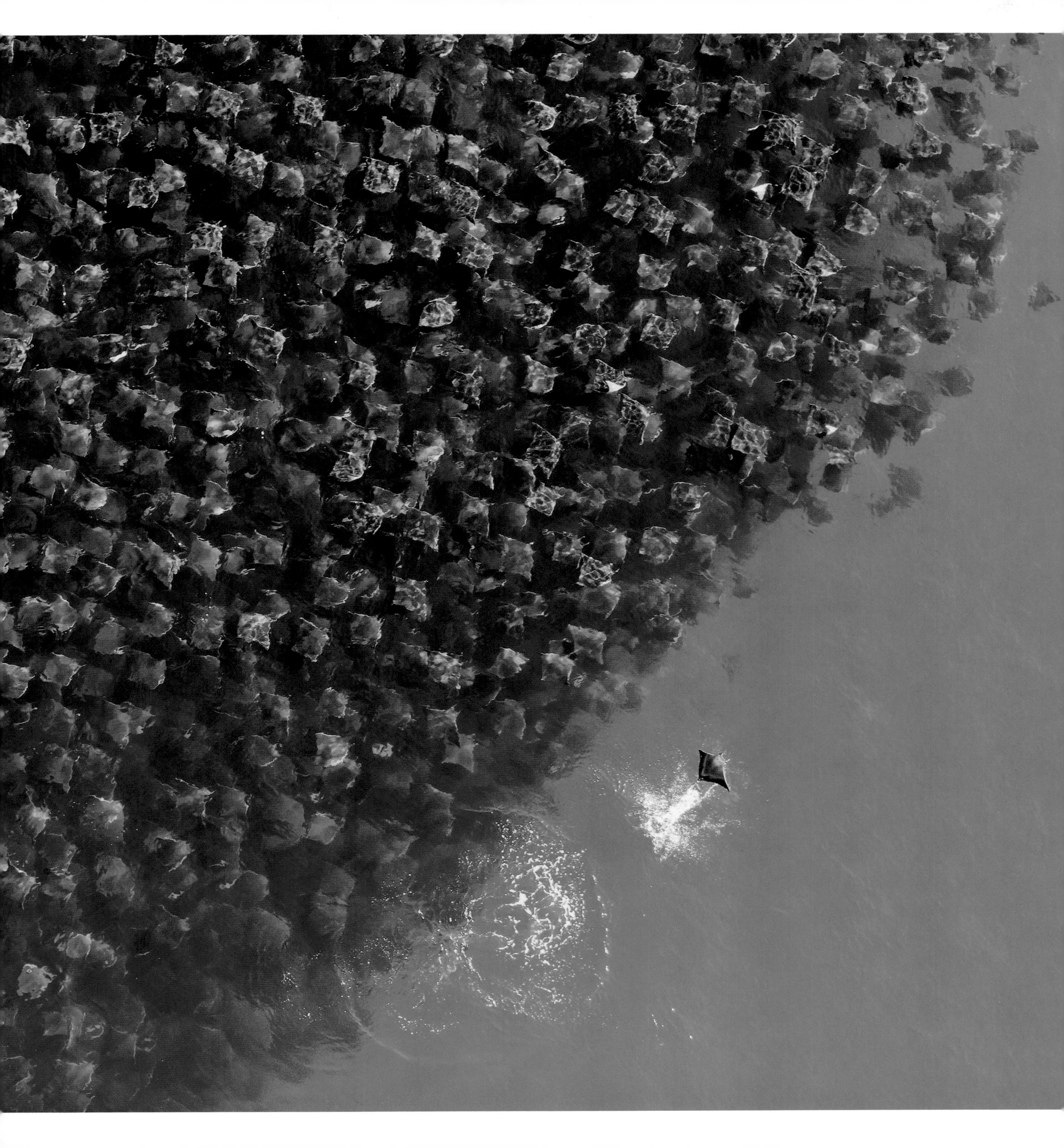

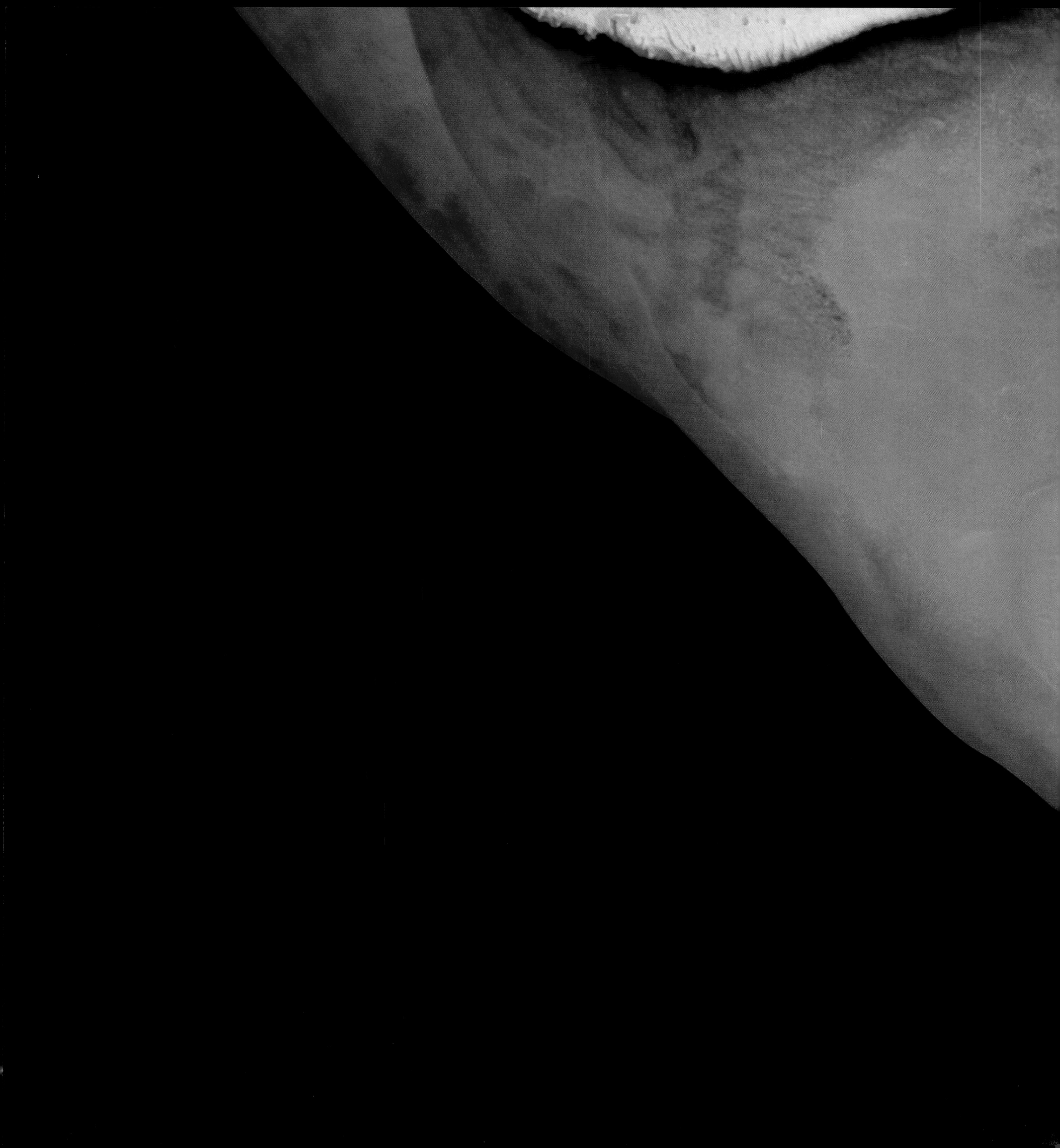

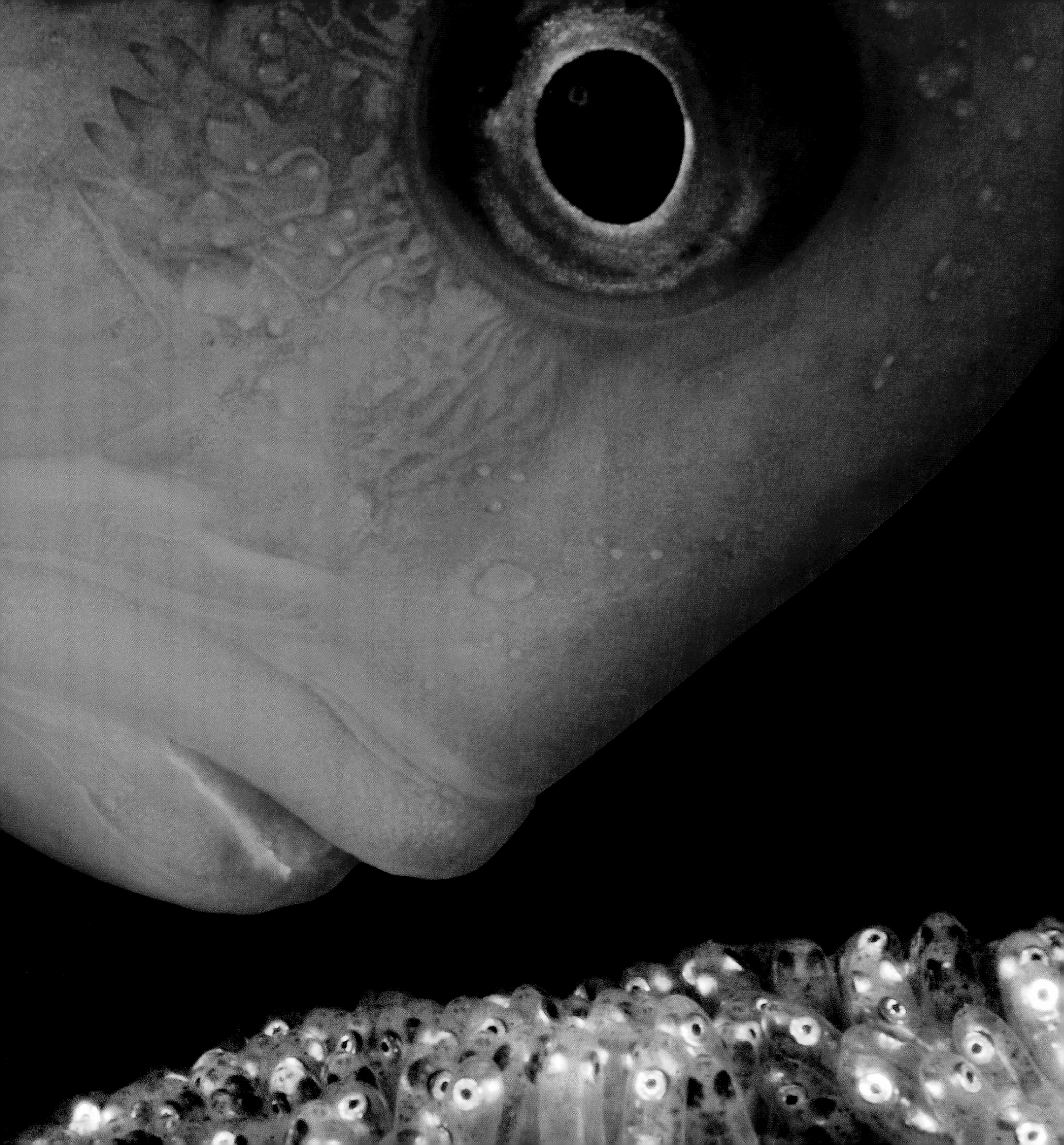

Andrew A. Rosenberg, Elizabeth R. Selig, Lindsey P. Fong, Leah Bunce Karrer, and Benjamin S. Halpern

MANAGING HUMAN IMPACTS ON THE OCEAN

Despite the incalculable services they provide to human communities, we currently exert unsustainable pressures on our oceans. We modify the shoreline and the ocean bottom in many places, overharvest its biota, mine its minerals, sail across its surface leaving behind a trail of noise and waste, and take for granted that it is the final repository for most of the waste we produce on land. We now know that we are affecting the global climate, fundamentally changing the temperature (Levitus et al., 2000) and chemistry of the ocean (Doney et al., 2009). Our impacts reach everywhere into the sea, and the effects on unseen environments can be profound (Halpern et al., 2008b; Katona, this volume).

The starting point for addressing the problems of human impacts on the ocean is to clearly remember that we do not "manage" the natural world—we manage people. Ocean life and ocean ecosystems are fragile, but can be remarkably resilient. If fish stocks are relieved from overfishing, if pollution is abated, and if other pressures are reduced, these systems can recover. These three simple facts—humans, not nature, can be managed; ocean life can be quite fragile; and that ocean ecosystems are remarkably resilient— show us clearly how to set priorities for ocean policy: focus on the human impacts, reduce their effects, and allow systems to respond and recover.

The Ocean—A Finite Resource

The enormity of the ocean has been its curse, because for millennia people believed it was impossible to harm an environment so vast. Our oceans and atmosphere still are viewed by many as the ultimate common-pool resources. All people feel they have the right to access and use the oceans. However, many of the current uses are unsustainable. Most individuals feel their effect on such a vast resource is tiny—but there are nearly seven billion of us. A single fisherman may not be able to imagine that a beautiful day on the water

LEFT: An insatiable market for reef fish, like snapper, coral trout, and groupers, in Hong Kong and other markets, is fueling a multibillion-dollar trade of live reef fish. In this image, a caretaker transfers live fish into fish pens in Tampakan, Kudat Bay, Sabah, Borneo, Malaysia.
Photograph by Jürgen Freund/ iLCP

spent catching a few fish can affect a fish stock, but there are over 70 million recreational fishing trips in coastal US waters each year (Coleman et al., 2004). Letting a plastic bag escape in the wind or losing the cover of a cooler at the beach may not seem like much of a problem, but a gyre of plastic the size of Texas has accumulated in the central Pacific made up of just such materials. Many fish stocks have been overfished to the point of collapse and coastal wetlands drained and paved over by development. We can and do manage these impacts, inevitably involving a great deal of debate and disagreement (Rosenberg, 2003), but the goal is clear: We must ensure that we do not use up the limited resources of our oceans.

Overarching policies and management goals can be established even at a global level, but ocean management action is necessarily local to regional. For example, there can be global agreements to manage fisheries or reduce pollution, and there is an overall United Nations Convention on the Law of the Sea that guides management, but ultimately action is needed at the national level to control human impacts on the ocean and within nations, states, or provinces, and so on, down to individual businesses and people.

Managing Human Impacts on the Ocean

Management of human activities that affect the ocean remains fragmented and uneven around the world. In the developed world there exists a framework of laws to control pollution, manage fisheries, and regulate shipping and coastal development. However, these laws are disconnected from one another and are unevenly enforced, when they are enforced at all. While the framework for protection is there, many ocean ecosystems remain subject to such harmful impacts as overfishing and pollution from the runoff of waste and nutrients. In the developing world, again the picture is uneven. Many countries have similar laws and regulations but lack the capacity to implement them in a meaningful way, or are unable to sustain that implementation for more than a few years. The economic imperative of development is everywhere. The enormous value of coastal land, fisheries, ports, and shipping keeps the pressure on. In most places, the management of these impacts is not keeping up.

The irony is that without better management, the things we value the most about ocean and coastal ecosystems will be lost, and economic development will collapse. In many areas, fishermen resist regulatory control, but it is overfishing that is destroying their livelihoods. A new coastal resort will not have any customers if the beauty of the coast is destroyed by poor development. And ineffective pollution controls, eased in the name of economic progress, have led to disastrous results around the world, both on land and in the sea.

We as a society have the capacity to manage our impacts on the environment, but do we have the will? To date the results are mixed, with some successes in managing fisheries, pollution, and other activities, but with far too many failures.

Depleting the Sea

Fisheries management is a good example of the challenges we face in developing strategies that promote sustainability. Recent reviews (National Research Council, 2006; Garcia and Rosenberg, 2010) have concluded that we have reached the global ceiling in marine fisheries production, and 40% of fisheries are now decreasing in production (Garcia, 2009). The United Nations Food and Agriculture Organization (FAO, 2009) suggests that at least 28% of the commercial species assessed are overexploited or depleted and a further 52% are being exploited to their maximum capacity. These may even be conservative estimates. Though controlling fishing pressure in some areas has contributed to the rebuilding of some depleted stocks, on average, biomass is still well below maximum sustained yield (maintaining the population size at the point of maximum growth rate) in most regions (Worm et al., 2009).

The problems of overfishing and stock decline have been blamed on weak fisheries controls (Beddington et al., 2007; Garcia 2009a,b; Mora et al., 2009). Although management authorities have set goals for sustainable use, progress has been hindered by an unwillingness or inability to bear the short-term social and economic costs of reducing fishing (Beddington et al., 2007). Large developed countries such as the United States and Japan, as well as the European Union, are spending twice as much on subsidies that encourage overfishing as they are on actions that protect oceans. Sixty percent of total global subsidies (US$27 million in 2003) go to support unsustainable fishing practices, including "capacity enhancing" boat construction and fuel, which encourage fisheries to bring in larger catches (Sumaila et al., 2010). This cycle of decline and rebuilding of fished stocks can incur significant costs because of lost catch, whereas sustained lower exploitation rates may promote greater stability of both biomass and catches (World Bank, 2009; Garcia and Rosenberg, 2010). In the long run, reducing fishing pressure (i.e., the exploitation rate) can actually result in increased catches from many stocks that are now depleted. That is, with fishing, we can often get more with less—which is better for the fish and for the fishermen.

Most management regimes have been built around the framework of maximum sustained yield, which sets goals for single species rather than ecosystems. Analyses of overfished areas reveals effects from fishers to predators and their prey species that can cause large ecological changes in the food web and overall productivity of the ecosystem (NRC, 2006; Worm et al., 2009). In other words, the effects of fishing are not just on the species that are targeted, like cod, tuna, or sharks, but on the ecosystem as a whole.

The tools most commonly used to reduce exploitation rates are restrictions on the type or amount of fishing gear or boats allowed in an area, closing areas to fishing, or reductions in the total allowable catch from the fleet as a whole, as well as allocating shares of the catch to a limited number of boats (Beddington et al., 2007; Worm et al., 2009; Costello et al., 2008).

Strong regulations, enforcement, and compliance are the backbone of successful conservation and rebuilding efforts (Mora et al., 2009). It is essential to have legislation preventing overexploitation, outlining clear rules, and setting targets for rebuilding (Beddington et al., 2007; Caddy et al., 2004). Governance frameworks have substantially improved, and techniques have been shown to be effective in individual cases; however, the global political will of governments must be marshaled to implement them effectively and eliminate loopholes (Ludwig et al., 1993; Brander, 2007). Given the added uncertainties of climate change, fishing agencies must act now rather than wait to begin rebuilding efforts only after stocks collapse (Ludwig et al., 1993; Brander, 2007).

Across the globe, developing countries are beginning to send their own commercial fleets out to fish the high seas. This presents a key problem for rebuilding stocks as fishing pressures move from the fishing fleets of industrialized nations to those of the developing world (Worm, 2009). Developing countries that have invested heavily in commercial fishing fleets will require assistance to reduce fishing pressure; initial financial losses may create strong resistance (Agnew et al., 2009).

Another significant problem is illegal, unreported, and unregulated (IUU) fishing, practices that seriously undermine efforts to rebuilt overfished stocks (Agnew et al., 2009). Effective controls on exploitation rates are still needed across vast areas of the ocean, including the high seas that lie beyond national jurisdiction (Pauly et al., 2003; Beddington et al., 2007; Mora et al., 2009).

Rebuilding Overfished Stock A Way Forward

Potential solutions may begin with the World Trade Organization and other agents. For example, the European Union rules adopted in 2010 prevent the importation of fish landed illegally from any part of the world, thus making a strong connection between trade and environmental protection (Garcia and Rosenberg, 2010).

The solution to the problem of overfishing is not that complicated: Reduce fishing pressure on key stocks. Fishing is one of those rare activities where less fishing can result in more yield if stocks are allowed to rebuild. And we have examples of successful rebuilding (Rosenberg et al., 2006). In New England, despite a remarkably contentious history of fisheries management, iconic and valuable stocks of haddock (*Melanogrammus aeglefinus*) and the Atlantic sea scallop (*Placopecten magellanicus*) have recovered from decades of overfishing and now support highly profitable and sustainable fisheries. There are other examples around the world (Worm et al., 2009) including haddock stocks that have been rebuilt in the North Sea, and swordfish (*Xiphias gladius*) off the eastern coast of the United States are rebounding. Overfishing is a problem we know how to solve, if we have the political will.

Rebuilding collapsed stocks may require trading short-term yields for conservation benefits. Fishing gear that has less impact on ocean habitats and results in less bycatch can help, along with a much more widespread use of ocean protected areas. Protecting some areas while allowing fishing in others provides a refuge for many species and not only rebuilds stocks but sustains them into the future. Changing the incentives for fishermen so that they can directly benefit by making conservation measures work is essential. Proven strategies include involving the community in fisheries management, and tradable catch and bycatch quotas (Beddington et al., 2007; Worm, 2009; Branch, 2008; Costello et al., 2008).

Fish for Food

The nutrition and livelihoods of millions of people worldwide rest critically on our ability to manage fisheries more responsibly. The global population is predicted to increase to 9.5 billion people by the year 2050 (U.S. Census Bureau, 2008). Total food requirements will increase by 100% (Tilman et al., 2002) as a function of both the increase in population and the additional global demand for animal protein as people in developing countries become more affluent (Keyzer et al., 2005). The resources available for agricultural production are likely to decrease concurrently with population growth due to competition for land and water and depletion of fossil fuel reserves. Using Life Cycle Analysis, it has been shown that seafood production has less environmental impact than other animal proteins (deVries and deBoer, 2010). To meet predicted demands for seafood by 2020, we may need to double aquaculture production. Alternatively, we will need to reform both how and for what we fish, targeting species lower on the food chain (Pitcher, 2008). For both aquaculture and wild fisheries, our goals must be to maintain and optimize production, in terms of catch composition, nutritional quality, fuel consumption, and ecological footprint. Recent interest in adopting ecosystem-based approaches to fisheries have led to a re-evaluation of management targets for fisheries and the role of managers in meeting broader marine conservation goals (Garcia et al., 2003).

Although small-scale fisheries have been touted as being more sustainable than large-scale operations, they face many disadvantages. Eliminating government subsidies would level the playing field, making large-scale fishing operations less profitable, to the benefit of smaller scale fisheries. Small-scale fisheries usually require only small capital investment, use lower technology gear and vessels (often non-motorized), and catch fish for subsistence or local markets (FAO, 2004). These fisheries produce as much annual catch for human consumption but use less than one-eighth the fuel as their industrial counterparts, and employ more than twelve million people worldwide, compared to half a million in

LEFT: Fisherman at a semi-permanent camp, at Tanjung Besi, Gam Island. These outsiders from Buton Island, Sulawesi, come here for months at a stretch to fish at night for small fish. Here men prepare to unload the night's catch into baskets. **Photograph by Tim Laman/ iLCP**

the industrial sector (Jacquet and Pauly, 2008). Subsidy money could instead be redirected toward improving the livelihoods and economic possibilities of fishing-community residents in industries other than fisheries, or allocated toward projects to rebuild fish stocks (Sumaila et al., 2010). Sumaila et al. further argue that if subsidies were removed, fishing would no longer be profitable, and stocks would have a chance to recover.

Eating Lower on the Food Chain

To maximize efficient use of current fishery products for human consumption, there are increasing calls to eat lower on the marine food chain (Hall, 2007; Grescoe, 2008), and to reserve small fish and shellfish for human consumption rather than processing them into fishmeal for livestock feed. Currently 36% of fish landed worldwide (some 30 million tons) are ground up each year into fishmeal and oil, mostly to feed farmed fish, chicken, and pigs (Alder et al., 2008). Pigs and chickens alone respectively consume six times and two times the amount of seafood as U.S. and Japanese consumers, respectively. It is further suggested that all agriculture and aquaculture need to revert back to less intensive systems, requiring only plant-based feeds for farm use (Pimentel and Pimentel, 2003).

The Challenge of Aquaculture

Aquaculture is a leading source of seafood, equivalent to capture fisheries, and is often seen as a way to meet the growing global demand for seafood. However, aquaculture operations have numerous environmental drawbacks. They can encroach on habitats, release nonnative fish into the environment through escapes, compete with wild-capture fisheries, and discharge antibiotics, hormones, parasiticides, and other additives into waterways.

In order to select efficient fish species to culture, identify appropriate sites for aquaculture operations, and set standards for responsible fish-farming practices, decision-makers must have a rigorous yet efficient way to quantify and compare the environmental impacts of seafood products. The Global Aquaculture Performance Index (based on the Environmental Performance Index, which ranks countries by their performance in categories, including fisheries) is one initiative designed to provide this information for marine finfish species (Mara et al., 2010). Using this tool, it has been found that the worst performing sectors of the industry (such as cobia and grouper) are also the fastest growing. As aquaculture expands, attention should be paid to ensure that the industry does not shift further toward poorer performers, at least until their practices improve significantly.

Ecosystem-Based Management

Fisheries are just one example of the need to improve the management of human impacts on the ocean. Almost every human activity or endeavor affects the ocean. New uses of the ocean continue to emerge, ranging from desalination plants along the coast to renewable energy and aquaculture facilities sited offshore. Eventually areas may be set aside for carbon sequestration to remediate the effects of global warming. Each time we use the ocean, we must carefully think through the impacts that result from our activities. Many proposed uses may conflict with one another. For instance, building an offshore energy facility—such as a wind farm, liquid natural gas (LNG) port, wave-power or tidal-power installation—takes up space and precludes some other coastal uses. We need coordinated management that directly confronts the problems of interactions and cumulative effects of human activities.

Managing all of the various kinds of human activities on or affecting the ocean is a major challenge. Ecosystem-based management (EBM) provides an approach to not only integrate disparate management agencies and their policies, but also to account for the needs of the whole ecosystem. Although implementation of EBM varies, the common goal is to sustain the delivery of critical ecosystem services that support human well-being (Rosenberg and McLeod , 2005; Leslie et al., 2008). Historically, we have managed most marine resources around a single species, sector, activity, or concern. Thus most developed and many developing countries have complex regulations covering fishing, shipping, waste disposal, and oil exploration that are based on statutory authority at the national level. In addition, there may be another layer of control at the local level. The coastal community may take direct responsibility for managing activities such as fishing or coastal development, for local use or benefit.

Although managing each sector individually seems a natural approach to dealing with complex problems, we have to move toward management that considers the needs and impacts of all sectors. Industries and activities are impacting a resource that is held in the public trust by government or the local community. In other words, the various benefits of a healthy ocean are for all people and every nation, not just those with immediate access or business on the ocean. The ocean, unlike land, is not "owned" by anyone, although the privilege to utilize the public resource may be conferred upon individuals or businesses. In the words of the United Nations Convention on the Law of the Sea, ocean resources are the "common heritage of mankind" (United Nations Division of Ocean Affairs, 1982).

Success in managing one activity or species can have unintended negative consequences for the whole ecosystem or may even fail with its focused target. Human activities have cumulative impacts on a species or ecosystem. Therefore, regulation of only one activity will not always be sufficient for sustainable management. At the same time, trying to regulate human impacts for only one species can neglect other species in the ecosystem that provide

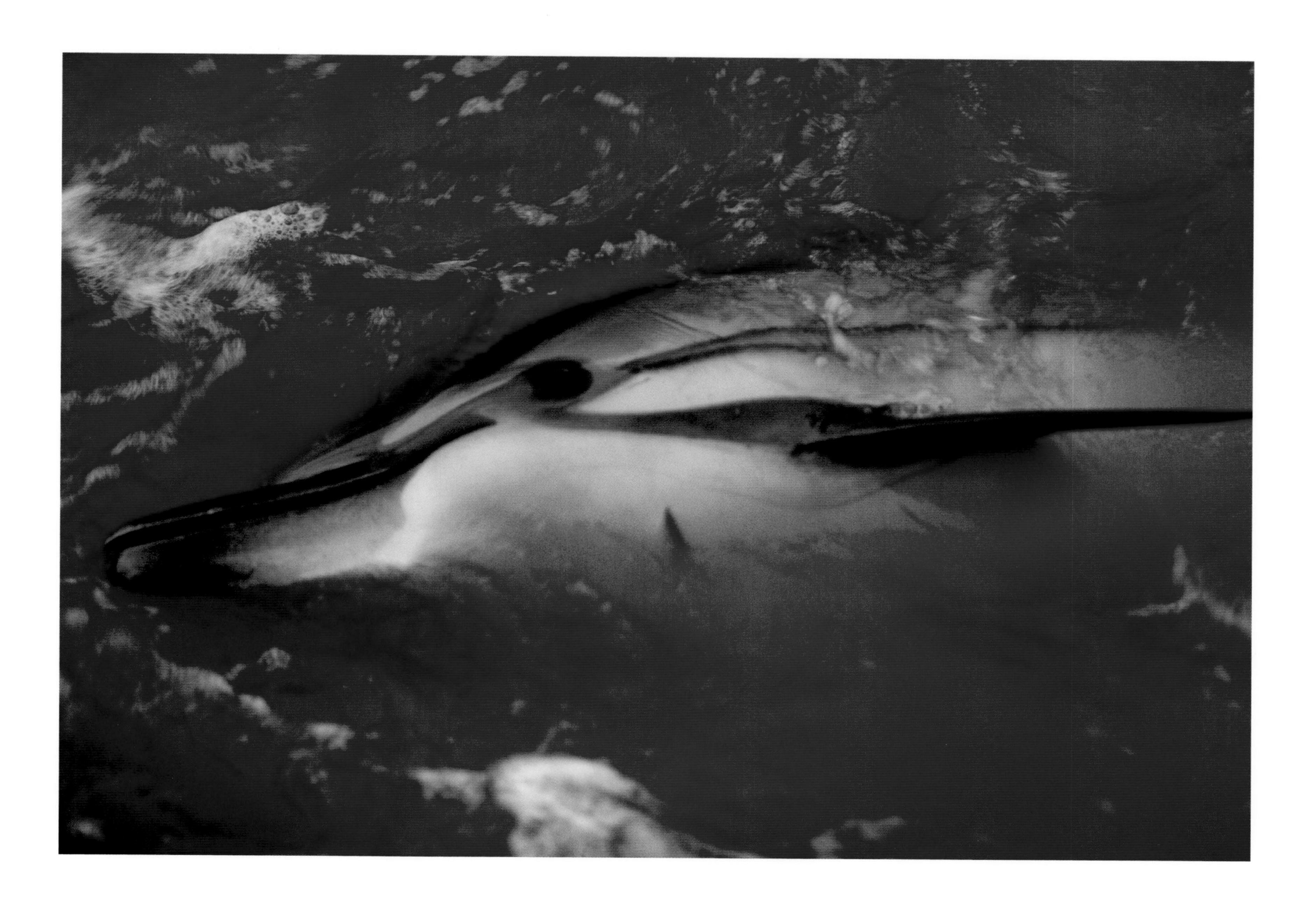

ABOVE: Dolphin drive hunting is the method used to kill several species of dolphins, like this striped dolphin (*Stenella coeruleoalba*), photographed in Futo, Japan. Hundreds of dolphins are massacred each year for meat while a few are sold alive to aquaria for live dolphin shows.
Photograph by David Doubilet/ iLCP

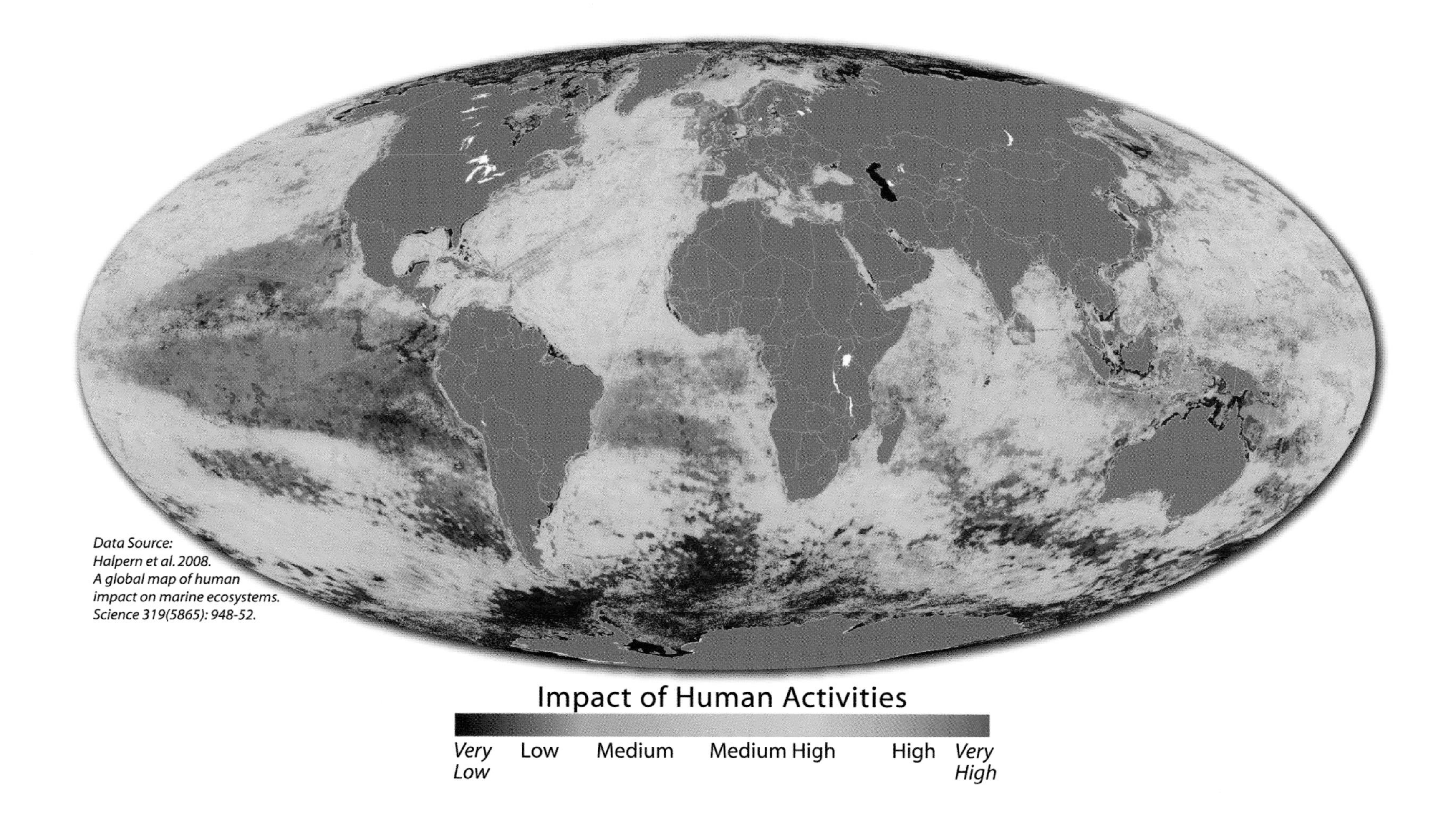

the habitat or food integral to the target species' needs for survival. For example, regulating commercial fishing based on the impacts on the target species alone may leave many other species, caught and discarded as unmarketable for one reason or another, vulnerable to depletion even as they play an important role in the functioning of an ecosystem. The prey of target species could still be overharvested, and other unregulated impacts like land-based runoff may undercut the efficacy of fishing regulations. The interdependencies of human activities and ecosystems require the holistic approach of ecosystem-based management.

Humans As Part of the Ecosystem

There are three things that distinguish ecosystem-based management from other types. First, EBM explicitly recognizes humans as part of the ecosystem and encourages management choices that acknowledge and address the tightly coupled nature of human and natural systems. People benefit from and have major influences on the natural world. The needs of communities and their impacts need to be carefully considered in order to design successful management interventions. Second, EBM requires us to assess the cumulative impacts of the full range of human activities on our natural world. Finally, EBM helps elucidate the inherent tradeoffs among different stakeholders, such as commercial and recreational fishermen, coastal developers, wastewater management agencies, conservationists, and private industry, thus informing management decisions. These three aspects of EBM offer a substantial advantage over sector-by-sector management because they acknowledge the multiple uses of the ocean, offer tools for assessing the consequences of those uses, and make transparent the outcomes of any management decision for each interested party (Rosenberg and McLeod, 2005; Halpern et al., 2008a; Rosenberg and Sandifer, 2009).

Ecosystem-based management can make use of a variety of existing management tools including traditional fishing regulations and marine protected areas (MPAs). Marine protected areas (MPAs) or national parks in the ocean can be designated nationally or locally. MPAs restrict activities in a designated area to give greater protection than surrounding areas. In some cases, all extractive activities are prohibited, but most MPAs allow multiple uses. An EBM approach would consider the impacts of an MPA on other sectors and work to integrate conservation, fishing, and other sectoral activities over the whole management area.

ABOVE: Cumulative human impact from fishing, shipping, organic and inorganic pollutants, and other activities on ocean ecosystems (From Halpern et al. *Science* 2008).

PRECEDING SPREAD: Sunken World War II aircraft, like this three-seat Japanese float plane photographed in the Solomon Sea, can be found all over the Pacific. These relics of war have become a popular tourism and diving destination, and they serve as artificial reefs as well. **Photograph by George Steinmetz/ iLCP**

EBM in Action: Lessons from the Field

Aspects of EBM have been applied to coastal marine systems around the world for nearly a decade, and success stories from these locations are beginning to offer lessons to shape future efforts.

A key step in EBM is identifying the goals of the coupled human–natural system. Incorporating the necessary social, economic, and biological data, and marshaling the political will necessary to form comprehensive ecosystem-based management plans can be challenging. EBM plans have been developed for many locations around the world, including Puget Sound on the West Coast of the United States and the Great Barrier Reef (GBR) in Australia. The successful implementation of these plans in Puget Sound and the GBR are just two key examples of the success of ecosystem-based management in different areas of the ocean.

The Puget Sound ecosystem has more than 41,500 square kilometers of terrestrial, marine, and freshwater habitat. Population within the region is projected to reach 5.4 million by 2025. The ecosystem is clearly under stress, with several species listed as threatened or endangered including key cultural symbols like orca whales (*Orcinus orca*) and Chinook salmon (*Oncorhynchus tshawytscha*) (Ruckelshaus et al., 2009). The Washington State Legislature created the Puget Sound Partnership (PSP) n 2007 was created out of concern for the future wellbeing of both the Puget Sound ecosystems and the humans that depend on them. [cite] Over the next year, this public-private coalition identified key ecosystem indicators and measurable social and ecological goals to improve the health of the Puget Sound (Ruckelshaus et al., 2009). The members of the PSP recognized that these goals also required coordination with Canadian authorities, because Puget Sound is part of the larger Georgia Basin ecosystem that extends into British Columbia, Canada. Several transboundary issues affect the health of Puget Sound including climate change, transportation and trade policies, and harvesting of wide-ranging species such as salmon (family Salmonidae) and herring (*Clupea* spp.) (McLeod and Ruckelshaus, 2009). PSP first developed an Action Agenda in 2008 to craft standards for a healthy Puget Sound and describe its current state of health as well as set priorities for management efforts and opportunities for federal, state, local, and private groups to coordinate their work. To adapt to changing conditions, the Action Agenda is now updated every two years (Puget Sound Partnership, 2011).

At 344,000 square kilometers, the Great Barrier Reef Marine Park (GBRMP) in Australia is one of the largest marine protected areas in the world. Created in 1975, the GBRMP underwent a major rezoning in 2004, increasing no-take areas from 4.5% to 33%. The Representative Areas Program of the Great Barrier Reef Marine Park Authority led the five-year process to determine how best to rezone the park to ensure different bioregions were protected and to maintain critical ecological functions such as connectivity (Day et al., 2002; Fernandes et al., 2005). The Great Barrier Reef Marine Park Authority tried to minimize the socioeconomic impacts of the rezoning by including in the planning process representatives from fishing and tourism industries as well as members of indigenous groups and conservation organizations. The Great Barrier Reef Marine Park is unique in that it is one large MPA, which is rare among areas being managed according to EBM principles. Key to the success of EBM at the Great Barrier Reef was the integration of user needs with conservation goals (Day et al., 2002; Fernandes et al., 2005). By zoning multiple activities over the whole marine park, the Representative Areas Program was able to conduct a broad ocean-zoning exercise that could serve as a model for future efforts.

At a national level, Rosenberg and colleagues (2009) compared efforts to implement more holistic management approaches in the U.S., Canada, Australia, New Zealand, and the European Union. These well-developed countries and regions have some of the strongest management capacity, but even here developing integrated management systems has been a challenge. As overarching frameworks in these four nations and the European Union have begun to tie together the disparate pieces of management, however, some progress has been made.

Internationally, the Convention for Conservation of Antarctic Living Marine Resources, the OSPAR (the Oslo and Paris Commission) Convention for the Northeast Atlantic, and the Baltic Sea Commission, to choose three examples, have developed integrated management systems in their respective areas by creating marine protected areas and by implementing shipping and fishing regulations to reduce the impacts of human activities and to manage future development.

Science for Management

Conservation and management depend on sound science. While humans have long valued and been fascinated by the sea, we invest little worldwide in the science needed to protect our oceans. During an informal hearing a few years ago in the U.S. House of Representatives, a congressman noted that it was proposed that the government spend billions on exploring Mars to investigate if there is water there, but we spend far less on exploring the ocean, and we know there is water here! We want our management actions to be based on the best science, but are we willing to support that science?

Scientists always want to know more, and so do policymakers. It would be nice to think that we could make decisions with all the information we need at hand, but in reality we must act while our scientific understanding is still incomplete. Over the last decade, the concept of a precautionary approach to management has

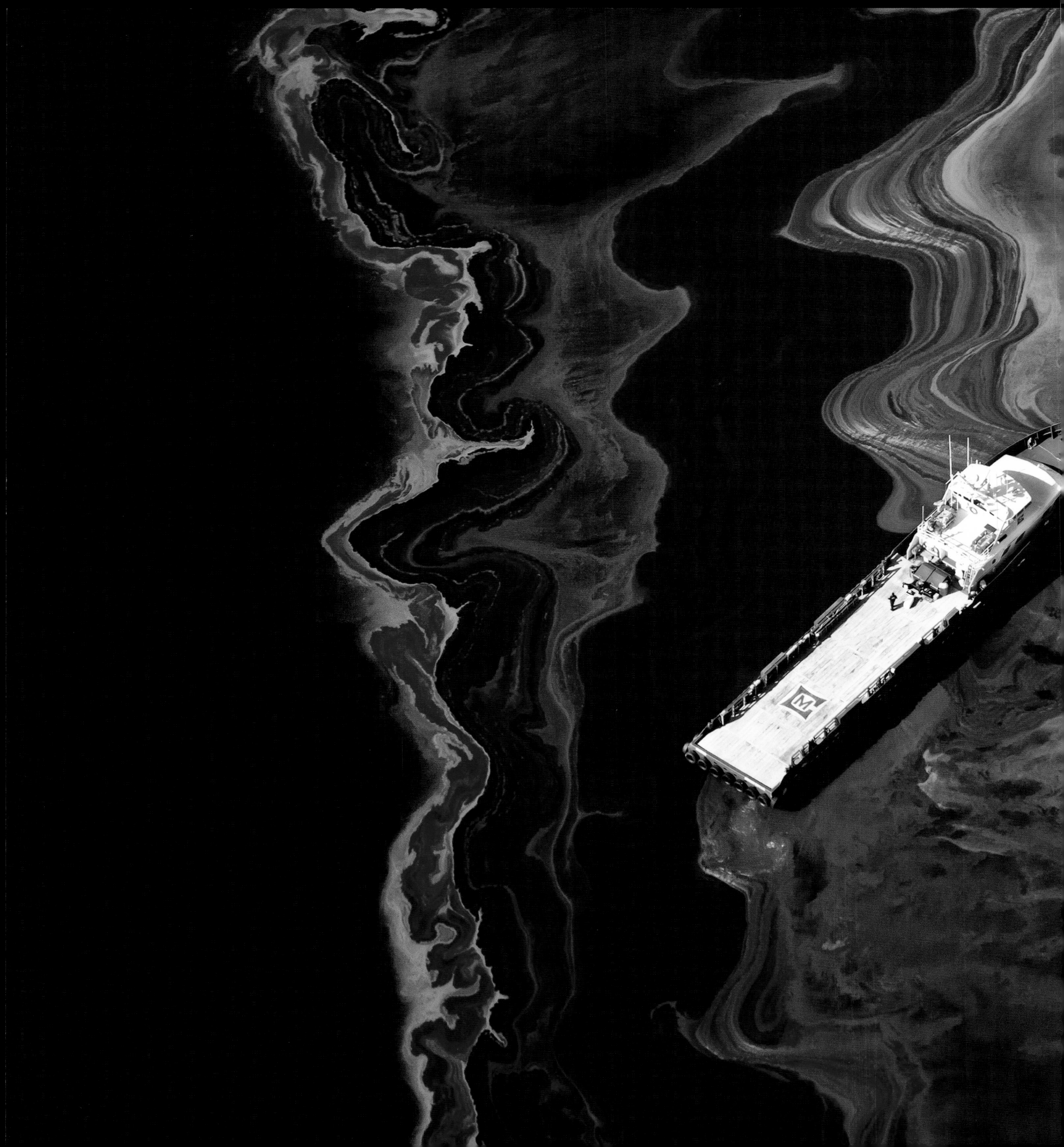

gained traction (Rosenberg, 2002). The precautionary approach means managers must exercise prudent foresight, barring activities that may cause major irreversible harm to an ecosystem and proceeding cautiously rather than reacting after damage has been done. In fisheries, for example, rather than allowing fishing effort to continue unchecked until all the science is in to set limits to fishing, ensure that increases are slow and can be dialed back as soon as signs of overfishing emerge. In pollution control, require testing before release of potentially harmful substances, rather than restricting them after harm has been demonstrated. In a precautionary management system, prudent foresight allows science to guide the decision-making process.

For science to inform decision making, results must be accessible, easily applicable, and understandable. Too often, tremendous effort goes into research that fails to inform conservation because no one makes the link between the results and relevant management decisions. Feeding science into decision making at the local and global level is a complex process requiring close collaboration between scientists and decision-makers, often facilitated by what Nancy Baron calls "science communicators" (Baron, 2010). Science communicators help establish partnerships between scientists and decision-makers; identify information needs based on management objectives; prioritize research studies based on those needs; draw out the key, management-relevant messages from the scientific results; synthesize these key messages into accessible forms (e.g., policy briefs, videos, posters); and, most importantly, facilitate discussions between decision-makers and scientists regarding the management implications at the appropriate times to influence management decisions.

In Abrolhos, Brazil, the Coraumbau Marine Extractive Reserve was established in part because science communicators, working with Conservation International, highlighted the importance of the mangroves as key nurseries for commercial fisheries and as critical to the livelihoods of over one thousand families as shown by socioeconomic and ecological analyses of the area. Similarly, in Fiji, science communicators facilitated discussions between scientists and village leaders regarding the ecological importance of a network of MMAs based on genetic analyses. These discussions led to village chiefs committing to stronger collaborative measures and establishment of new locally managed marine areas.

Incentives: Motivating Sustainable Production and Purchasing

When developing regulations (e.g., gear restrictions, bans on destructive activities, zoning of shoreline development, pollution controls), one of the challenges regulators face is a mismatch between stakeholders who lose over the short term and those who benefit over the long term. This mismatch necessitates economic incentives to compensate individuals or communities that incur short-term losses by adopting sustainable practices. Conservation investors (NGOs, government agencies, corporations) use incentives as tools to engage resource users (local residents, fishers, developers) and motivate them to change unsustainable practices, such as destructive fishing or clear-cutting of mangroves (Niesten and Gjertsen, 2010). Three of the most widely used approaches on the production side are:

BUY-OUTS. Conservation investors purchase resource rights or equipment with the intention of retiring them, thereby reducing the overall level of harvest. Resource owners or users are typically compensated with an up-front, one-time cash payment, followed by government enforcement to ensure illegal practices have indeed stopped.

ALTERNATIVE LIVELIHOODS. Conservation investors train and equip resource users in alternative livelihoods to replace unsustainable activities. Income or harvest for their own consumption may be derived from entirely new economic activities or revised forms of previous activities, such as less destructive methods of fishing, which may be achieved through fishery and aquaculture improvement projects (FAIPs). These projects help a fishery or aquaculture operation to mitigate its environmental and/or social impacts as well as leveraging associated market benefits.

CONSERVATION AGREEMENTS. Resource-users sign contracts agreeing to abstain from unsustainable activities in exchange for benefits that are conditional on conservation performance. Benefits may be in the form of cash, services, or goods, and are provided periodically when conservation performance targets are met and verified.

Another way to use incentives to support conservation is to enlist the power of consumers and the marketplace. Producers can only meet the demand for sustainable practices if consumers are aware of the possibilities and benefits of those practices. Creating consumer demand for ocean-friendly, "blue" products and services confers a market advantage on those producers who modify their business practices. A notable example of this is new awareness of sustainable seafood, affecting consumers' choices at the seafood counter and at restaurants. Market-based approaches have been used in many types of businesses from Walmart to seafood retailers (Walmart, 2008; FishWise, 2011).

Since the 1960s, worldwide per capita consumption of marine fishes has nearly doubled (World Health Organization, 2006) and demand is expected to increase as wealth increases in populous countries such as China and India. The politics of fishery management favor continued exploitation—making over-fishing a seemingly intractable problem that is hard to address through management alone (Rosenberg, 2003).

PRECEDING SPREAD: Aerial view of the oil leak from the Deepwater Horizon wellhead during the BP oil crisis in the Gulf of Mexico in 2010. **Photograph by Daniel Beltrá/ iLCP**

This is because even though fisheries depend upon public resources (national and international), they tend to be out of sight and out of mind for the majority of the public—except fishermen, who unsurprisingly are generally pushing back against regulation and restrictions.

Recognizing that the growing demand for seafood has contributed to the marine fisheries crisis, it is fitting that efforts be directed at influencing the human appetite and hence public awareness and demand (Grescoe, 2008). In recent years, efforts have begun to raise awareness and encourage what is popularly referred to as "sustainable seafood," generally referring to products produced by responsible fishing that minimizes environmental impacts. Demand-side initiatives by retailers and consumers include eco-labeling, certification systems, seafood guides, purchasing policies, and boycotts (Roheim and Sutinen, 2006; Halweil, 2006; Marine Aquaculture Task Force, 2007). By stimulating consumer appetite for seafood from well-managed fishing stocks, these programs aim to create market-based incentives for better fisheries management through the supply chain. Additionally, public opinion and pressure can sway political will and encourage governmental efforts to manage in sustainable ways. Notable campaigns include "Give Swordfish a Break," "Take a Pass on Chilean Sea Bass," "Farmed and Dangerous Salmon," and "Caviar Emptor" (Roheim and Sutinen, 2006).

Eco-labels are used to designate products that have been independently certified as meeting defined sets of standards. At the start of the seafood supply chain, certification schemes encourage fishers to comply with conservation and management rules, and may help reduce illegal, unreported, and unregulated fishing. Certification schemes, such as the Marine Stewardship Council, Friend of the Sea, and Responsible Aquaculture Program Certified Best Aquaculture Practices and their resulting eco-labels, should be backed by a "chain-of-custody" procedure documenting each stage of production and certifying that the fish or shellfish came from a sustainably managed source (Wessells et al., 2001).

Processors, wholesalers, and retailers can then purchase seafood from accredited fisheries and place eco-labels on their products, as a marketing advantage to an increasingly aware public. (Gudmundsson and Wessells, 2000). Consumers benefit from having increased information concerning the products they purchase and greater choice of products with varying environmental qualities, as well as the ability to make informed choices regarding the purchase of those seafood products, and the continued availability (sustainability) of their favorite seafood in the future.

Eco-labels have raised concerns, however. Those concerns include consumer confusion over differing definitions of sustainability and inconsistent interpretation of data to declare a given fish as sustainably or unsustainably sourced. If chain-of-custody procedures are insufficient or lacking entirely, the credibility of eco-labels may also be called into question. While many sustainable seafood programs are addressing these concerns, most eco-labels still lack direct regulation, placing the onus on consumers to educate themselves about their options (Jacquet et al., 2010).

In addition to eco-labelling, there are several well-established guides to "wise seafood choices" available; in the U.S., sources include Monterey Bay Aquarium, the Blue Ocean Institute, Environmental Defense, and NOAA. Such guides allow consumers easy access to sustainability rankings through websites, seafood-choice wallet cards, smartphone applications, or color-coded displays at the seafood counter. These systems have been criticized for being too general in their categorization of ratings and recommendations, but they do provide a basis for consumers to make more informed decisions on purchasing, which can influence suppliers around the world.

Restaurants, supermarkets, and other retailers are also being encouraged to adopt company policies reducing their purchases of unsustainable products and stocking their menus and seafood counters with more sustainable offerings. Sustainable seafood purchasing policies can be a strategic addition to other Earth-friendly initiatives and public marketing strategy, attractive to consumers because it relieves them of the burden of researching their seafood selections. Other business advantages of sourcing from the variety of available sustainable seafood products on the market include a more stable supply and price, and reduced vulnerability to regulatory changes, consumer boycotts, and other shocks of supply and demand. Conversely, if environmentally problematic species continue to be marketed, their supplies are likely to remain limited and unpredictable.

Improving our management of human activities and their impacts on the ocean will require action from local to international scales, from kitchen tables to the decks of fishing vessels, from corporate boardrooms to legislative chambers. In many places, local communities still have purview over many land-use decisions as well as many aspects of economic development. These ordinary citizens must not only see the value of the natural marine system as important for their communities, but they must also obtain the economic benefits. For example, keeping coastal habitats intact, rather than replacing them with hotels, shrimp farms, recreational harbors, and the like must be seen as bringing long-term economic benefits to local communities. These benefits may be better coastal water quality, nursery habitats for young fish to support recreational and commercial fisheries, and protection from storms or other natural hazards. While such economic benefits may be hidden compared to more politically heralded creation of jobs or tax revenues from a hotel, imagine the cost of trying to "build" such services as nature is already providing through ecosystems. We have ample examples of places where the loss of ecosystem services such as natural hazard

RIGHT: Off the northern coast of British Columbia, Canada, First Nation Gitga'at fishers depend heavily on healthy marine resources, like this Dungeness crab (*Metacarcinus magister*). The Gitga'at harvest crabs in the spring along with a bounty of other sea products to store and consume through the cold winter months.
Photograph by Cristina Goettsch Mittermeier/ iLCP

protection have resulted in a great toll in human lives, livelihoods, and economic losses. Hurricane Katrina in the Gulf of Mexico, tsunamis in Southeast Asia and Japan, and coastal landslides in Central America were all certainly exacerbated because the coastal mangroves and salt marshes that protect the coast had been destroyed in the name of development.

We are just beginning to recognize another service provided by coastal ecosystems, that of sequestering carbon and mitigating the pace of climate change. "Blue carbon" (Nellemann et al., 2010) refers to carbon stored when habitats such as mangrove areas, seagrass beds, and salt marshes are allowed to remain intact and flourishing. These ecosystems pump large amounts of carbon into the sediment and hold it there for hundreds of years, effectively removing carbon dioxide from the atmosphere. But when such marine and coastal vegetation is removed and the sediment is disturbed, the carbon will be re-released, adding to greenhouse gas emissions much in the manner of deforestation in tropical forests. Recorded loss rates of coastal habitats have been very high in the 2010's, so protecting these habitats may provide a major tool for reducing greenhouse gas emissions. Because of this, we should compensate local communities that keep their coastal ecosystems intact as carbon offsets for other areas. Such a "payment for ecosystem services" scheme can provide additional revenue that, along with preserving these same habitats for fisheries production, sediment capture, and water quality benefits and wildlife habitat, could change the balance toward development that conserves nature rather than destroying it.

Ecosystem-based management (EBM) can help to ensure that multiple activities are managed sustainably for both the natural ecosystems and the people that rely on them. We can implement EBM by developing spatial plans for coastal and ocean areas that resolve conflicts between different interests and stakeholders and favor development that conserves nature and the services that it provides. Such spatial plans are common on land but, as noted above, ocean activities have often been managed in a patchwork fashion, as if they are unconnected to each other. New policies in Europe, the United States, Canada, Australia, and New Zealand have established the principles of EBM and marine spatial planning (e.g., Rosenberg et al., 2009; Obama, 2010; EC, 2007). While the implementation of spatial plans poses a major challenge, it has the potential to dramatically improve our management of coastal areas, not only in developed countries but also across the developing world. One important benefit of such planning efforts is that they necessarily require bringing together information on all aspects of ocean activities in one comprehensive map or database. Yet the starting point for any plan is not complete information on all aspects of the marine environment, but remembering

LEFT: A coral farmer tends to his unusual crop. The World Fish Center in the Solomon Islands teaches local people how to cultivate coral to replenish ailing coral reefs.
Photograph by Jürgen Freund/ iLCP

to take the precautionary approach, framing the data that do exist and refining that data over time to guide development.

In any marine spatial plan, we cannot ignore the goal of maintaining (or restoring) natural systems and their services. Creating marine spatial plans and valuing the natural services provided by coastal areas when planning development will be a key part of future "green" economic development. Along our coasts, as well as on land, if we can factor natural capital and the services that flow from that capital into our development planning, we can place our economic development on a new path that is durable and sustainable in supporting human communities around the world.

We will need to complement ecosystem-based management with international policy agreements to effectively conserve ocean resources for future generations. International treaties such as the United Nations Law of the Sea and multinational agreements such as The United Nations Framework Convention on Climate Change (UNFCCC) will play a key role in the future management of ocean resources. With rising sea level, ocean acidification, increased storm intensity, and other effects, coastal areas are the front lines of the battle against climate change. The contribution of coastal areas to carbon sequestration will be important for reducing greenhouse gas emissions, and adaptation to ongoing climate change will be critical in coastal areas (National Research Council, 2010). The new Cancun Agreements (2010) represent an important step forward, but legally binding agreements to reduce emissions from all the participating nations will be essential for preventing dangerous climate change.

The success of future ocean management will also require Regional Fisheries Management Organizations (RFMOs) to adopt international fishing regulations. These organizations are responsible for managing stocks of tuna, sea turtles, and sharks that move within national boundaries and among the regions outside national jurisdiction known as the High Seas. Without coordinated efforts, these species can be overfished in one location, undermining management efforts in another. While the RFMOs have been operating for decades, in too many cases they have been ineffective in preventing overexploitation. These regional organizations are made up of member states from each region, so it is member governments that must meet the challenge of upholding the public trust. Through the RFMOs, the regional governments must enact regulations that don't just protect their fishing industry's share of the catch, but that protect the very resources these fisheries exploit.

Another international agreement with important implications for ocean health is the Convention on Biological Diversity (CBD). At the 2010 meeting in Nagoya, Japan, the parties to the CBD agreed to protect 10% of oceans that lie within national jurisdiction. Currently, approximately 1% of the ocean is protected in marine protected areas (MPAs). Such targets can galvanize political will for creating and enlarging MPAs. Setting international targets for protection facilitates the possibility of developing a coherent network of protected areas and the conservation of species critical for ecosystem services. The term "marine managed areas" is often used interchangeably with "marine protected areas" as an inclusive way of describing MPAs with different types of protections, ranging from those allowing multiple uses to areas of complete protection (Orbach and Karrer, 2010).

Efforts continue to harness the power of the marketplace to connect with other efforts and translate to change on the water. Innovative ideas to expand promotion of sustainably sourced seafood products include combining labeling information with health and fair trade information, and even utilizing celebrity endorsements. To unite efforts in engaging buyers, suppliers, and businesses, a Conservation Alliance for Seafood Solutions has formed to improve and connect certification schemes and labeling, expand sustainable product availability and traceability, and influence policy and management.

In the future, the goal of ocean management must be to keep ocean ecosystems, the life support system for the planet, healthy and functioning. Reducing human impacts at all levels is important, and different sectors can't work in isolation or wait for each other to take up the challenge. As the waters of the oceans are all connected, so are the solutions. Ultimately, integrated management offers the way to control impacts and maintain the oceans for future generations. As stated unequivocally in the United Nations Law of the Sea, the oceans are the common heritage of mankind. It is a heritage we have the responsibility to admire, respect—and protect.

RIGHT: A man stands among giant clam beds in Kiribati's Phoenix Islands Protected Area, the largest designated marine protected area and one of five natural sites added to the UNESCO World Heritage list. **Photograph by Paul Nicklen/ National Geographic Stock/ iLCP**

FOLLOWING PAGE: A kayaker paddles into the sunset off the coast of the Mexican Riviera, Quintana Roo, Mexico. **Photograph by Claudio Contreras/ iLCP**

FLOTATION AID - TYPE III PFD
WATERSPORT VEST
SIZES: MEDIUM

EPILOGUE

All photographers have subjects that make their hearts beat faster and their pulse race. Some thrive in the frozen wilderness of the north, stalking bears, wolves, and caribou; others stake and claim their territory in the sweltering heat of rain forest or the desert. All photographers are witness to our planet's natural history. They endure equal measures of exciting chase when their subject comes into focus, followed by tedious stakeouts when nothing for days—or weeks is happening.

Now add water. Not only is it much harder to locate a subject underneath the dark ocean, but the underwater photographer also endures long stints in rocking vessels, less-than-calm seas, cold water—and the resultant seasickness. Armed with heavier, bulkier, and more-likely-to-fail equipment, the brave aquanaut has one hour of life-giving air to find a breathtaking shot, come up with an artistic rendition of the subject—all the while hoping that their regulators and compressors do not fail, as their very lives depend on them.

There is nothing heroic here, just a simple recognition that the kind of photography we do is needed now more than ever. Natural photography adds visual and textual dimensions to the urgent questions confronting mankind; questions about sustainability and survival, about policy and management. These questions are critical, but they can and do seem theoretical and abstract without the visual documentation of the photograph to make them real. We believe that powerful imagery can bring them to life, make them relevant. To capture simple moments eloquently, and to translate them visually, so that the universal human experience is recorded for future generations—that is the job you have given us, and we have given ourselves as conservation photographers.

So—although most people will never know who we are, what we do, or how we do it, let alone the price we pay for it—we are convinced that what they eventually see is worth recording, not just through our images, but through our stories and our scars. Our job is to coax people from the comfort of their routine, to set the imagination alight, to ignite a spark of wonder, to whisper possibility. We want to convey what it feels like to thrive among the animals, scenery and the natural beauty of the planet we have come to fight for and love. Conservation photography, and the powerful message it conveys, is part of our DNA. The causes we fight so tirelessly for are forever burned into our soul. The result is that we photograph not because we need to, but because we must.

Cristina G. Mittermeier
Founder and Fellow of the ILCP

Shari Sant Plummer
President of Code Blue and Director of the Board of iLCP

ABOUT THE AUTHORS

Gregory S. Stone is Senior Vice President and Chief Scientist for Oceans at Conservation International and Senior Vice President for Exploration and Conservation for the New England Aquarium. He pioneered research in Antarctica on marine mammals and later ice ecology and has written prolifically for science and popular publications, including *Nature* and *National Geographic*. His book about Antarctica, *Ice Island*, won the 2003 National Outdoor Book Award for Nature and the Environment. In addition to writing, he has produced an award-winning series of marine conservation films.

A specialist in undersea technology and exploration, Stone has piloted deep-sea submersibles, lived in undersea habitats, and logged thousands of hours scuba diving in all five oceans. His speaking engagements, given around the world, include an invited talk aboard TED.com's Mission Blue Voyage in 2010 and an address in Davos, Switzerland, to the World Economic Forum, for which he chairs the Global Agenda Council on Ocean Governance. Since 2000, Stone has led the effort to create one of the world's largest marine protected areas around the Phoenix Islands in the ocean nation of Kiribati. The Phoenix Islands Protected Area marks the first use of market-based mechanisms to conserve ocean biodiversity, while encouraging economic opportunity for local communities. In 2010, the Phoenix Islands Protected Area was inscribed as a World Heritage Site.

Among other accolades and professional associations, Stone has been a National Fellow of the Explorers Club and a Pew Fellow for Marine Conservation. He is the recipient of the National Science Foundation/US Navy Antarctic Service Medal for his research in Antarctica, and the Boston *Globe* named him one of the five "Bostonians of the Year" in 2008. He now makes his home in Christchurch, New Zealand.

Russell A. Mittermeier is President of Conservation International, a position he has occupied since 1989. His areas of expertise include primatology, herpetology, tropical biology, and biodiversity conservation. In addition to his work with CI, he has a long association with the International Union for the Conservation of Nature (IUCN), where he has served as Chairman of the IUCN Species Survival Commission (SSC) Primate Specialist Group since 1977, as a member of the Steering Committee of the SSC since 1984, and as a Regional Councillor for North America and the Caribbean since 2004.

Most recently, he was elected a Vice President for IUCN for the period 2009–2012. Mittermeier's work has taken him to 146 countries on seven continents, and he has conducted field work in more than twenty—with much of his work having focused on Amazonia (particularly Brazil and Suriname), the Atlantic forest region of Brazil, and Madagascar. He received his PhD from Harvard University in 1977 and has published more than 658 scientific and popular papers and twenty-three books.

Among the honors he has received are the Order of the Golden Ark of the Netherlands (1995), the Grand Sash and Order of the Yellow Star of the Republic of Suriname (1998), the Order of the Southern Cross of the Brazilian Government (1998), the Aldo Leopold Award from the American Society of Mammalogists (2004), the Sir Peter Scott Award of IUCN's Species Survival Commission (2008), and Harvard University's Roger Tory Peterson Medal (2009).

Octavio Aburto-Oropeza completed his PhD from the Center for Marine Biodiversity and Conservation at the Scripps Institution of Oceanography in San Diego, California, USA. He was a professor at Universidad Autónoma de Baja California Sur in La Paz, Mexico, from 1997 to 2003. In1998, Aburto-Oropeza became the director of the Reef Fauna Project, and he has been the principal Mexican researcher for several research and fisheries policy grants, funded by Mexican and international organizations.

Aburto-Oropeza's research has focused on commercially exploited reef fish and their fisheries in the Gulf of California, as well as the management of marine protected areas in the region. A member of ILCP, he has photographed marine ecosystems in Mexican coastal waters since 1994, and his photographs have been used in outreach campaigns for marine conservation.

Claudio Campagna is a conservationist with two affiliations: the Wildlife Conservation Society, with headquarters in New York, New York, and the National Research Council of Argentina. Before devoting his career to pursuing conservation objectives, he was a physician, having graduated from the University of Buenos Aires. Dr. Campagna earned his doctorate in animal behavior from the University of California at Santa Cruz. For his work on the conservation of the Patagonian Sea, he became a Pew Fellow in marine conservation. Claudio divides his efforts between three areas: field research on the biology of marine mammals, conducted at Peninsula Valdes (Argentina), conservation work, and writing essays and fiction.

Convinced of the urgent need to promote the conservation agenda using creative communication tools, he served as the scientific consultant on Isabella Rossellini's series for the Sundance Channel, "Green Porno." Campagna is published widely in the field of scientific and popular literature and serves in several international marine conservation committees and specialist groups, such as the IUCN Species Survival Commission (SSC) and the World Economic Forum's Future of the Ocean Commission.

Kent E. Carpenter is a professor of Biological Sciences at Old Dominion University, in Norfolk, Virginia, and manager of the Marine Biodiversity Unit of the Species Programme of the International Union for Conservation of Nature (IUCN). His primary research interests are in the conservation, evolution, and biogeography of marine fishes, with a special interest in the saltwater species of Southeast Asia. Current active research includes phylogeographic studies in the Coral Triangle using the population genetics of a variety of marine vertebrates and invertebrates, and the molecular phylogenetics of modern bony fishes.

Carpenter is also Principal Investigator on the IUCN/Conservation International Global Marine Species Assessment (GMSA), supported by the Otto Haas Charitable Trust 2, an advised fund at the New Hampshire Charitable Foundation. The IGMSA is conducting the first global review of every marine vertebrate species, as well as selected marine invertebrates and marine plants—approximately 20,000 species—to determine their conservation status and risk of extinction under IUCN Red List Criteria. At Old Dominion University, he teaches courses in Ichthyology, Marine Conservation Biology, and Speciation and Systematics.

Laurence P. Madin is Senior Scientist and the Executive Vice President and Director of Research at the Woods Hole Oceanographic Institution (WHOI) in Woods Hole, Massachusetts. He grew up in northern California and received his PhD from the University of California, Davis. His main research interests are in the biology of oceanic and deep-sea zooplankton, particularly medusae, siphonophores, ctenophores, and pelagic tunicates. He was among the first biologists to use scuba and submersibles to study oceanic plankton in the early 1970s.

Some of Larry's recent research has been on the population dynamics and biogeochemical effects of salp blooms in the Antarctic and elsewhere, distribution of macro-plankton and fishes in the Arabian Sea, biodiversity of oceanic plankton in the Sargasso Sea, and development of new instrumentation for sampling and exploration. Madin was previously the Chair of the WHOI Biology Department and Director of WHOI's Ocean Life Institute. He continues to pursue interests in the biodiversity, ecology, evolution, and conservation of oceanic animals, and in the impacts of climate change and human activity on marine ecosystems.

ABOUT THE AUTHORS

David Obura is Director of CORDIO (Coastal Oceans Research and Development Indian Ocean) East Africa and a coral biologist with the New England Aquarium. Obura received his PhD from the University of Miami in 1995 on coral bleaching and life history strategies, which has developed into a primary research interest in climate change, coral bleaching, and the resilience of coral reefs. He also helps develop monitoring techniques and research tools with artisanal fishers in East Africa, and surveys remote reefs in the central Pacific and the Indian Ocean. Obura chairs IUCN's Coral Specialist Group and the Climate Change and Coral Reefs Working Group. He lives in Mombasa, Kenya.

Enric Sala is a marine ecologist who dedicates his career to restoring ocean health. A former Professor at Scripps Institution of Oceanography, he is a National Geographic Ocean Fellow. Sala's work includes exploration, research, communication, and policy. His scientific publications are widely recognized and used for real-world conservation efforts such as the creation of marine reserves. Sala has been an Aldo Leopold Leadership Fellow (2005), a Pew Fellow in Marine Conservation (2006), and a World Economic Forum's Young Global Leader (2008). Sala's experience and scientific expertise contribute to his service on scientific advisory boards of international environmental organizations.

Sebastian Troëng is Vice President of Marine Conservation for Conservation International. He holds a doctorate in animal zoology from University of Lund, Sweden. He has worked with marine research and conservation for the past fifteen years in places like Greece, Fiji, Australia, Indonesia, Sri Lanka, Costa Rica, and Panama. Before joining CI, Troëng worked for Wetlands International and Caribbean Conservation Corporation, where he coordinated the longest-running sea turtle research and conservation program in the world in Tortuguero, Costa Rica. He has published extensively on sea turtle migrations, conservation, and the economic benefits of nonextractive use of sea turtles. In 2010, Troëng was recognized as one of the "Devex 40 Under 40" International Development Leaders, the only environmental conservationist recognized.

Cristina Goettsch Mittermeier is a Mexican-born photographer and fisheries biologist who began her career as a writer and photographer in 1996. While co-editing a series of fine art books for CEMEX and Conservation International, Cristina discovered a gap in the photography industry. In 2005 she founded the International League of Conservation Photographers (iLCP), to unite a prestigious group of photographers in visually communicating conservation issues. In 2009, Cristina was named one of Sony's Artisans of Imagery and she now uses Sony's Alpha 900 system to photograph the fragile relationship between humans and nature.

She dedicates her time to traveling the world to lecture and photograph subjects ranging from conservation science to indigenous cultures.

Peter A. Seligmann is Chairman and Chief Executive Officer of Conservation International (CI), and has been a leader in creating conservation solutions for the past thirty-five years. Since he founded the organization in 1987, CI has earned a reputation as an organization on the cutting edge, creating innovative and lasting solutions to the threats facing humanity, biodiversity, and the natural systems that sustain us all. He has developed strong partnerships between CI and leaders in science, industry, government, entertainment, and communities around the world. He continues to prove that healthy ecosystems are essential for the present and future well being of humanity and all life on Earth. As an experienced diver, Peter has worked intensively for sound management of marine ecosystems. He serves on the advisory councils of the Jackson Hole Land Trust, Ecotrust, the Wild Salmon Center, and several other not-for-profit organizations. Peter is a member of the Council on Foreign Relations, and he also is a member of the Environment Committee of the International Public Policy Advisory Board for The Coca-Cola Company. President Clinton named him a member of the Enterprise for the Americas Board in 2000. He began his career in 1976 at The Nature Conservancy, serving as the organization's western region land steward.

RIGHT: A herd of walruses (*Odobenus rosmarus*) sun themselves on the beach at Cape Pierce National Wildlife Refuge, Alaska.
Photograph by Art Wolfe/ Art Wolfe Stock/ iLCP

REFERENCES

INTRODUCTION: STONE, MITTERMEIER, ABURTO-OROPEZA, ET AL.

Balter, M. 2008. "Ancient Algae Suggest Sea Route for First Americans." *Science* 320, no. 5877: 729–729. doi:10.1126/science.320.5877.729.

Caldwell, L. K. 1970. *Environment: A Challenge for Modern Society.* Garden City, NY: Natural History Press. Published for the American Museum of Natural History.

Christensen, Norman L., Ann M. Bartuska, James H. Brown, Stephen Carpenter, Carla D'Antonio, Robert Francis, et al. 1996. "The Report of the Ecological Society of America Committee on the Scientific Basis for Ecosystem Management." *Ecological Applications* 6, no. 3: 665. doi:10.2307/2269460.

Cogan, C. B., B. J. Todd, P. Lawton, and T. T. Noji. 2009. "The Role of Marine Habitat Mapping in Ecosystem-Based Management." *ICES Journal of Marine Science* 66, no. 9: 2033-2042. doi:10.1093/icesjms/fsp214.

Craighead, Frank. 1979. *Track of the Grizzly.* San Francisco: Sierra Club Books.

Fagundes, Nelson J. R., Ricardo Kanitz, Roberta Eckert, Ana C. S. Valls, Mauricio R. Bogo, Francisco M. Salzano, et al. 2008. "Mitochondrial Population Genomics Supports a Single Pre-Clovis Origin with a Coastal Route for the Peopling of the Americas." *The American Journal of Human Genetics* 82, no. 3: 583-592. doi:10.1016/j.ajhg.2007.11.013.

Fuller, R. 1969. *Operating Manual for Spaceship Earth.* Carbondale: Southern Illinois University Press.

Grumbine, R. Edward. 1994. "What Is Ecosystem Management?" *Conservation Biology* 8, no. 1: 27-38. doi:10.1046/j.1523-1739.1994.08010027.x.

Leopold, Aldo. 1941. "Wilderness As a Land Laboratory." *Living Wilderness* 6, no. 3.

———. 1949. *A Sand County Almanac, and Sketches Here and There.* New York: Oxford University Press.

McLeod, K. L., J. Lubchenco, S. R. Palumbi, and A. A. Rosenberg. 2005. Scientific Consensus Statement on Marine Ecosystem-Based Management. Signed by 217 academic scientists and policy experts with relevant expertise and published by the Communication Partnership for Science and the Sea at http://compassonline.org/?q=EBM.

Millennium Ecosystem Assessment. 2005. *Ecosystems and Human Well-Being: Synthesis.* Washington DC: Island Press.
http://www.millenniumassessment.org/en/Products.aspx

NOAA (National Oceanic and Atmospheric Administration). 1996. Magnuson-Stevens
Fishery Management and Conservation Act amended through 11 October 1996. NOAA
Technical Memorandum NMFS-F/SPO-23.

United Nations Convention on Biological Diversity, Rio de Janeiro, June
1-14, 1992.

US Commission on Ocean Policy. 2004. *An Ocean Blueprint for the 21st Century: Final Report of the U.S. Commission on Ocean Policy.* Washington DC.

Wright, G. M., and B. H. Thompson. 1935. *Fauna of the National Parks of the United States.* Fauna Series No. 2. Washington DC: National Park Service.

Yaffee, S. L. 1996. "Ecosystem Management in Practice: The Importance of Human Institutions." *Ecological Applications* 6, no. 3: 724. doi:10.2307/2269472.

CHAPTER 1:
KATONA, HALPERN, AND STONE

Ausubel, J. H., D. T. Crist, and P. E. Waggoner (eds.). 2010. *First Census of Marine Life 2010. Highlights of a Decade of Discovery.* Washington DC: Census of Marine Life International Secretariat. Consortium for Ocean Leadership.

Balmford, A., P. Gravestock, N. Hockley, C. J. McClean, and C. M. Roberts. 2004. "The Worldwide Costs of Marine Protected Areas." *PNAS* 101 (26): 9694–9697.

Beaumont, N. J., M. C. Austen, J. P. Atkins, D. Burdon, S. Degraer, T. P. Dentinho, et al. 2007. "Identification, Definition and Quantification of Goods and Services Provided by Marine Biodiversity: Implications for the Ecosystem Approach." *Mar. Pollution Bull.* 54:253–265.

LEFT: Green iguana (*Iguana iguana*). A portrait of a female overlooking a breeding colony on a small Island in Lake Gatun, Barro Colorado Island, Panama. **Photograph by Christian Ziegler/ Minden Pictures/ National Geographic Stock/ iLCP**

RIGHT: A rare albino baby green sea turtle (*Chelonia mydas*). These turtles are being artificially incubated to increase their chances of survival. **Photograph by Daniel Beltrá/ Greenpeace/ iLCP**

Boyd, C., T. M. Brooks, S. H. M. Butchart, G. J. Edgar, G. A. B. da Fonseca, F. Hawkins et al. 2008. "Spatial Scale and the Conservation of Threatened Species." *Conservation Letters* 1 (2008): 37–43. Available online at: http://www.azoresbioportal.angra.uac.pt/files/publica-coes_Conserv%20Theatned%20species.pdf.

Burke, T.A., J. S. Litt, and M. A. Fox. 2000. "Linking Public Health and the Health of the Chesapeake Bay." *Environmental Research Section A* 82:143–149. Available online at: http://www.jhsph.edu/bin/y/z/Health_conf_linking.pdf. (Also see http://www.eco-check.org/reportcard/chesapeake/2009/)

Carté, B. K. 1996. "Biomedical Potential of Marine Natural Products." *Bioscience* 46: 271–286.

Chivian, E., and A. Bernstein (eds.). 2008. *Sustaining Life: How Human Health Depends on Biodiversity.* New York: Oxford University Press.

Costanza, R., R. d'Arge, R. de Groot, S. Farber, M. Grasso, B. Hannon, et al. 1997. "The Value of the World's Ecosystem Services and Natural Capital." *Nature* 387: 253–260.

Daily, G. C., S. Alexander, P. R. Ehrlich, L. Goulder, J. Lubchenco, P. A. Matson, et al. 1997. "Ecosystem Services: Benefits Supplied to Human Societies by Natural Ecosystems." Issues in Ecology 2: 1–16. Available online at: http://www.epa.gov/owow/watershed/wacademy/acad2000/pdf/issue2.pdf.

de Leeuw, N. H., C. Richard, A. Catlow, H. E. King, A. Putnis, K. Muralidharan, et al. 2010. "Where on Earth Has Our Water Come From?" *Chem. Commun.*, 46, 8923–8925.

FAO. 2006. *The State of World Fisheries and Aquaculture.* Rome: Food and Agriculture

Organization of the United Nations.

Farver, S. C., R. Costanza, and M. A. Wilson. 2002. "Economic and Ecological Concepts for Valuing Ecosystem Services." *Ecological Economics*, special issue: *The Dynamics and Value of Ecosystem Services: Integrating Economic and Ecological Perspectives* 41: 375–392.

Proclamation No. 8031, 71 Fed. Reg. 122 (June 26, 2006). "Establishment of the Northwestern Hawaiian Islands Marine National Monument."
Proclamation No. 8112, 72 Fed. Reg. 43 (March 6, 2007). Amending Proclamation 8031 of June 15, 2006 to read, "Establishment of the Papah naumoku kea Marine National Monument."

Gell, F. R., and C. M. Roberts. 2003. "Benefits Beyond Boundaries: The Fishery Effects of Marine Reserves and Fishery Closures." *Trends in Ecology and Evolution* 18: 448–455.

Halpern, B. S., S. Walbridge, K. A. Selkoe, C. V. Kappel, F. Micheli, C. D'Agrosa et al. 2008. "A Global Map of Human Impact on Marine Ecosystems." *Science* 319: 948–952.

Halpern, B. S., and R. R. Warner. 2002. "Marine Reserves Have Rapid and Lasting Effects." *Ecology Letters* 5: 361–366.

HELCOM 2010. "Ecosystem Health of the Baltic Sea 2003–2007. HELCOM Initial Holistic Assessment." *Balt. Sea Environ.* Proc. No. 122.

Hsieh, H. H., and D. Jewitt. 2006. "A Population of Comets in the Main Asteroid Belt." *Science* 312(5772): 561–563.

Hussain, S. S., A.Winfrow-Giffin, D. Moran, L. A. Robinson, A. Fofana, O. A. L. Paramor et al. 2010. "An Ex Ante Ecological Economic Assessment of the Benefits Arising from Marine Protected Areas Designation in the UK." *Ecological Economics* 69(4): 828–838.

Jah, R.K., and X. Zi-rong. 2004. "Biomedical Compounds from Marine Organisms." *Mar. Drugs* 2: 123–146.

McLeod, K. L., and H. M. Leslie (eds.). 2009. *Ecosystem-Based Management for the Oceans.* Washington DC: Island Press.

Millennium Ecosystem Assessment. 2005. *Ecosystems and Human Well-being: Current State and Trends.* Washington DC: Island Press.

Molnar, J. L., R. L. Gamboa, C. Revenga, and M. D. Spalding. 2008. "Assessing the Global Threat of Invasive Species to Marine Biodiversity." *Frontiers in Ecology and the Environment* 6: 485–492. Available online at http://groups.ucanr.org/Ballast_Outreach/files/48598.pdf

Myers, R. A., and B. Worm. (2003). "Rapid Worldwide Depletion of Predatory Fish Communities." *Nature* 423: 280–283.

Orbach M., and L. Karrer. 2010. *Marine Managed Areas: What, Why, and Where.* Arlington, VA: Conservation International, Science and Knowledge Division. Available online at: http://www.conservation.org/Documents/CI_MMAS_Science-to-Action_marine_managed_areas_what_why_where.pdf.

Pauly, D., R. Watson, R., and J. Alder, J. (2005). "Global Trends in World Fisheries: Impacts on Marine Ecosystems and Food Security." *Phil. Trans. R. Soc. Lond.* Ser. B, 360, 5–12.

Pressey, R. J., and M. C. Bottrill. 2009. "Approaches to Landscape- and Seascape-Scale Conservation Planning: Convergence, Contrasts and Challenges. *Oryx* 43(4): 464–475. Available online at: http://www.uq.edu.au/spatialecology/docs/Publications/2009_Pressy_Bottrill_ApproachesToLandscape.pdf.

Ruckelshaus, M., and K. M. A. Chan. 2010. "Characterizing Changes in Marine Ecosystem Services." *Biology Reports* 2: 54. Available online at: http://f1000.com/reports/b/2/54/pdf.

Ruckelshaus, M., and A. D. Guerry. 2009. "Valuing Marine Ecosystems?" *Mar. Scientist* 26: 26–29.

Shin, Y.-J., and L. J. Shannon. 2010. "Using Indicators for Evaluating, Comparing, and Communicating the Ecological Status of Exploited Marine Ecosystems. 1. The IndiSeas Project." *ICES Journal of Marine Science*, 67: 686–691. Available online at: http://icesjms.oxfordjournals.org/content/67/4/686.full.pdf+html

Snelgrove, P. W. R. 2010. *Discoveries of the Census of Marine Life: Making Ocean Life Count.* Cambridge, UK: Cambridge University Press.

Stone, G. 2011. "Phoenix Rising." *National Geographic*, January.

Stone, G. S., L. P. Madin, K. Stocks, G. Hovermale, P. Hoagland, M. Schumacher, et al. 2003. "Seamount Biodiversity, Exploitation and Conservation." In L. Glover and S. Earle (eds.), *Ocean's End: An Agenda for Action.* Washington DC: Island Press, 43–70.

Swartz, W., E. Sala, S. Tracey, R. Watson, and D. Pauly. 2010. "The Spatial Expansion and Ecological Footprint of Fisheries (1950 to Present)." *PLoS ONE* 5 (12) e15143. Available online at: http://www.plosone.org/article/info:doi/10.1371/

journal.pone.0015143f

Talberth, J., K. Wolowicz, J. Venetoulis, M. Gelobter, P. Boyle, and B. Mott. 2006. *The Ecological Footprint of Nations: Measuring Humanity's Impact on Marine Ecosystems.* Oakland, CA: Redefining Progress. Available online at www.redefiningprogress.org

Teuten, E. L., J. M. Saquing, D. R. U. Knappe, M. A. Barlaz, S. Jonsson, A. Björn, et al. 2009. "Transport and Release of Chemicals from Plastics to the Environment and to Wildlife. *Phil. Trans. R. Soc. B* 2009 364, 2027–2045.

UNESCO 2002. Intergovernmental Oceanographic Commission (IOC). The Final Design Plan for the HOTO (Health of the Ocean) Module of GOOS (Global Ocean Observing System). *GOOS Report* No. 99. IOC/INF-1167. Available online at http://www.jodc.go.jp/info/ioc_doc/INF/125135e.pdf.

Villa, F.A., and Gerwick, L. 2010. "Marine Natural Product Drug Discovery: Leads for Treatment of Inflammation, Cancer, Infections, and Neurological Disorders." *Immunopharmacology and Immunotoxicology* 32 (2): 228–237. See also http://www.actforconservation.org/wp/wp-content/uploads/2009/10/medicines-from-nature_-website.pdf.

White House Council on Environmental Quality. 2010. *Final Recommendations of the Interagency Ocean Policy Task Force.* http://www.whitehouse.gov/files/documents/OPTF_FinalRecs.pdf. Accessed January 11, 2011.

Zachos, J. C., U. Röhl, S. A. Schellenberg, A. Sluijs, D. A. Hodell, D. C. Kelly, et al. 2005. "Rapid Acidification of the Ocean During the Paleocene-Eocene Thermal Maximum." *Science* 308 (5728): 1611–1615.

Zalasiewicz, J., M. Williams, W. Steffen, and P. Crutzen. 2010. "The New World of the Anthropocene." *Environ. Sci. Technol. 44* (7): 2228–2231. Available online at http://pubs.acs.org/doi/pdfplus/10.1021/es903118j.

CHAPTER 2: MADIN AND HAMNER

Alldredge, A. L. 1972. "Abandoned Larvacean Houses: A Unique Food Source in the Pelagic Environment." *Science* 177: 885–887.

Alldredge, A. L. 1981. "The Impact of Appendicularian Grazing on Natural Food Concentrations *in situ*." *Limnol. Oceanogr.* 26: 247–257.

Berger, W. H. 2007. "Cenozoic Cooling, Antarctic Nutrient Pump, and the Evolution of Whales." *Deep-Sea Research II* 54: 2399–2421.

Bertness M. D., S. D. Gaines, and M. E. Hay. 2001. *Marine Community Ecology.* Sunderland, MA: Sinauer Associates.

Clements, F. E. 1916. *Plant Succession: An Analysis of the Development of Vegetation.* Washington Publications. Washington DC: Carnegie Institute.

———. 1936. "Nature and Structure of the Climax." *Journal of Ecology* 24: 252–284.

Cuthill, I. C. 2005. "The Study of Function in Behavioural Ecology." *Animal Biology* 55: 399–417.

Darwin, C. 1859. *The Origin of Species by Means of Natural Selection, or the Preservation of Favored Races in the Struggle for Life.* New York Modern Library.

Daskalov, G. 2002. "Overfishing Drives a Tophic Cascade in the Black Sea." *Marine Ecology Progress Series* 225: 53–63. doi:10.3354/meps225053.

Dawson, M. N., and W. M. Hamner. 2008. "A Biophysical Perspective on Dispersal and the Geography of Evolution in Marine and Terrestrial Systems." *J. R. Soc. Interface* 5: 135–150.

Elton, C. S. 1939. "On the Nature of Cover." *Journal Wildlife Management* 3: 332–338.

Elton, C. S. 1966. *The Pattern of Animal Communities.* Wiley.

Falkowski, P. G., M. E. Katz, A. H. Knoll, A. Quigg, J. A. Raven, O. Schofield, et al. 2004. "The Evolution of Modern Eukaryotic Phytoplankton." *Science* 305: 354–360.

Flannery, T. F. 1994. *The Future Eaters.* Melbourne: Reed Books.

Futuyma, Douglas. 2005. *Evolution.* Sunderland, MA: Sinauer Associates.

Gilmer, R. W. 1972. "Free Floating Mucus Webs: A Novel Feeding Adaptation in the Open Ocean." *Science* 176: 1239–1240.

Gilmer, R. W. 1974. "Some Aspects of Feeding in Thecomatous Pteropod Molluscs." *J. Exp. Mar. Biol. Ecol.* 15: 127–144.

Gopnik, Morgan. 1995. *Understanding Marine Biodiversity: A Research Agenda for the Nation.* Washington DC: National Academies Press.

Hamner, W. M. 1974. "Blue-Water Plankton." *Natl. Geogr. Mag.* 146: 530–545.

Hamner, W. M. 1995. "Predation, Cover, and Convergent Evolution in Epipelagic Oceans." *Mar. Fresh. Behav. Physiol.* 26: 71–89.

Hamner, W. M., P. P. Hamner, S. W. Strand, and R. W. Gilmer. 1983. "Behavior of Antarctic Krill, *Euphausia superba*: Chemoreception, Feeding, Schooling, and Molting. *Science* 220: 433–435.

Hamner, W. M., L. P. Madin, A. L. Alldredge, R. W. Gilmer, and P. P. Hamner. 1975. "Underwater Observations of Gelatinous Zooplankton: Sampling Problems, Feeding Biology, and Behavior." *Limnol. Oceanogr.* 20: 907–917.

Harbison, G. R., and R. W. Gilmer. 1976. "The Feeding Rates of the Pelagic Tunicate *Pegea confoederata* and Two Other Salps." *Limnol. Oceanogr.* 21: 517–528.

Hessler, R. R., and H. L. Sanders. 1967. "Faunal Diversity in the Deep Sea." *Deep-Sea Res.* 14: 65–78.

Johnsen, S. 2007. "Does New Technology Inspire New Directions? Examples Drawn from Pelagic Visual Ecology." *Integrative Comparative Biology* 47: 799–807.

Johnson, C. 2006. *Australia's Mammal Extinctions: A 50,000 Year History.* Cambridge, UK: Cambridge University Press.

Kroll, Gary. 2008. *America s Ocean Wilderness: A Cultural History of Twentieth-Century Exploration.* Lawrence, KS: University Press of Kansas.

Lalli, C., and R. W. Gilmer. 1989. *Pelagic Snails: The Biology of Holoplanktonic Gastropod Mollusks.* Palo Alto, CA: Stanford University Press.

Lipps, J. H., and E. D. Mitchell. 1976. "Trophic Model for the Adaptive Radiations and Extinctions of Pelagic Marine Mammals." *Paleobiology* 2: 147–155.

Llope, Marcos, G. M. Daskalov, Tristan A. Rouyer, Vesselina Mihneva, Kung-Sik Chan, Alexander N. Grishin, and et al. 2011. "Overfishing of Top Predators Eroded the Resilience of the Black Sea System Regardless of the Climate and Anthropogenic Conditions." *Global Change Biology* 17, no. 3: 1251–1265. doi:10.1111/j.1365-2486.2010.02331.x.

Longhurst, Alan, and Daniel Pauly. 1987. *Ecology of Tropical Oceans*. San Diego: Academic Press.

Madin, L. P. 1974. "Field Observations on the Feeding Behavior of Salps (Tunicata: Thaliacea)." *Mar. Biol.* 25: 143–147.

Marx, F. G., and M. D. Uhen. 2010. "Climate, Critters, and Cetaceans: Cenozoic Drivers of the Evolution of Modern Whales." *Science* 327: 993–996.

Nishizawa, S., M. Fukuda, and N. Inowe. 1954. "Photographic Study of Suspended Matter and Plankton in the Sea." *Bull. Pac. Fish. Hokkaido Univ.* 5: 36–40.

Ocean Studies Board. 2000. *50 Years of Ocean Discovery: National Science Foundation, 1950–2000.* Washington DC: National Academies Press.

Ramirez-Llodra, E., A. Brandt, R. Danovaro, B. De Mol, E. Escobar, C. R. German, et al. 2010. "Deep, Diverse and Definitely Different: Unique Attributes of the World's Largest Ecosystem." *Biogeosciences* 7: 2851–2899.

Rex, Michael A., and Ron J. Etter. 2010. *Deep-Sea Biodiversity: Pattern and Scale.* Cambridge, MA: Harvard University Press.

Ricklefs, R. E. 2007. *The Economy of Nature.* 5th ed. New York: W. H. Freeman.

Riisgård, H. U., and P. S. Larsen. 2010. "Particle Capture Mechanisms in Suspension-Feeding Invertebrates." *Mar Ecol Prog Ser.* 418: 255–293.

Robison, B. H. 2009. "Conservation of Deep Pelagic Biodiversity." *Cons. Biology* 23: 847–858.

Robison, B. H., R. E. Sherlock, and K. R. Reisenbichler. 2010. "The Bathypelagic Community of Monterey Canyon." *Deep-Sea Research II* 57: 1551–1556.

Ryther, J. H. 1969. "Photosynthesis and Fish Production in the Sea." *Science* 166: 72–76.

Schippers, Axel, Lev N. Neretin, Jens Kallmeyer, Timothy G. Ferdelman, Barry A. Cragg, R. John Parkes, et al. 2005. "Prokaryotic Cells of the Deep Sub-Seafloor Biosphere Identified As Living Bacteria." *Nature* 433, no. 7028: 861–864. doi:10.1038/nature03302.

Simon, M., M. Johnson, P. Tyack, and P. T. Madsen. 2009. "Behaviour and Kinematics of Continuous Ram Filtration in Bowhead Whales (*Balaena mysticetus*). *Proc. R. Soc. B* 276: 3819–3828.

Sutherland, K. R., L. P. Madin, and R. Stocker. 2010. "Filtration of Submicrometer Particles by Pelagic Tunicates." *Proc. Nat. Acad. Sci.* 107: 15129–15134.

Tunnicliffe, Verena. 1992. "Hydrothermal-Vent Communities of the Deep Sea." *American Scientist* 80, no. 4: 336–349.

Tyler, Paul. 2003. *Ecosystems of the Deep Oceans.* Amsterdam, New York: Elsevier.

Van Dover, Cindy. 2000. *The Ecology of Deep-Sea Hydrothermal Vents.* Princeton, NJ: Princeton University Press.

Wangersky, P J. 1974. "Particulate Organic Carbon: Sampling Variability." *Limnol. Oceanogr.* 19: 980–984.

Whittaker, R. H. 1975. *Communities and Ecosystems.* 2nd ed. New York: Macmillan.

Zaret, T. M. 1975. "Strategies for Existence of Zooplankton Prey in Homogeneous Environments." *Verh. Internat. Verein. Limnol.* 19: 1484–1489.

CHAPTER 3: CARPENTER, POLIDORO, HARWELL, AND SANCIANGO

Algeo, T. J., Z. Q. Chen, M. L. Fraiser, and R. J. Twitchett. 2011. "Terrestrial-Marine Teleconnections in the Collapse and Rebuilding of Early Triassic Marine Ecosystems." *Palaeogeography* doi: 10.1016/j.palaeo.2011.01.011.

Allen, G. R. 2007. "Conservation Hotspots of Biodiversity and Endemism for Indo-Pacific Coral Reef Fishes." *Aquatic Conservation: Marine and Freshwater Ecosystems* DOI: 10.1002/aqc.880.

Allen, G. R., and T. B. Werner. 2002. "Coral Reef Fish Assessment in the 'Coral Triangle' of Southeastern Asia." *Environmental Biology of Fishes* 65: 209–214.

Alroy, J. 2008. "Dynamics of Origination and Extinction in the Marine Fossil Record." PNAS 105. Suppl. 1: 11536-11542.

Alroy, J., M. Aberhan, D. J. Bottjer, M. Foote, F. T. Fiirsich, P. J. Harries, et al. 2008. "Phanerozoic Trends in the Global Diversity of Marine Invertebrates." *Science* 321: 97–100.

Bouchet, P. 2006. "The Magnitude of Marine Biodiversity." In C. M. Duarte (ed.), *The Exploration of Marine Biodiversity: Scientific and Technological Challenges.* Paris: Natural History Museum, 30–64.

Briggs, J. C. 2005. Coral Reefs: Conserving the Evolutionary Sources. *Biological Conservation* 126: 297–305.

Butchart, S. M., M. Walpole, B. Collen, A. van Strien, J. P. W. Scharlemann, R. E. A. Almond, et al. 2010. "Global Biodiversity: Indicators of Recent Declines." *Science* 328: 1164–1168.

Camhi, M. D., S. V. Valenti, S. V. Fordham, S. L. Fowler, and C. Gibson. 2009. *The Conservation Status of Pelagic Sharks and Rays: Report of the IUCN Shark Specialist Group Pelagic Shark Red List Workshop.* Newbury, UK: IUCN Species Survival Commission Shark Specialist Group.

Carpenter, K. E., M. Abrar, G. Aeby, R. B. Aronson, S. Banks, A. Bruckner, et al. 2008. "One-Third of Reef-Building Corals Face Elevated Extinction Risk from Climate Change and Local Impacts." *Science* 321: 560–563.

Carpenter, K. E., and Springer, V. G. 2005. "The Center of the Center of Marine Shorefish Distribution: The Philippines Islands." *Environmental Biology of Fishes* 72: 467–480.

Chaloupka, M., N. Kamezaki, and C. Limpus. 2008. "Is Climate Change Affecting the Population Dynamics of the Endangered Pacific Loggerhead Sea Turtle?" *Journal of Experimental Marine Biology and Ecology* 136: 136–143.

LEFT: Tucked within the tentacles of an anemone was the expressive eye of an anemone fish—suggestive of its innocence, curiosity, and beauty. **Photograph by Keith Ellenbogen/ iLCP**

Cheung, W. W. L., V. W. Y. Lam, J. L. Sarmiento, K. Kearney, R. Watson, and D. Pauly. 2009. "Predicting Global Marine Biodiversity Impacts Under Climate Change Scenarios." *Fish and Fisheries* 10: 235–251.

Dulvy, N. K., J. K. Baum, S. Clarke, L. J. V. Compagno, E. Cortes, A. Domingo, et al. 2008. "You Can Swim But You Can't Hide: The Global Status and Conservation of Oceanic Pelagic Sharks and Rays." *Aquatic Conservation: Marine Freshwater Ecosystem* 18: 459–482.

Dulvy, N. K., Y. Sadovy, Y., and J. D. Reynolds. 2003. "Extinction and Vulnerability in Marine Populations." *Fish and Fisheries* 4: 25–64.

Eckert, K. L. 1995. "Anthropogenic Threats to Sea Turtles." In K. A. Bjorndal (ed.), *Biology and Conservation of Sea Turtles.* Washington DC: Smithsonian Institution Press, 611–612.

Fish, M. R., I. M. Côté, J. A. Gill, A. P. Jones, S. Renshoff, and A. R. Watkinson. 2005. "Predicting the Impact of Sea-Level Rise on Caribbean Sea Turtle Nesting Habitat." *Conservation Biology* 19: 482–491.

Glavin, T. 2007. *The Sixth Extinction: Journeys Among the Lost and Left Behind.* New York: Thomas Dunne.

Goombridge, B., and M. D. Jenkins. 2000. *Global Biodiversity: Earth's Living Resources in the 21st Century.* Cambridge, UK: World Conservation Press.

Grassle, J. F., and N. J. Maciolek. 1992. "Deep-Sea Species Richness: Regional and Local Diversity Estimates from Quantitative Bottom Samples." *American Naturalist* 139: 313–341.

Gray, J. S. 1997. "Gradients of Marine Biodiversity." In R. Ormond, J. Gage, and J. F. Grassle (eds.) *Marine Biodiversity: Patterns and Processes.* Cambridge, UK: Cambridge University Press, 18–34.

Gray, J. S., G. C. B. Poore, K. I. Ugland, R. S. Wilson, F. Olsgard, and O. Johannessen. 1997. "Coastal and Deep-Sea Benthic Diversities Compared. *Marine Ecology Progress Series* 159: 97–103.

Gray, J. S. 2001. "Marine Diversity: The Paradigms in Patterns of Species Richness Examined." *Scientia Marina* 65: 41–56.

Halpern, B. S., S. Walbridge, K. A. Selkoe, C. V. Kappel, F. Micheli, C. D'Agrosa, et al. 2008. "A Global Map of Human Impact on Marine Ecosystems." *Science* 319: 948–952.

Hawkes, L. A., A. C. Broderick, M. H. Godfrey, and B. J. Godley. 2007. "Investigating the Potential Impacts of Climate Change on a Marine Turtle Population." *Global Change Biology* 13: 923–932.

Hawkins, J. P., C. M. Roberts, and V. Clark. 2000. "The Threatened Status of Restricted-Range Coral Reef Fish Species." *Animal Conservation* 3: 81–88.

IUCN. 2001. *IUCN Red List Categories and Criteria Version 3.1*, accessed February 15, 2011, http://www.redlist.org/info/categories_criteria2001.html.

IUCN. 2010. *IUCN Red List of Threatened Species*, accessed December 1, 2010, http://www.iucnredlist.org.

Jablonski, D., and D. M. Raup. 1995. "Selectivity of End-Cretaceous Marine Bivalve Extinctions." *Science* 268: 389–391

Jackson, J. B. C., M. X. Kirby, W. H. Berger, K. A. Bjorndal, L. W. Botsford, B. J. Bourque, et al. 2006. "Historical Overfishing and the Recent Collapse of Coastal Ecosystems." *Science* 293: 629–637.

Jacobsen, N. D., R. J. Twitchett, and L. Krystyn. 2009. "Palaeoecological Methods for Assessing Marine Ecosystem Recovery Following the Late Permian Mass Extinction Event." *Palaeogeography, Palaeoclimatology and Palaeoecology* DOI: 10.1016/j.palaeo.2010.04.024

Knoll, A. H., R. K. Bambach, J. L. Payne, S. Pruss, and W. W. Fischer. 2007. "Paleophysiology and End-Permian Mass Extinction." *Earth and Planetary Science Letters* 256: 295–313.

Levinton, J. S. 1995. *Marine biology. Function, Biodiversity, Ecology.* New York: Oxford University Press.

Lotze, H. K., H. S. Lenihan, B. J. Bourque, R. H. Bradbury, R. G. Cooke, M. C. Kay, et al. 2006. "Depletion, Degradation, and Recovery Potential of Estuaries and Coastal Seas." *Science* 312: 1806–1809.

Marshall, C. R. 2006. "Explaining the Cambrian "Explosion" of Animals." *Annual Review of Earth Planetary Science* 34: 355–84.

Myers, R. A., and B. Worm. 2003. "Rapid Worldwide Depletion of Predatory Fish Communities." *Nature* 423: 280–283.

Polidoro, B. A., K. E. Carpenter, L. Collins, N. C. Duke, A. M. Ellison, J. C. Ellison, et al. 2010. "The Loss of Species: Mangrove Extinction Risk and Geographic Areas of Global Concern." *PLoS ONE* 5 (4): e10095. DOI: 10.1371/journal.pone.0010095.

Polidoro, B. A., S. R. Livingstone, K. E. Carpenter, B. Hutchinson, R. B. Mast, N. Pilcher, et al. 2009. "Status of the World's Marine Species." In J.-C. Vié, C. Hilton-Taylor, and S. N. Stuart (eds.), Wildlife *in a Changing World.* Gland, Switzerland: Island Press, IUCN.

Reaka-Kudla, M. L. 1997. "The Global Biodiversity of Coral Reefs: A Comparison with Rain Forests." In M. L. Reaka-Kudla, D. E. Wilson, and E. O. Wilson (eds.), *Biodiversity II.* Washington, DC: Joseph Henry Press, 83–108.

Reynolds, J. E., W. F. Perrin, and R. R. Reeves. 2005. *Marine Mammal Research: Conservation Beyond Crisis.* Baltimore: Johns Hopkins University Press.

Roberts, C. M., and J. P. Hawkins. 1999. "Extinction Risk in the Sea." *Trends in Ecology and Evolution* 14: 241–246.

Roberts, C. M., C. J. McClean, J. E. N. Veron, J. P. Hawkins, G. R. Allen, D. E. McAllister, et al. 2002. "Marine Biodiversity Hotspots and Conservation Priorities for Tropical Reefs." *Science* 295: 1280–1284.

Roy, K., D. Jablonski, J. W. Valentine, and G. Rosenberg. "Marine Latitudinal Diversity Gradients: Tests of Causal Hypotheses." *Proceedings of the National Academy of Sciences USA* 95: 3699–3702.

Sadovy, Y. 2007. "Workshop for Global Red List Assessments of Groupers Family Serranidae; Subfamily Epinephelinae." *Final Report, IUCN Species Survival Commission Groupers and Wrasses Specialist Group*, The University of Hong Kong.

Sala, E., and N. Knowlton. 2006. "Global Marine Biodiversity Trends." *Annual Review of Environmental Resources* 31: 93–122.

Sanders, H. L. 1968. "Marine Benthic Diversity: A Comparative Study." *American Naturalist* 102: 243–282.

Schipper, J., J. S. Chanson, F. Chiozza, N. A. Cox, M. Hoffmann, V. Katariya, J. Lamoreux et al. 2008. "The Status of the World s Land and Marine Mammals: Diversity, Threat, and Knowledge." *Science* 322, no. 5899: 225–230. doi:10.1126/science.1165115.

Short, F. T., B. Polidoro, S. R. Livingstone, K. E. Carpenter, S. Bandeira, S., J. S. Bujang, et al. 2011. "Extinction Risk Assessment of the World's Seagrass Species." *Science* 332: 225–230.

Stevens, J. D., R. Bonfil, N. K. Dulvy, and P. A. Walker. 2000. "The Effects of Fishing on Sharks, Rays, and Chimaeras (Chondrichthyans), and the Implications for Marine Ecosystems." *ICES Journal of Marine Science* 57: 476–494.

Venter, J. Craig, Karin Remington, John F. Heidelberg, Aaron L. Halpern, Doug Rusch, Jonathan A. Eisen, et al. 2004. "Environmental Genome Shotgun Sequencing of the Sargasso Sea." *Science* 2 April 2004: 304 (5667), 66–74. Published online 4 March 2004 [DOI:10.1126/science.1093857]

Veron, J. E. N. 1995. *Corals in Space and Time: The Biogeography and Evolution of the Scleractinia.* Sydney: University of New South Wales Press.

Veron, J. E. N., L. M. Devantier, E. Turak, A. L. Green, S. Kininmonth, M. Stafford-Smith, and N. Peterson. 2009. "Delineating the Coral Triangle." *Galaxea, Journal of Coral Reef Studies* 11: 91–100.

CHAPTER 4: MAST, FARRIOR, HEMPHILL, HENDERSON ET AL.

Alvarez, R., and G. Medina-Vogel. 2008. "*Lontra felina.*" *IUCN Red List of Threatened Species.* Version 2010.4. www.iucnredlist.org. Accessed May 17, 2011.

Bouchet, P. 2006. "The Magnitude of Marine Biodiversity." In C. M. Duarte (ed.), *The Exploration of Marine Biodiversity: Scientific and Technological Challenges.* Paris: Natural History Museum.

Calliet, G. M., J. A. Musick, C. A. Simpendorfer, and J. D. Stevens. 2005. "Ecology and Life History Characteristics of Chondrichthyan Fish." In G. H. Burgess, G. M. Cailliet, M. Camhi, R. D. Cavanagh, S. V. Fordham, S. L. Fowler, et al. (eds.), *Sharks, Rays and Chimaeras: The Status of the Chondrichthyan Fishes. Status Survey,* 461. Gland, Switzerland and Cambridge, UK: IUCN/SSC, Shark Specialist Group.

Carpenter, K. E., B. Polidoro, H. Harwell, and J. Sanciangco. 2011. "Ocean Biodiversity." In G. S. Stone, R. A. M. Mittermeier, O. Aburto-Oropeza, C. Campagna, K. E. Carpenter, L. P. Madin, et al., (eds.), *Oceans: Heart of Our Blue Planet.* Arlington, VA: ILCP/Earth in Focus Editions, pp. TK.

Clarke, S. C., M. K. McAllister, E. J. Milner-Gulland, G. P. Kirkwood, G. J. Michielsens, D. J. Agnew, E. K. Pikitch, H. Nakano, and M. S. Shivji. 2006. "Global Estimates of Shark Catches Using Trade Records From Commercial Markets." *Ecology Letters* 9 (2006): 1115–1126.

Durner, D. M., J. P. Whiteman, H. J. Harlow, S. C. Amstrup, E. V. Regehr, and M. Ben-David. 2011. "Consequences of Long-Distance Swimming and Travel Over Deep-Water Pack Ice for a Female Polar Bear During a Year of Extreme Sea Ice Retreat." *Polar Biology* DOI: 10.1007/s00300-010-0953-2.

Dotson, R. C., and K. D. Hyrenbach. 2001. "Post-Breeding Movements of a Male Black-Footed Albatross (Phoebastria nigripes)." *Marine Ornithology* 29: 7–10.

Ferretti, F., B. Worm, G. L. Britten, M. R. Heithaus, and H. K. Lotze. 2010. "Patterns and Ecosystem Consequences of Shark Declines in the Ocean." *Ecology Letters* 13 (8): 1055–1071.

Field, I. C., M. G. Meekan, R. C. Buckworth, and C. J. A. Bradshaw. "Susceptibility of Sharks, Rays, and Chimaeras to Global Extinction." *Advances in Marine Biology* 56 (2009): 275–363.

Food and Agriculture Organization of the United Nations. 2007. *The State of World Fisheries and Aquaculture 2006.* Rome: Food and Agriculture Organization of the United Nations.

Grassle, J. F., and N. J. Maciolek. 1992. "Deep-Sea Species Richness: Regional and Local Diversity Estimates from Quantitative Bottom Samples." *American Naturalist* 139 (1992): 313–341.

Harrison, P. 1996. *Seabirds of the World.* Princeton, NJ: Princeton University Press.

International Seafood Sustainability Foundation (ISSF). 2010. *2010 Update on the Status of the Tuna Stocks in the Eastern Pacific Ocean (EPO).* Scientific Advisory Committee of the Inter-American Tropical Tuna Commission (IATTC).

International Union for the Conservation of Nature. *IUCN Red List of Threatened Species 2010.* Accessed January 2011: www.iucnredlist.org.

Johnson, A. M. 1982. "Status of Alaska Sea Otter Populations and Developing Conflicts with Fisheries." In *Transactions of the 47th North American Wildlife and Natural Resources Conference, Washington DC*: 293–299.

Kenyon, K. W. 1969. "The Sea Otter in the Eastern Pacific Ocean." *North American Fauna* 68. Washington DC: US Department of the Interior.

Kovacs, K. 2008. "Monachus tropicalis." In *International Union for the Conservation of Nature (IUCN).* IUCN Red List of Threatened Species. Accessed January 6, 2011. www.iucnredlist.org

Lavigne, D. M. "Harp Seal Pagophilus groenlandicus." 2009. In W. F. Perrin, J. G. M. Thewissen, and B. Wursig (eds.), *Encyclopedia of Marine Mammals, vol. 2.* San Diego: Academic Press, 542–546.

Lilley, R. "Colossal Squid Has World's Biggest Eyes." 2008 (April). *National Geographic.* Accessed February 24, 2011: http://news.nationalgeographic.com/news/2008/04/080430-AP-new-zealand.html.

MarineBio.org. "Marine Invertebrates." *MarineBio.org.* Last modified on November 20, 2010. Accessed February 21, 2011: http://marinebio.org/oceans/marine-invertebrates.asp

Mast, R. B., and A. G. J. Rhodin. "Sea Turtles." 2003. In T. Brooks, G. A. B. da Fonseca, P. R. Gil, M. Hoffmann, W. R. Konstant, R. B. Mast, et al. (eds.), *Wildlife Spectacles.* CEMEX—Agrupacion Sierre Madre, Mexico: Conservation International, 233–237.

LEFT: Scuba diver explores a giant kelp (*Macrocystis pyrifera*; also known as strap kelp) forest. Tasman Peninsula, Tasmania, Australia. **Photograph by Gary Bell/ Oceanwide Images**

Mittermeier, C., and S. A. Earle. "Hammerhead Sharks." 2003. In T. Brooks, G. A. B. da Fonseca, P. R. Gil, M. Hoffmann, W. R. Konstant, R. B. Mast, et al. (eds.), *Wildlife Spectacles.* CEMEX—Agrupacion Sierre Madre, Mexico: Conservation International, 243–246.

MSNBC. *It's Official: Caribbean Monk Seal Is Extinct.* Last modified on June 6, 2008. http://www.msnbc.msn.com/id/25007277/ns/us_news-environment/

National Marine Fisheries Service. *Hawaiian Monk Seal (Monachus schauinslandi).* Accessed February 2010: http://www.nmfs.noaa.gov/pr/species/mammals/pinnipeds/hawaiianmonkseal.html

Nellaiappan, K., and M. Sugumaran. 1996. "On the Presence of Prophenoloxidase in the Hemolymph of the Horseshoe Crab, *Limulus.*" *Comp. Biochem. and Physio. Part B: Biochem. and Molecular Biol.* 113(1): 163-168.

Schindler, D. E., T. E. Essington, J. F. Kitchell, C. Boggs, and R. Hilborn. "Sharks and Tunas: Fisheries Impacts on Predators with Contrasting Life Histories." *Ecological Applications* 12 (2002): 735–748.

Snover, M. L., A. A. Hohn, L. B. Crowder, and S. S. Heppell. 2007. "Age and Growth in Kemp's Ridley Sea Turtles: Evidence from Mark—Recapture and Skeletochronology." In P. T. Plotkin (ed.), *Biology and Conservation of Ridley Sea Turtles.* Baltimore: The Johns Hopkins University Press.

Spotila, J. R., A. E. Dunham, A. J. Leslie, A. C. Steyermark, P. T. Plotkin, and F. V. Paladino. 1996. "Worldwide Population Decline of Dermochelys coriacea: Are Leatherback Turtles Going Extinct?" *Chelonian Conservation and Biology* 2: 209–222.

United States Fish and Wildlife Service. *Midway Atoll Wildlife Refuge: Tsunami 2011.* Last modified on March 28, 2011. http://www.fws.gov/midway/tsunami.html

United States Fish and Wildlife Service. Population Status of the Northern Sea Otter. Accessed May 2011. http://alaska.fws.gov/fisheries/mmm/seaotters/history.html

Wilson, E. O. 1984. *Biophilia.* Cambridge, MA: Harvard University Press.

CHAPTER 5: TROËNG, BRYANT, DUTRA, ERDMANN ET AL.

Bensted-Smith, R. and H. Kirkman. 2010. *Comparison of Approaches to Management of Large Marine Areas.* Cambridge, UK: Fauna & Flora International, and Washington DC: Conservation International. http://www.conservation.org/documents/CI_FFI_Management_of_Large_Marine_Areas.pdf

Edgar, G. J., S. A. Banks, S. Bessudo, J. Cortés, H. M. Guzman, S. Henderson, et al. (in press). "Variation in Reef Fish and Invertebrate Communities with Level of Protection from Fishing Across the Eastern Tropical Pacific Seascape." *Global Ecology and Biogeograph.*

Francini-Filho, R. B, and R. L. Moura. 2008. "Evidence for Spillover of Reef Fishes from a No-Take Marine Reserve: An Evaluation Using the Before-After Control-Impact (BACI) Approach." *Fisheries Research* 93: 346-356.

Gutiérrez, N. L., R. Hilborn, and O. Defeo. 2011. "Leadership, Social Capital and Incentives Promote Successful Fisheries." *Nature* doi:10.1038/nature09689.

McLeod, K. L., J. Lubchenco, S. R. Palumbi, and A. A. Rosenberg. 2005. *Scientific Consensus Statement on Marine Ecosystem-Based Management.* Signed by 217 academic scientists and policy experts with relevant expertise and published by the Communication Partnership for Science and the Sea at http://compassonline.org/?q=EBM.

6. SEASCAPES: EASTERN TROPICAL PACIFIC (HENDERSON, ARJONA, CHALÉN, DIAZGRANADOS, ET AL.)

Baum, J., S. Clarke, A. Domingo, M. Ducrocq, A. F. Lamónaca, N. Gaibor, et al. 2008. *IUCN Red List of Threatened Species. Version 2010.4.* Accessed January 15, 2010: http://www.iucnredlist.org/

Christie, D. M., R. A. Duncan, A. R. McBirney, M. A. Richards, W. M. White, and K. S. Harpp. 1992. "Drowned Islands Downstream from the Galápagos Hot Spot Imply Extended Speciation Times." *Nature* 355: s246–248.

Edgar, G. J., S. A. Banks, M. Brandt, R. H. Bustamante, A. Chiriboga, S. A. Earle, et al. 2010. "El Niño, Fisheries and Animal Grazers Interact to Magnify Extinction Risk for Marine Species in Galápagos." *Global Change Biology* 16: 2876–2890.

Edgar, G. J., S. A. Banks, S. Bessudo, J. Cortes, H. Guzman, S. Henderson, et al. (in press). "Variation in Reef Fish and Invertebrate Communities with Level of Protection from Fishing Across the Eastern Tropical Pacific Seascape." *Global Ecology and Biology.*

FAO. 2005. *FAO Fisheries Circular No. 821*, Revision 9: 1961–2005.

Hearn, A., J. Ketchum, A. P. Klimley, E. Espinoza, and C. Peñaherrera. 2010. "Hotspots Within Hotspots? Hammerhead Shark Movements Around Wolf Island, Galápagos Marine Reserve." *Marine Biology* 157 (9): 1899–1915.

Hearn, A. 2008. "The Rocky Path to Sustainable Fisheries Management and Conservation in the Galápagos Marine Reserve." *Ocean & Coastal Management*: 51 (8–9): 567–574.

Ketchum, J. T. 2007. "Seascape Species and Biological Hotspots: A New Approach to Structure Conservation Action in the Marine Environment." *9th Annual Bay Area Conservation Biology Symposium, University of California-Berkeley, February 2007.*

Kirby, M. X., D. S. Jones, and B. J. MacFadden. 2008. "Lower Miocene Stratigraphy Along the Panama Canal and Its Bearing on the Central American Peninsula." *PLoS One* 3 (7).

IATTC Fish Catch Statistics. http://www.iattc.org/Catchbygear/IATTC-Catch-by-species1.html. Accessed on January 15, 2010.

Pidgeon, E. 2010. "Carbon Sequestration by Coastal Marine Habitats: Important Missing Sinks." In D. Laffoley, and G. D. Grimsditch (eds.), *The Management of Natural Coastal Carbon Sinks.* Gland, Switzerland: IUCN, 47–51.

THE CORAL TRIANGLE: ERDMANN

Agostini, V. N. 2009. "Ecosystem-Based Management and Marine Protected Areas: Coming Together in Working Seascapes." *Marine Ecosystems and Management* 2(3): 6.

Allen, G. R. 2007. "Conservation Hotspots of Biodiversity

and Endemism for Indo-Pacific Coral Reef Fishes." *Aquatic Conservation: Marine and Freshwater Ecosystems* 18(5): 541–556.

Allen, G. R., and M. V. Erdmann. 2009. "Reef Fishes of the Bird's Head Peninsula, West Papua, Indonesia." *Check List* 5(3): 587–628.

Barber, P. H., S. R. Palumbi, M. V. Erdmann, and M. K. Moosa. 2000. "A Marine Wallace's Line?" *Nature* 406: 692–693.

Barber, P. B., M. V. Erdmann, and S. R. Palumbi. 2006. "Comparative Phylogeography of Three Codistributed Stomatopods: Origins and Timing of Regional Lineage Diversification in the Coral Triangle." *Evolution* 60(9): 1825–1839.

Briggs, J. C. 1974. *Marine Biogeography.* New York: McGraw-Hill.

Briggs, J. C. 2005. "Coral Reefs: Conserving the Evolutionary Sources." *Biological Conservation* 126: 297–305.

Burke, L., E. Selig, and M. Spalding. 2002. *Reefs at Risk in Southeast Asia.* Washington DC: World Resources Institute.

Carr, L., and R. Mendelsohn. 2003. "Valuing Coral Reefs: A Travel Cost Analysis of the Great Barrier Reef." *Ambio* 32: 353–357.

Christie, P., A. White, and E. Deguit. 2002. "Starting Point or Solution? Community-Based Marine Protected Areas in the Philippines." *Journal of Environmental Management.* 66:441–454.

DeBoer, T. S., M. D. Subia, Ambariyanto, M. V. Erdmann, K. Kovitvongsa, and P. H. Barber. 2008. "Phylogeography and Limited Genetic Connectivity in the Endangered Giant Boring Clam, *Tridacna crocea*, Across the Coral Triangle." *Conservation Biology* 22(5): 1255–1266.

DeVantier, L., and E. Turak. 2009. *Coral Reefs of Brunei Darussalam.* Fisheries Department, Ministry of Industry and Primary Resources, Brunei Darussalam.

Edyvane, K., N. de Carvalho, S. Penny, A. Fernandes, C. B. de Cunha, A. L. Amaral, et al. 2009. *Conservation Values, Issues and Planning in the Nino Konis Santana Marine Park, Timor Leste – Final Report.* Ministry of Agriculture and Fisheries, Government of Timor Leste.

Ekman, S. 1934. Indo-Westpazific und Atlanto-Ostpazific, eine tiergeographische studie. *Zoogeographica* 2: 320–374.

Ekman, S. 1953. *Zoogeography of the Sea.* London: Sidgwick and Jackson.

Erdmann, M. V., L. Pet-Soede, and A. Cabanban. 2002. "Destructive Fishing Practices." In B. A. Best, R. S. Pomeroy, and C. M. Balboa (eds.), *Implications for Coral Reef Management and Policy: Relevant Findings from the 9th International Coral Reef Symposium.* Washington DC: US Agency for International Development, 78–81.

Erdmann, M. V. 2007. "Stomatopod Crustaceans of Northern Papua." 499-502 In A. J. Marshall, and B. Beehler (eds.), *The Ecology of Papua.* Singapore: Periplus Editions, 499–502.

Gordon, A., and R. Fine. 1996. "Pathways of Water Between the Pacific and Indian Oceans in the Indonesian Seas."*Nature.* 379:146–149.

Gosliner, T. M. 2002. "Biodiversity, Endemism, and Evolution of Opisthobranch Gastropods on Indo-Pacific Coral Reefs." *Proceedings of the 9th International Coral Reef Symposium* 2: 937–940.

Green, A. L. and P. Lokani. 2004. "Designing a Resilient Network of Marine Protected Areas in Kimbe Bay, West New Britain, Papua New Guinea." Townsville, Australia: The Nature Conservancy.

Green, A. L., and P. J. Mous. 2004. "Delineating the Coral Triangle, Its Ecoregions, and Functional Seascapes." *Report on an Expert Workshop Held at the Southeast Asia Centre for Marine Protected Areas, Bali Indonesia (30April–2May 2003).* Bali, Indonesia: The Nature Conservancy.

Groombridge, B., and M. D. Jenkins. 2002. *World Atlas of Biodiversity. Earth's Living Resources in the 21st Century.* Berkeley: University of California Press.

Halas, D., and R. Winterbottom. 2009. "A Phylogenetic Test of Multiple Proposals for the Origins of the East Indies Coral Reef Biota." *Journal of Biogeography* 36: 1847–1860.

Hall, R. 1998. "The Plate Tectonics of Cenozoic SE Asia and the Distribution of Land and Sea." In R. Hall, and J. D. Holloway (eds.), *Biogeography and Geological Evolution of Southeast Asia.* Leiden: Backhuys Publishers, 99–132.

Hoegh-Guldberg, O., H. Hoegh-Guldberg, J. E. N. Veron, A. Green, E. D. Gomez, J. Lough, et al. 2009. *The Coral Triangle and Climate Change: Ecosystems, People and Societies at Risk.* Brisbane, Australia: World Wildlife Federation.

Hoeksema, B. W. 2007. "Delineation of the Indo-Malayan Centre of Maximum Marine Biodiversity: The Coral Triangle." In W. Renema (ed.), *Biogeography, Time and Place: Distributions, Barriers and Islands.* Dordrecht, The Netherlands: Springer. 117–118.

McLeod, E., and R. Salm. 2006. *Managing Mangroves for Resilience to Climate Change.* Gland, Switzerland: IUCN.

McLeod, E., J. Hinkel, A. T. Vafeidis, R. J. Nicholls, N. Harvey, and R. Salm. 2010. "Sea-Level Rise Vulnerability in the Countries of the Coral Triangle." *Sustainability Science* 5(2): 207–224.

McManus, J. W. 1985. "Marine Speciation, Tectonics, and Sea Level Changes in Southeast Asia." *Proceedings of Fifth International Coral Reef Congress, Tahiti.* 4: 133–138.

Mous, P., J. Pet, Z. Arifin, R. Djohani, M. V. Erdmann, A. Halim, Met al. 2005. "Policy Needs to Improve Marine Capture Fisheries Management and to Define a Role for Marine Protected Areas in Indonesia." *Fisheries Management and Ecology* 12: 259–268.

Pidgeon, E. 2009. "Carbon Sequestration by Coastal Marine Habitats: Important Missing Sinks." In D. Laffoley, and G. Grimsditch (eds.), *The Management of Natural Coastal Carbon Sinks.* Gland, Switzerland: IUCN, 47–51.

Randall, J. E. 1998. "Zoogeography of Shorefishes of the Indo-Pacific Region." *Zoological Studies* 37(4): 227–268.

Regional Plan of Action: Coral Triangle Initiative on Coral Reefs, Fisheries and Food Security. 2008. Coral Triangle Secretariat, Jakarta, Indonesia. Available at: http://www.cti-secretariat.net/

Schuttenberg, H., and D. Bizot. 2002. *The Status of Coral Reef Management in Southeast Asia: A Gap Analysis.* Bangkok, Thailand: UNEP East Asian Seas Regional Coordinating Unit.

Spalding, M. D., C. Ravilious, and E. P. Green. 2001. *World Atlas of Coral Reefs.* Prepared at the UNEP World Conservation Monitoring Center. Berkeley: University of California Press.

Spalding, M. D., M. Taylor, C. Ravilious, F. Short, and E. P. Green. 2003. "Global Overview. The Distribution and Status of Seagrasses." In E. P. Green, and F. T. Short (eds.), *World Atlas of Seagrasses.* Berkeley: University of California Press, 5–26.

Veron, J. E. N., L. M. Devantier, E. Turak, A. L. Green, S. Kininmonth, M. Stafford-Smith, et al. 2009. "Delineating the Coral Triangle." *Galaxea: Journal of Coral Reef Studies* 11: 91–100.

Voris, H. K. 2000. "Maps of Pleistocene Sea Levels in Southeast Asia: Shorelines, River Systems and Time Durations." *Journal of Biogeography* 27: 1153–1167.

Wallace, C. C. 1997. "The Indo-Pacific Centre of Coral Diversity Re-Examined at Species Level." *Proceedings of the Eighth International Coral Reef Symposium* 1: 365–370.

Wells, F. E. 2002. "Centres of Species Richness and Endemism of Shallow Water Marine Molluscs in the Tropical Indo-West Pacific." *Proceedings of the Ninth International Coral Reef Symposium* 2: 941–945.

THE PATAGONIAN SEA: CAMPAGNA, FALABELLA, AND ZAVATTIERI

Acha, E. M., H. W. Mianzan, R. A. Guerrero, M. Favero, and J. Bava. 2004. "Marine Fronts at the Continental Shelf of Austral South America. Physical and Ecological Processes." *Journal of Marine Systems* 44: 83–105.

Boersma, D, J. Ogden, G. Branch, R. Bustamante, C. Campagna, G. Harris, et al. 2004. "Lines on the Water: Ocean Use Planning Within Large Marine Ecosystems." In L. K. Glover and S. A. Earle (eds.), *Defying Ocean's End. An Agenda for Action.* Washington, DC: Island Press.

Campagna, C., A. R. Piola, M. R. Marin, M. Lewis, and T. Fernández. 2006. "Southern Elephant Seal Trajectories, Fronts and Eddies in the Brazil/Malvinas Confluence." *Deep-Sea Research* I 53:1907–1924.

Campagna, C., E. W. Sanderson, P. B. Coppolillo, V. Falabella, A. R. Piola, S. Strindberg, et al. 2007. "A Species Approach to Marine Ecosystem Conservation." *Aquatic Conservation: Marine and Freshwater Ecosystem* 17:S122-S147 DOI: 10.1002/aqc.918

Croxall, J.P., and A. G. Wood. 2002. "The Importance of the Patagonian Shelf for Top Predator Species Breeding at South Georgia." *Aquatic Conservation: Marine and Freshwater Ecosystems* 12(1): 101–118.

Falabella, V., C. Campagna, and J. Croxall, (eds.). 2009. *Atlas del Mar Patagónico. Especies y Espacios.* Published by Wildlife Conservation Society and BirdLife International.

Foro para la Conservación del Mar Patagónico y Áreas de Influencia. 2008. *Síntesis del estado de conservación del Mar Patagónico y áreas de influencia.* Puerto Madryn, Argentina: Edición del Foro.

Halpern, B. S., S. Walbridge, K. A. Selkoe, C. V. Kappel, F. Micheli , C. D'Agrosa, et al. 2008. "A Global Map of Human Impact on Marine Ecosystems." *Science* 319: 948–952

THE POLAR OCEANS: ASHJIAN

Ainley, D. G., and DeMaster. 1990. "The Upper Trophic Levels in Polar Marine Ecosystems." In W. O. Smith Jr. (ed.), *Polar Oceanography, Part B: Chemistry, Biology, and Geology.* San Diego: Academic Press, 599–630.

Armstrup, S. C. 2003. "Polar Bear." In G. A. Feldhammer, B. C. Thompson, and J. A. Chapman (eds.), *Wild Mammals of North America: Biology, Management, and Conservation.* 2nd ed. Baltimore: Johns Hopkins University Press, 587–610.

Arrigo, K. R., G. L. van Dijken, and S. Bushinsky. 2008. "Primary Production in the Southern Ocean, 1997–2006." *J. Geophys. Res.* 113: doi: 10.1029/2007JC004551.

Arrigo, K. R., G. van Dijken, and S. Pabi. 2008. "Impact of a Shrinking Arctic Ice Cover on Marine Primary Production. *J. Geophys. Res.* Lett. 3: doi: 10/1029/2008GL035028.
Atkinson, A., V. Siegel, E. Pakhomov, and P. Rothery. 2004. "Long-Term Decline in Krill Stock and Increase in Salps Within the Southern Ocean." *Nature* 432: 100–103.

Atkinson, A., V. Siegel, E. A. Pakhomov, P. Rothery, V. Loeb, R. M. Ross, et al. 2008. "Oceanic Circumpolar Habitats of Antarctic Krill." *Mar. Ecol. Prog.* Ser. 362: 1–23.

RIGHT: Plastic pollution is a huge problem for all marine animals. Many species, including sea turtles, mistake floating plastic bags for jellyfish and will die as a result of swallowing them. Sipadan Island, Malaysia.
Photograph by Gary Bell/ Oceanwide Images

Carmack, E. C. 1990. "Large-Scale Physical Oceanography of Polar Oceans." In W. O. Smith, Jr. (ed.), *Polar Oceanography, Part A: Physical Science.* San Diego: Academic Press, 171–222.

Cooper, L. W., C. J. Ashjian, S. L. Smith, L. A. Codispoti, J. Grebmeier, R. G. Campbell, et al. 2006. "Rapid Seasonal Sea-Ice Retreat in the Arctic Could Be Impacting Pacific Walrus (*Odobenus rosmarus divergens*) Recruitment." *Aquatic Mammals* 32: 98–102.

Ducklow, H. W., K. Baker, D. B. Martinson, L. B. Quetin, R. M. Ross, R. C. Smith, et al. 2007. "Marine Pelagic Ecosystems: The West Antarctic Peninsula." *Phil. Trans. R. Soc.* B 362: 67–94.

Forcada, J., and P. N. Trathan. 2009. "Penguin Responses to Climate Change in the Southern Ocean." *Global Change Biol.* 15: 1618–1630.

Forcada, J., P. N. Trathan, K. Reid, and E. J. Murphy. 2005."The Effects of Global Climate Variability in Pup Production of Antarctic Fur Seals." *Ecology* 86: 2409–2417.

Fraser, W. R., W. Z. Trivelpiece, D. G. Ainley, and S. G. Trivelpiece. 1992. "Increases in Antarctic Penguin Populations: Reduced Competition with Whales or a Loss of Sea Ice Due to Environmental Change?" *Polar Biol.* 11: 525–531.

Grebmeier, J. M., W. O. Smith Jr., and R. J. Conover. 1995. "Biological Processes on Arctic Continental Shelves: Ice-Ocean-Biota Interactions." In W. O. Smith Jr. and J. M. Grebmeier (eds.), *Arctic Oceanography: Marginal Ice Zones and Continental Shelves.*" Washington DC: American Geophysical Union, 231–262.

Grebmeier, J. M., J. E. Overland, S. E. Moore, E. V. Farley, E. C. Carmack, L. W. Cooper, et al. 2006. "A Major Ecosystem Shift Observed in the Northern Bering Sea." *Science* 311: 1461–1464.

Hopcroft, R. R., K. Kosbokova, and A. I. Pinchuk. 2010. "Zooplankton Community Patterns in the Chukchi Sea During Summer 2004." *Deep-Sea Res.* II 57: 27–39.

Jakobsson, M. 2002. "Hypsometry of the Arctic Ocean and Its Constituent Seas." *Geochemistry, Geophysics, Geosystems* 3(5), 1028, doi: 10.1029/2001GC000302.

Jakobsson, M. 2004. "Correction to 'Hypsometry and volumes of the Arctic Ocean and its constituent seas.'" *Geochemistry, Geophysics, Geosystems* 5. Q02005, doi: 10.1029/2004GC000694.

Kock, K-H., K. Reid, J. Croxall, and S. Nicol. 2007. "Fisheries in the Southern Ocean: An Ecosystem Approach." *Phil. Trans. R. Soc.* B 362: 2333–2349.

Laidre, K. L., I. Stirling, L. F. Lowry, Ø. Wiig, H-J. Mads Peter, and S. H. Ferguson. 2008. "Quantifying the Sensitivity of Arctic Marine Mammals to Climate-Induced Habitat Change." *Ecol. App.* 18: S97–S125.

Loeb, V., V. Siegel, O. Holm-Hansen, R. Hewitt, W. Fraser, W. Trivelpiece, et al. 1997. "Effects of Sea-Ice Extent and Krill or Salp Dominance on the Antarctic Food Web." *Nature* 387: 897–900.

Macdonald, R. W., E Sakshaug, and R. Stein. 2004. "The Arctic Ocean: Modern Status and Recent Climate Change." In R. Stein and R. W. Macdonald (eds.), The *Organic Carbon Cycle in the Arctic Ocean.* Berlin/Heidelberg: Springer-Verlag, 6–20.

Marr, J. W. S. 1962. The Natural History and Geography of the Antarctic Krill (*Euphausia superba* Dana). *Discovery Rep.* 32: 33–464.

Maslanik, J. A., C. Fowler, J. Stroeve, S. Drobot, J. Zwally, D. Yi, et al. 2007. "A Younger, Thinner Arctic Ice Cover: Increased Potential for Rapid, Extensive Sea-Ice Loss." *Geophys. Res.* Lett. 32: doi: 10.1029/2007GL32043.

Mayewski, P. A., M. P. Meredith, C. P. Summerhayes, J. Turner, A. Worby, P. J. Barrett, et al. 2009. "State of the Antarctic and Southern Ocean Climate System." *Reviews of Geophysics* 47, doi: 10.1029/2007RG000231.

Melnikov, I. A. 1997. *The Arctic Sea Ice Ecosystem.* Amsterdam: Gordon and Breach.

Meredith, M. P., and J. C. King. 2005. "Rapid Climate Change in the Ocean West of the Antarctic Peninsula During the Second Half of the 20th Century." *Geophys. Res. Lett.* 32, doi: 10.1029/2005GL024042.

Moline, Mark A., Nina J. Karnovsky, Zachary Brown, George J. Divoky, Thomas K. Frazer, Charles A. Jacoby, et al. 2008. "High Latitude Changes in Ice Dynamics and Their Impact on Polar Marine Ecosystems." *Annals of the New York Academy of Sciences* 1134, no. 1: 267–319. doi:10.1196/annals.1439.010.

Monnett, C., and J. S. Gleason. 2006. "Observations of Mortality Associated with Extended Open-Water Swimming by Polar Bears in the Alaskan Beaufort Sea." *Polar Biol.* 29: 681–687.

Montes-Hugo, M., S. C. Doney, H. W. Duklow, W. Fraser, D. Martinson, S. E. Stammerjohn, et al. 2009. "Recent Changes in Phytoplankton Communities Associated with Rapid Regional Climate Change Along the Western Antarctic Peninsula." *Science* 323: 1470–1473.

Moore, S. E., and H. P. Huntington. 2008. "Arctic Marine Mammals and Climate Change: Impacts and Resilience." *Ecol. App.* 18: S157–S165.

Nicol, S., A. Worby, and R. Leaper. 2008. "Changes in the Antarctic Sea Ice Ecosystem: Potential Effects on Krill and Baleen Whales." *Marine and Freshwater Research* 59: 261–283.

Pabi, S., G. L. Dijken, and K. R. Arrigo. 2008. "Primary Production in the Arctic Ocean, 1998–2006." *J. Geophys Res.* 113: doi: 10.1029/2007JC004578.

Regehr, E. V., N. J. Lunn, S. C. Amstrup, and I. Stirling. 2007. "Effects of Earlier Sea Ice Breakup on Survival and Population Size of Polar Bears in Western Hudson Bay." *J. Wildlife Management* 71: 2673–2683.

Regehr, E. V., C. M. Hunter, H. Caswell, S. C. Amstrup, and I. Stirling. 2010. "Survival and Breeding of Polar Bears in the Southern Beaufort Sea in Relation to Sea Ice." *J. Animal Ecol.* 79: 117–127.

Rode, K., S. Amstrup, and E. Regehr. 2010. "Reduced Body Size and Cub Recruitment in Polar Bears Associated with Sea Ice Decline." *Ecological Applications* 20: 768–782.

Smith, S. L., and S. B. Schnack-Schiel. 1990. "Polar Zooplankton." In W. O. Smith Jr. (ed.), *Polar Oceanography, Part B: Chemistry, Biology, and Geology.* San Diego: Academic Press, 527–598.

Smith Jr., W. O., D. G. Ainley, and R. Cattaneo-Vietti. 2007. "Trophic Interactions Within the Ross Sea Continental Shelf Ecosystem." *Phil. Trans. R. Soc.* B 362, 95–111.

Smith, W. O. Jr., and J. C. Comiso. 2008. "Influence of Sea Ice on Primary Production in the Southern Ocean: A Satellite Perspective." *J. Geophys. Res.* 113: doi: 10.1029/2007JC004251.

Stirling, I., N .J. Lunn, and J. Iacozza. 1999. "Long-Term Trends in the Population Ecology of Polar Bears in Western Hudson Bay in Relation to Climate Change." *Arctic* 52: 294–306.

Stone, G. 2003. *Ice Island: Expedition to Antarctica's Largest Iceberg.* Boston: Bunker Hill. (Winner of the 2003 National Outdoor Book Award for Nature and the Environment)

Stroeve, J., M. Serreze, S. Drobot, S. Gearheard, M. Holland, J. Maslanik, et al. 2008. "Arctic Sea Ice Extent Plummets in 2007." *EOS Transactions American Geophysical Union* 89: 13–20.

THE MEDITERRANEAN SEA: SALA

Ballesteros, E. 1992. *Els Vegetals i la Zonació Litoral: Espècies, Comunitats i Factors que Influeixen en la Seva Distribució.* Arxius de la Secció de Ciències, CI. Barcelona: Institut d'Estudis Catalans.

Boudouresque, C. F., A. Meinesz, M. A. Ribera, and E. Ballesteros. 1995. "Spread of the Green Alga *Caulerpa taxifolia* (Caulerpales, Chlorophyta) in the Mediterranean: Possible Consequences of a Major Ecological Event." *Sci. Mar.* 59:21–29.

CIESM. 2011. *CIESM Atlas of Exotic Species in the Mediterranean.* http://www.ciesm.org/online/atlas/intro.htm

Coll, M., C. Piroddi, J. Steenbeek, K. Kaschner, F. Ben Rais Lasram, J. Agguzi, et al. 2010. "The Biodiversity of the Mediterranean Sea: Estimates, Patterns, and Threats." *PLoS ONE* 5(8): e11842.

Ferretti, F., R. A. Myers, F. Serena, and H. K. Lotze. 2008. "Loss of Large Predatory Sharks from the Mediterranean Sea." *Conservation Biology* 22: 952–964.

Garcia-Castellanos, D., F. Estrada, I. Jiménez-Munt, C. Gorini, M. Fernàndez, J. Vergés, et al. 2009. "Catastrophic Flood of the Mediterranean After the Messinian Crisis." *Nature* 462, 778–781.

Garrabou, J., and J. G. Harmelin. 2002. "A 20-Year Study on Life-History Traits of a Harvested Long-Lived Temperate Coral in the NW Mediterranean: Insights into Conservation and Management Needs." *Journal of Animal Ecology* 71: 966–978.

Goñi, R., R. Hilborn, D. Díaz, S. Mallol, and S. Adlerstein. 2010. "Net Contribution of Spillover from a Marine Reserve to Fishery Catches." *Mar Ecol Prog Ser* 400: 233–243.

Guidetti, P., and E. Sala. 2007. "Community-Wide Effects of Marine Reserves in the Mediterranean Sea." *Marine Ecology Progress Series* 335: 43–56.

Johnson, W. M., and Lavigne, D. M. 1999. "Monk Seals in Antiquity: The Mediterranean Monk Seal (*Monachus monachus*) in Ancient History and Literature." *Mededelingen* 35. Leiden: The Netherlands Commission for International Nature Protection.

Licandro, P., D. V. P. Conway, M. N. Daly Yahia, M. L. Fernandez de Puelles, S. Gasparini, J. H. Hecq, et al. 2010. "A Blooming Jellyfish in the Northeast Atlantic and Mediterranean." *Biology Letters* 6 (5): 688.

Margalef, R. (ed.). 1985. Western Mediterranean. Oxford: Pergamon Press.

MacKenzie, B. R., H. Mosegaard, A. A. Rosenberg. 2009. "Impending Collapse of Bluefin Tuna in the Northeast Atlantic and Mediterranean." *Conservation Letters* 2: 26–35.

Merino, G., F. Maynou, and J. Boncoeur. 2009. "Bioeconomic Model for a Three-Zone Marine Protected Area: A Case Study of Medes Islands (Northwest Mediterranean)." *ICES Journal of Marine Science* 66: 147–154.

Perez, T., J. Garrabou, S. Sartoretto, J. G. Harmelin, P. Francour, J. Vacelet. 2000. "Mass Mortality of Marine Invertebrates: An Unprecedented Event in the Northwestern Mediterranean." *C. R. Acad. Sci. Ser. III Sci. Vie* 323: 853–865.

Sala, E. 2004. "The Past and Present Topology and Structure of Mediterranean Subtidal Rocky Shore Food Webs." Ecosystems 7: 333–340.

Zabala, M., and E. Ballesteros. 1989. "Surface-Dependent Strategies and Energy Flux in Benthic Marine Communities Or, Why Corals Do Not Exist in the Mediterranean." *Scientia Marina* 53: 3–17.

THE CENTRAL PACIFIC OCEAN: TAEI, DONOGHUE, STONE, AND WRIGLEY

Burke, L., K. Reytar, M. Spalding, and A. Perry. 2011. *Reefs at Risk: Revisited.* Washington, DC: World Resources Institute. http://www.wri.org/publication/reefs-at-risk-revisited.

Gillett, R., and A. Langley. 2007. *Tuna for Tomorrow? Some of the Science Behind an Important Fishery in the Pacific Islands.* Updated 2007. Manila, Philippines: Asian Development Bank and Secretariat of the Pacific Community.

Hau ofa, E. 2008. "Our Sea of Islands." In *We Are the Ocean: Selected Works.* Honolulu: University of Hawaii Press.

Pacific Islands Forum Secretariat. 2009. *Final Communiqué of the 40th Pacific Islands Forum, Cairns.* In Cairns, Australia, August 5.

———. 2010. *Final Communiqué of the 41st Pacific Islands Forum, Port Vila, Vanuatu: Framework for a Pacific Oceanscape.* In Port Vila, Vanuatu, August 4.

Pippard, H. 2009. *The Pacific Islands: An Analysis of the Status of Species As Listed on the 2008 IUCN Red List of Threatened Species.* Suva, Fiji: IUCN Regional Office for Oceania.

Pratt, C., and H. Govan. 2010. Our Sea of Islands, Our Livelihoods, Our Oceania. Framework for a Pacific Oceanscape: A Catalyst for Implementation of Ocean Policy. Apia, Samoa: South Pacific Regional Environment Programme (SPREP).

SPREP 2010. *Ocean Voices: Lessons from the Whales for the CBD: Humpback Whales in Oceania.* Apia, Samoa: Secretariat of the Pacific Regional Environment Programme (SPREP).

UNESCO World Heritage Committee. 2010. *Report of the Decisions Adopted by the World Heritage Committee at Its 34th Session.* Brasilia, Brazil, July 25- August 3, 2010. http://whc.unesco.org/en/sessions/34COM/.

LEFT: A tourist boat travels along Na Pali coast, Kauai, Hawai'i. **Photograph by Frans Lanting/ iLCP**

THE WESTERN INDIAN OCEAN: OBURA

Adger, N.A., T. P. Hughes, C. Folke, S. R. Carpenter, and J. Rockstrom. 2005. "Social-Ecological Resilience to Coastal Disasters." *Science* 309: 1036–1039.

de Ruijter, W. P. M., H. Ridderinkhof, J. R. E. Lutjeharms, M. W.Schouten, and C. Veth 2002. "Observations of the Flow in the Mozambique Channel." *Geophys. Res. Lett.*, 29(10), 1502, doi:10.1029/2001GL013714.

Donner, S. D. 2009. Coping with Commitment: Projected Thermal Stress on Coral Reefs Under Different Future Scenarios. *PLoS ONE* 4(6): e5712. doi:10.1371/journal.pone.0005712

IPCC. 2007. "Climate Change 2007: The Physical Science Basis Summary for Policymakers. Intergovernmental Panel on Climate Change." *WMO/UNEP.*

McNeely, J. A., R. A. Mittermeier, T M. Brooks, F. Boltz, and N. Ash. 2009. *The Wealth of Nature: Ecosystem Services, Biodiversity, and Human Well-Being.* CEMEX Conservation Book Series. Arlington, VA: CEMEX.

Richmond, M. D. 2001. "The Marine Biodiversity of the Western Indian Ocean and Its Biogeography: How Much Do We Know?" In M. D. Richmond, and J. Francis (eds.). *Marine Science Development in Tanzania and Eastern Africa. Proceedings of the 20th Anniversary Conference on Advances in Marine Science in Tanzania. 28 June–1 July, 1999, Zanzibar, Tanzania.* IMS/WIOMSA, 241–262.

Rosen, B. 1971. "The distribution of reef coral genera in the Indian Ocean." *Symposium of the Zoological Society of London* 28: 263–299.

Schott, F. A., J. P. McCreary, and S. P. Xie. 2009. "Indian Ocean Circulation and Climate Variability." *Rev. Geophys.*, 47, RG1002, doi:10.1029/2007RG000245.

Sheppard, C. 1987. "Coral Species of the Indian Ocean and Adjacent Seas: A Synonymized Compilation and Some Regional Distributional Patterns." *Atoll Research Bulletin* 307: 1–32.

Veron, J. E. N. 2000. *Corals of the World.* Townsville: Australian Institute of Marine Science.

Wilkinson, C., O. Linden, H. Cesar, G. Hodgson, J. Rubens, and A. Strong. 1999. "Ecological and Socioeconomic Impacts of 1998 Coral Mortality in the Indian Ocean: An ENSO Impact and a Warning of Future Change? *Ambio* 28: 188–196.

THE ABROLHOS SEASCAPE: DUTRA, DE MOURA, AND KAUFMAN

Andriolo, A., P. G. Kinas, M. H. Engel, C. C. A. Martins, and A. M. Rufino. 2010. "Humpback Whales Within the Brazilian Breeding Ground: Distribution and Population Size Estimate." *Endangered Species Research* 11:233–243.

Dutra, G. F., G. R. Allen, T. Werner, and S. A. McKenna. 2006. "A Rapid Marine Biodiversity Assessment of the Abrolhos Bank, Bahia, Brazil." *RAP Bulletin of Biological Assessment* 38.

Francini-Filho, R., and R. Moura. 2008a. "Evidence for Spillover of Reef Fishes from a No-Take Marine Reserve: An Evaluation Using the Before-After Control-Impact Approach." *Fisheries Research* 93: 346–356.

Francini-Filho, R., and R. Moura. 2008b. "Dynamics of Fish Assemblages on Coral Reefs Subjected to Different Management Regimes in the Abrolhos Bank, Eastern Brazil." *Aquatic Conservation* 18: 1166–1179.

Francini-Filho, R. B., R. L. Moura, F. L. Thompson, R. M. Reis, L. Kaufman, R. K. P. Kikuchi, et al. 2008. "Diseases Leading to Accelerated Decline of Reef Corals in the Largest South Atlantic Reef Complex (Abrolhos Bank, Eastern Brazil). *Mar. Pollut. Bull.* 56:1008–1014.

Leão, Z. M. A. N., R. K. P. Kikuchi, and V. Testa. 2003. "Corals and Coral Reefs of Brazil." In J. Cortés (ed.), *Latin America Coral Reefs.* Amsterdam: Elsevier Science, 9–52.

Marchioro, G. B., M. A. Nunes, G. F. Dutra, R. L. Mour, and P. G. P. Pereira. 2005. "Avaliação dos Impactos da Exploração e Produção de Hidrocarbonetos no Banco dos Abrolhos e Adjacências." [Evaluation of the Impacts of Exploration and Production of Oil and Natural Gas in the Abrolhos Bank and Adjacent Areas] *Megadiversidade* 1: 225–310.

Moura, R. L., 2003. "Brazilian Reefs as Priority Areas for Biodiversity Conservation in the Atlantic Ocean." In *Proceedings of the 9th International Coral Reef Symposium* 2, 917–920.

Moura, R., and K. Lindeman. (2007). "A New Species of Snapper (*Perciformes: Lutjanidae*) from Brazil, with Comments on the Distribution of Lutjanus griseus and L. apodus." *Zootaxa* 1422: 31–43.

Ribeiro, M. C., J. P. Metzger, A. C. Martensen, F. J. Ponzoni, and M. M. Hirota. 2009. "The Brazilian Atlantic Forest: How Much Is Left, and How Is the Remaining Forest Distributed? Implications for Conservation." *Biological Conservation* 142: 1141–1146.

Wedekin, L. L., M. H. Engel, A. Azevedo, P. G. Kinas, A. Andriolo, and P. C. Simões-Lopes. (2010). "Density and Abundance of the Humpback Whale in the Brazilian Breeding Ground (Stock A): Aerial Survey, 2008." Working Paper SC-62-SH-28, presented at the *Scientific Committee of the International Whaling Commission (IWC), 62nd Annual Meeting*, Agadir, Morocco.

Werner, T. B., L. P. Pinto, G. F. Dutra, and P. G. P. Pereira. 2000. "Abrolhos 2000: Conserving the Southern Atlantic's Richest Coastal Biodiversity into the Next Century." *Coastal Management* 28: 99–108.

THE GULF OF CALIFORNIA: (ABURTO-OROPEZA AND MITTERMEIER)

Aburto-Oropeza, O., Exequiel Ezcurra, Gustavo Danemann, Víctor Valdez, Jason Murray, and Enric Sala. 2008. "Mangroves in the Gulf of California Increase Fishery Yields." *Proceedings of the National Academy of Sciences* 105: 10456–10459.

Aburto-Oropeza, O., M. Caso, B. Erisman, and E. Ezcurra, eds. 2011. *Log of the Deep Sea: An Expedition to the Gulf of California.* Instituto Nacional de Ecología, UC MEXUS, Scripps Institution of Oceanography, Mexico, D.F.

Alder, J., B. Campbell, V. Karpouzi, K. Kaschner, and D. Pauly. 2008. "Forage Fish: From Ecosystems to Markets." *Annual Reviews in Environment and Resources* 33: 153–166.

Alvarez-Borrego, S. 2010. "Physical, Chemical, and Biological Oceanography of the Gulf of California." In R. C. Brusca (ed.), *The Gulf of California. Biodiversity and Conservation.* Arizona: The University of Arizona Press, 24–48.

Brusca, R., M. E. Hendrickx. 2010. "Invertebrate Biodiversity

FOLLOWING SPREAD: A Caribbean reef shark (*Carcharhinus perezi*) swims at sunset just beneath the surface while a school of Yellow-tail Snappers trail just behind. French Cay, Turks and Caicos Islands.
Photograph by Mauricio Handler

and Conservation in the Gulf of California." In R. C. Brusca (ed.), *The Gulf of California. Biodiversity and Conservation.* Arizona: The University of Arizona Press, 72–95.

Erisman, B., Gustavo A. Paredes, Tomas Plomozo-Lugo, Juan J. Cota-Nieto, Philip Hastings, and Octavio Aburto-Oropeza. 2011. "Spatial Structure of Commercial Marine Fisheries in Northwest Mexico." *ICES Journal of Marine Sciences* doi: 10.1093/icesjms/fsq179.

Ezcurra, E. 1998. *Conservation and Sustainable Use of Natural Resources in Baja California: An Overview.* San Diego Dialogue's Forum Fronterizo policy luncheon series, The San Diego Union-Tribune and Sempra Energy, and Public Policy Institute of California, 15.

Gamez, A. E., (ed.), 2008. *Turismo y sustentabilidad en Cabo Pulmo, BCS.* San Diego State University, Universidad Autónoma de Baja California Sur, y Consejo Nacional de Ciencia y Tecnología.

Hastings, P. A., L. T. Findley, A. M. Van der Heiden. 2010. "Fishes of the Gulf of California." In R. C. Brusca (ed.), *The Gulf of California. Biodiversity and Conservation.* Arizona: The University of Arizona Press, 96–118.

Ledesma-Vazquez J., A. L. Carreño. 2010. "Origin, Age, and Geological Evolution of the Gulf of California." In R. C. Brusca (ed.), *The Gulf of California. Biodiversity and Conservation.* Arizona: The University of Arizona Press, 7–23.

Sala, E., O. Aburto-Oropeza, G. Paredes, I. Parra, J. C. Barrera, and P. K. Dayton. 2002. "A General Model for Designing Networks of Marine Reserves." *Science* 298: 1991–1993.

Urbán, J. R. 2010. "Marine Mammals of the Gulf of California." In R. C. Brusca (ed.), *The Gulf of California. Biodiversity and Conservation.* Arizona: The University of Arizona Press, 188–209.

Velarde, E., E. Ezcurra, M. A. Cisneros-Mata, , M. F. Lavín. 2004. "Seabird Ecology, El Niño Anomalies, and Prediction of Sardine Fisheries in the Gulf of California." *Ecol. Appl.* 14: 607–615.

CHAPTER 7: ROSENBERG, SELIG, FONG, KARRER, AND HALPERN

Agnew, D. J., J. Pearce, G. Pramod, T. Peatman, G. Watson, J. Beddington, and T. J. Pitcher. 2009. "Estimating the Worldwide Extent of Illegal Fishing." *PLoS ONE*, 4, 1–8.

Alder, J., B. Campbell, V. Karpouzi, K. Kaschner, and D. Pauly. 2008. "Forage Fish: From Ecosystems to Markets." *Annual Review of Environment and Resources* 33, no. 1: 153–166.

Baron, N. 2010. *Escape from the Ivory Tower: A Guide to Making Your Science Matter.* Washington DC: Island Press.

Beddington, J. R., D. J. Agnew, and C. W. Clark. 2007. "Current Problems in the Management of Marine Fisheries." *Science* 316, no. 5832: 1713–1716.

Branch, T. 2008. "Not All Fisheries Will Be Collapsed in 2048." *Marine Policy* 32, no. 1: 38–39.

Brander, K. M. 2007. "Climate Change and Food Security Special Feature: Global Fish Production and Climate Change." *Proceedings of the National Academy of Sciences* 104, no. 50: 19709–19714.

Caddy J. F., and D. J. Agnew. 2004. "An Overview of Recent Global Experience with Recovery Plans for Depleted Marine Resources and Suggested Guidelines for Recovery Planning." *Reviews of Fish Biology and Fisheries* 14, 43–112.

Coleman, F. C. 2004. "The Impact of United States Recreational Fisheries on Marine Fish Populations." *Science* 305, no. 5692: 1958–1960.

Commission of the European Communities. 2007. *An Integrated Maritime Policy for the European Union.*

Committee on Ecosystem Effects of Fishing: Phase II—Assessments of the Extent of Change and the Implications for Policy, National Research Council. 2006. *Dynamic Changes in Marine Ecosystems: Fishing, Food Webs, and Future Options.* Ocean Studies Board Report. National Academies Press.

Costello, C., S. D. Gaines, and J. Lynham. 2008. "Can Catch Shares Prevent Fisheries Collapse?" *Science* 321, no. 5896: 1678–1681.

Day, J., L. Fernandes, A. Lewis, G. De'ath, S. Slegers, B. Barnett, et al. 2002. "The Representative Areas Program for Protecting the Biodiversity of the Great Barrier Reef World Heritage Area." In M. K. Moosa, S. Soemodihardjo, A. Soegiarto, K. Romimohtarto, A. Nontji, Soekarno and Suharsono (eds.). *Proceedings of the Ninth International Coral Reef Symposium.* Bali, 687–696.

de Vries, M., and I. J. M. de Boer. 2010. "Comparing Environmental Impacts for Livestock Products: A Review of Life Cycle Assessments." *Livestock Science* 128, no. 1-3: 1–11.

Doney, S. C., V. J. Fabry, R. A. Feely, and J. A. Kleypas. 2009. "Ocean Acidification: The Other CO_2 Problem." *Annual Review of Marine Science* 1, no. 1: 169–192.

FAO. 2005. *Increasing the Contribution of Small-Scale Fisheries to Poverty Alleviation and Food Security.* FAO Technical Guidelines for Responsible Fisheries. No. 10. Rome: Food and Agriculture Organization of the United Nations.

FAO. 2009. *The State of World Fisheries and Aquaculture 2008.* Rome, Italy: FAO. http://www.fao.org/fishery/sofia/en.

Fernandes, L., J. Day, A. Lewis, S. Slegers, B. Kerrigan, D. Breen, et al. 2005. "Establishing Representative No-Take Areas in the Great Barrier Reef: Large-Scale Implementation of Theory on Marine Protected Areas." *Conservation Biology* 19, no. 6: 1733–1744.

FishWise 2011. *Mission.* http://fishwise.org/our-organization. Accessed March 30, 2011.

Garcia, S. M. 2009. *Rising to Depletion? Towards a Dialogue on the State of National Marine Fisheries.* Preliminary report. Washington DC: (World Bank) Global Program on Fisheries (PROFISH). Agricultural and Rural Development. Sustainable Development Network.

Garcia, S. M. 2009a. Governance, Science and Society. The Ecosystem Approach to Fisheries. In R. Quentin Grafton, R. Hilborn, D. Squires, M. Tait, and M. Williams (eds.), *Handbook of Marine Fisheries Conservation and Management.* Oxford, UK: Oxford University Press, 87–98.

Garcia, S. M., and A. A. Rosenberg. 2010. "Food Security and Marine Capture Fisheries: Characteristics, Trends, Drivers and Future Perspectives." *Philosophical Transactions*

of the Royal Society B: Biological Sciences 365, no. 1554: 2869–2880.

Garcia, S. M., A. Zerbi, C. Aliaume, T. Do Chi, and G. Lasserre. 2003. *The Ecosystem Approach to Fisheries. Issues, Terminology, Principles, Institutional Foundations, Implementation and Outlook.* FAO Fisheries Technical Paper.

Grescoe, T. 2008. *Bottomfeeder: A Seafood Lover s Journey to the End of the Food Chain.* 1st ed. New York: Bloomsbury USA.

Gudmundsson, E., & Wessells, C. R. 2000. "Ecolabeling Seafood for Sustainable Production: Implications for Fisheries Management." *Marine Resource Economics,*15, 97–113.

Hall, M. 2007. "Eat More Anchovies." *Conservation Magazine*, 8(3).
http://www.conbio.org/cip/article30713.cfm. Accessed January 10, 2011.

Halpern, B. S., K. L. McLeod, A. A. Rosenberg, and L. B. Crowder. 2008. "Managing for Cumulative Impacts in Ecosystem-Based Management Through Ocean Zoning." *Ocean & Coastal Management*, 51, 203–211.

Halpern, B. S., S. Walbridge, K. A. Selkoe, C. V. Kappel, F. Micheli, C. D Agrosa, et al. 2008. "A Global Map of Human Impact on Marine Ecosystems." *Science* 319, no. 5865: 948–952.

Halweil, B. 2006. "Catch of the Day: Choosing Seafood for Healthier Oceans." *Worldwatch Institute.* Worldwatch Paper #172. http://www.worldwatch.org/node/4707. Accessed January 11, 2011.

Jacquet, J., Hocevar J., S. Lai, P. Majluf, N. Pelletier, T. Pitcher, et al. 2010. "Conserving Wild Fish in a Sea of Market-Based Efforts." *Oryx*, 44(1), 45–56.

Jacquet, J., and D. Pauly. 2008. "Funding Priorities: Big Barriers to Small-Scale Fisheries." *Conservation Biology* 22, no. 4: 832–835.

Keyzer, M. A., M. D. Merbis, I. F. P. W. Pavel, and C. F. A. van Wesenbeeck. 2005. "Diet Shifts Towards Meat and the Effects on Cereal Use: Can We Feed the Animals in 2030?" *Ecological Economics* 55, no. 2: 187–202. doi:10.1016/j.ecolecon.2004.12.002.

Leslie, H. M., A. A. Rosenberg, and J. Eagle. 2008. "Is a New Mandate Needed for Marine Ecosystem-Based Management?" *Frontiers in Ecology and the Environment*, 6, 43–48.

Levitus, S. 2000. "Warming of the World Ocean." *Science* 287, no. 5461: 2225–2229.

Ludwig, D., R. Hilborn, and C. Walters. 1993. "Uncertainty, Resource Exploitation, and Conservation: Lessons from History." *Science* 260, no. 5104: 17–36.

Mara, V., A. de Sherbinin, and T. Srebotnjak. 2010. *2010 Environmental Performance Index.* http://epi.yale.edu.

Marine Aquaculture Task Force. 2007. *Sustainable Marine Aquaculture: Fulfilling the Promise; Managing the Risks.* Report of the Marine Aquaculture Task Force. http://www.pewtrusts.org/uploadedFiles/wwwpewtrustsorg/Reports/Protecting_ocean_life/Sustainable_Marine_Aquaculture_final_1_07.pdf. Accessed November 26, 2008.

McLeod, K. L., and H. M. Leslie. 2009. "State of Practice." In K. O. McLeod and H. Leslie (eds.), *Ecosystem-Based Management of the Ocean.* Washington, DC: Island Press, 314–324.

Mora, C., O. Aburto-Oropeza, A. A. Bocos, P. M. Ayotte, S. Banks, A. G. Bauman, et al. 2011. "Global Human Footprint on the Linkage Between Biodiversity and Ecosystem Functioning in Reef Fishes." S. P. Ellner, Editor. *PLoS Biology* 9, no. 4: e1000606. doi:10.1371/journal.pbio.1000606.

Mora, C., R. A. Myers, M. Coll, S. Libralato, T. J. Pitcher, R. U. Sumaila, et al. 2009. "Management Effectiveness of the World's Marine Fisheries." C. Roberts, Editor. *PLoS Biology* 7, no. 6: e1000131. doi:10.1371/journal.pbio.1000131.

National Research Council. 2010. *Adapting to the Impacts of Climate Change.* Washington DC: The National Academies Press. 272p.

Nellemann, C., E. Corcoran, C. M. Duarte, L. Valdés, C. De Young, L. Fonseca, et al. (eds.). 2009. *Blue Carbon. A Rapid Response Assessment.* United Nations Environment Programme, GRID-Arendal. www.grida.no

Niesten, E., and H. Gjertsen. 2010. *Economic Incentives for Marine Conservation.* Arlington, VA: Conservation International, Science and Knowledge Division.

Obama, B. 2010. *Executive Order: Stewardship of the Ocean, Our Coasts, and the Great Lakes.*

Orbach, M., and L. Karrer. 2010. *Marine Managed Areas: What, Why, and Where.* Arlington, VA: Conservation International, Science and Knowledge Division.

Pauly, D., J. Alder, E. Bennet, V. Christensen, P. Tyedmers, and R. Watson. 2003. "The Future for Fisheries." *Science*, 302, 1359–1361.

Pimentel, D., and M. Pimentel. 2003. "Sustainability of Meat-Based and Plant-Based Diets and the Environment." *American Journal of Clinical Nutrition* 78, no. 3: 660S–663S.

Pitcher, T. J. 2008. "The Sea Ahead: Challenges to Marine Biology from Seafood Sustainability." *Hydrobiologia* 606, no. 1: 161–185.

Roheim, C. A., and J. Sutinen. 2006. "Trade and Marketplace Measures to Promote Sustainable Fishing Practices." *Natural Resources, International Trade and Sustainable Development.* Issue Paper No. 3. Geneva, Switzerland: International Centre for Trade and Sustainable Development and the High Seas Task Force.

Rosenberg, A. A. 2002. "The Precautionary Approach from a Manager's Perspective." *Bull. Marine Sci.* 70: 577–588.

Rosenberg, A. A. 2003. "Managing to the Margins: The Overexploitation of Fisheries." *Frontiers in Ecology and the Environment* 1, no. 2: 102–106.

Rosenberg, A. A., and K. L. McLeod. 2005. "Implementing Ecosystem-Based Approaches to Management for the Conservation of Ecosystem Services." *Marine Ecology-Progress Series*, 300, 270–274.

Rosenberg, A. A., and P. A. Sandifer. 2009. "What Do Managers Need?" In K. O. McLeod and H. Leslie (eds.), *Ecosystem-Based Management of the Ocean.* Washington DC: Island Press, 13–32.

Rosenberg, A. A., J. H. Swasey, and M. Bowman. 2006. "Rebuilding US fisheries: Progress and Problems." *Frontiers in Ecology and the Environment* 4: 303–308.

Rosenberg, A. A., M. Mooney-Seus, I. Kiessling, C. B. Mogensen, R. O'Boyle, J. Peacey. 2009. "Lessons from

RIGHT: Plumose anemone (*Metridium senile*), Lofoten, Norway.
Photograph by Magnus Lundgren/ Wild Wonders of Europe

National-Level Implementation Across the World." In K. O. McLeod and H. Leslie (eds.), *Ecosystem-Based Management of the Ocean.* Washington DC: Island Press, 294–313.

Ruckelshaus, M. H., T. Essington, and P. Levin. 2009. Puget Sound, Washington, USA. In K. McLeod and H. M. Leslie (eds.), *Ecosystem-Based Management for the Oceans.* Washington DC: Island Press, 201–226.

Sumaila, U. R., A. S. Khan, A. J. Dyck, R. Watson, G. Munro, P. Tydemers, et al. 2010. "A Bottom-Up Re-estimation of Global Fisheries Subsidies. *Journal of Bioeconomics,* 12(3), 201–225.

Tilman, D., K. G. Cassman, P. A. Matson, R. Naylor, and S. Polasky. 2002. "Agricultural Sustainability and Intensive Production Practices." *Nature* 418, no. 6898: 671–677.

U. S. Census Bureau. 2008. *Total Midyear Population for the World: 1950–2050.* http://www.census.gov/ipc/www/idb/worldpop.html.

Wessells, C. R., K. Cochrane, C. Deere, P. Wallis, and R. Willmann. 2001. "Product Certification and Eco-Labelling for Fisheries Sustainability." *Fisheries Technical Paper 422.* Rome: Food and Agriculture Organization of the United Nations. ftp://ftp.fao.org/docrep/fao/005/y2789e/y2789e00.pdf. Accessed January 8, 2011.

World Health Organization. 2006. *Global and Regional Food Consumption Patterns and Trends: Availability and Consumption of Fish.* http://www.who.int/nutrition/topics/3_foodconsumption/en/index5.html. Accessed January 6, 2011.

Worm, B., R. Hilborn, J. K. Baum, T. A. Branch, J. S. Collie, C. Costello, et al. 2009. "Rebuilding Global Fisheries." *Science* 325, no. 5940 (July 31): 578–585.

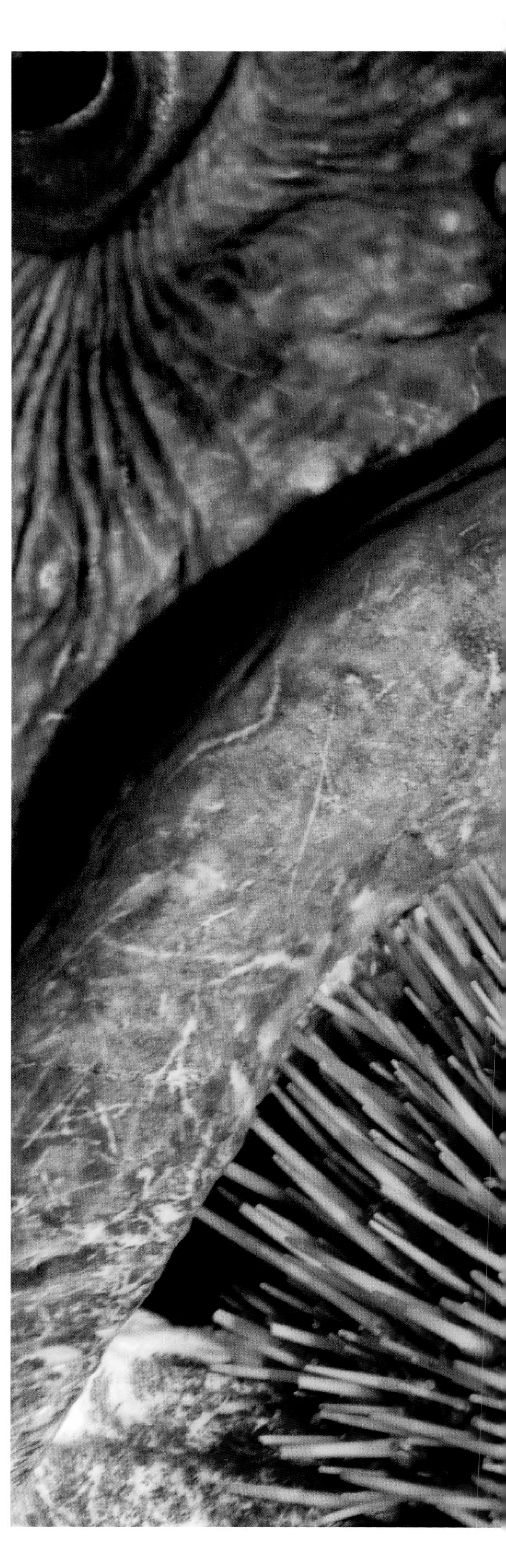

RIGHT: Atlantic wolf fish (*Anarhichas lupus*), Atlantic marine life, Saltstraumen, Bodö, Norway.
Photograph by Magnus Lundgren/ Wild Wonders of Europe

PRECEDING SPREAD: Nudibranch (*Phyllodesmium longicirrum*). Philippines, Indo-West Pacific.
Photograph by Gary Bell/ Oceanwide Images

RIGHT: Lionfish (*Pterois antennata*) hunting at dusk, Challenger Bay, Great Barrier Reef, Australia. Beautiful in the habitat where it belongs, this voracious fish has become a severe threat. An invasive species, the lionfish is devastating reef fish populations along the Florida coast and into the Caribbean.
Photograph by David Doubilet/ iLCP

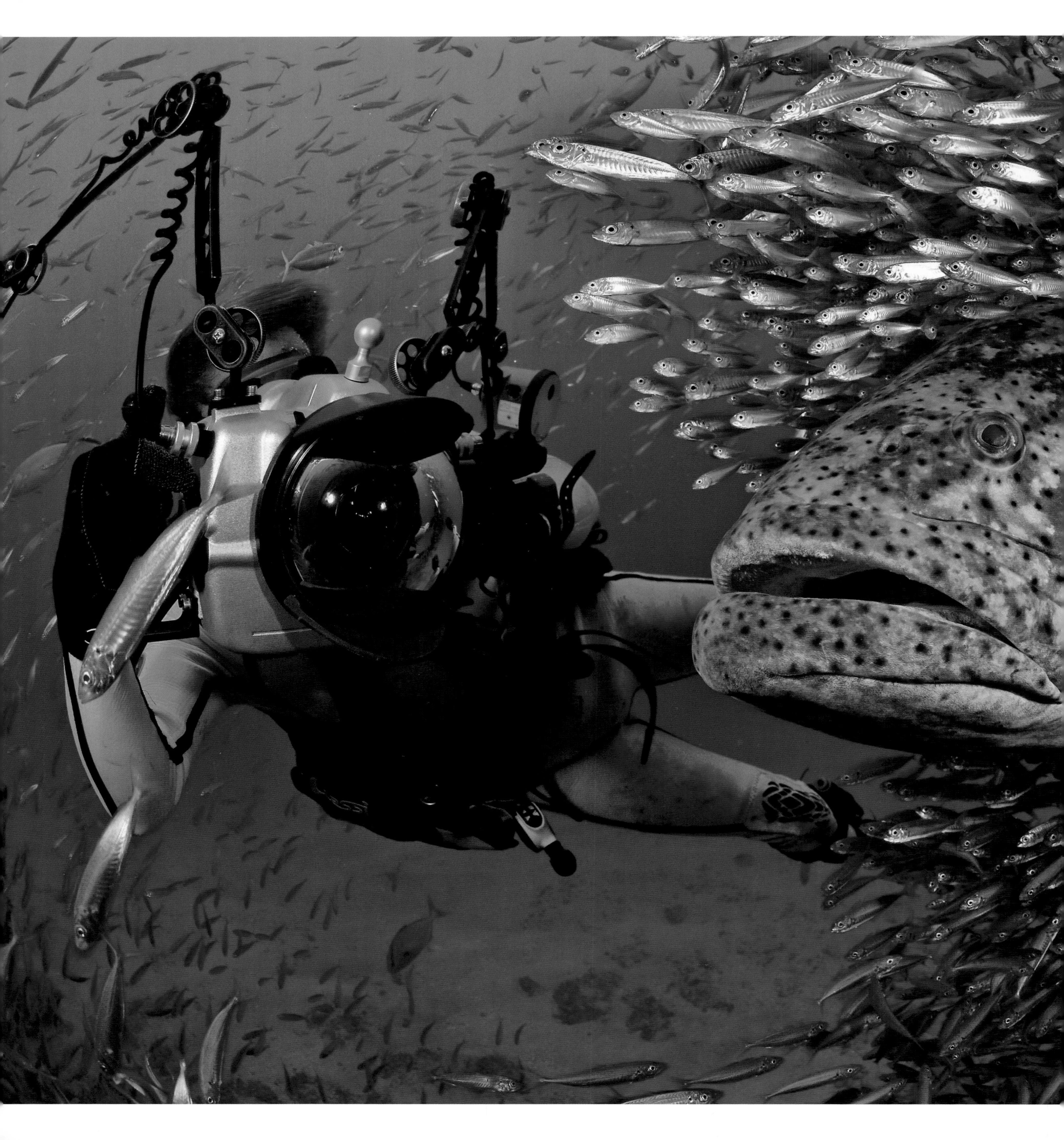

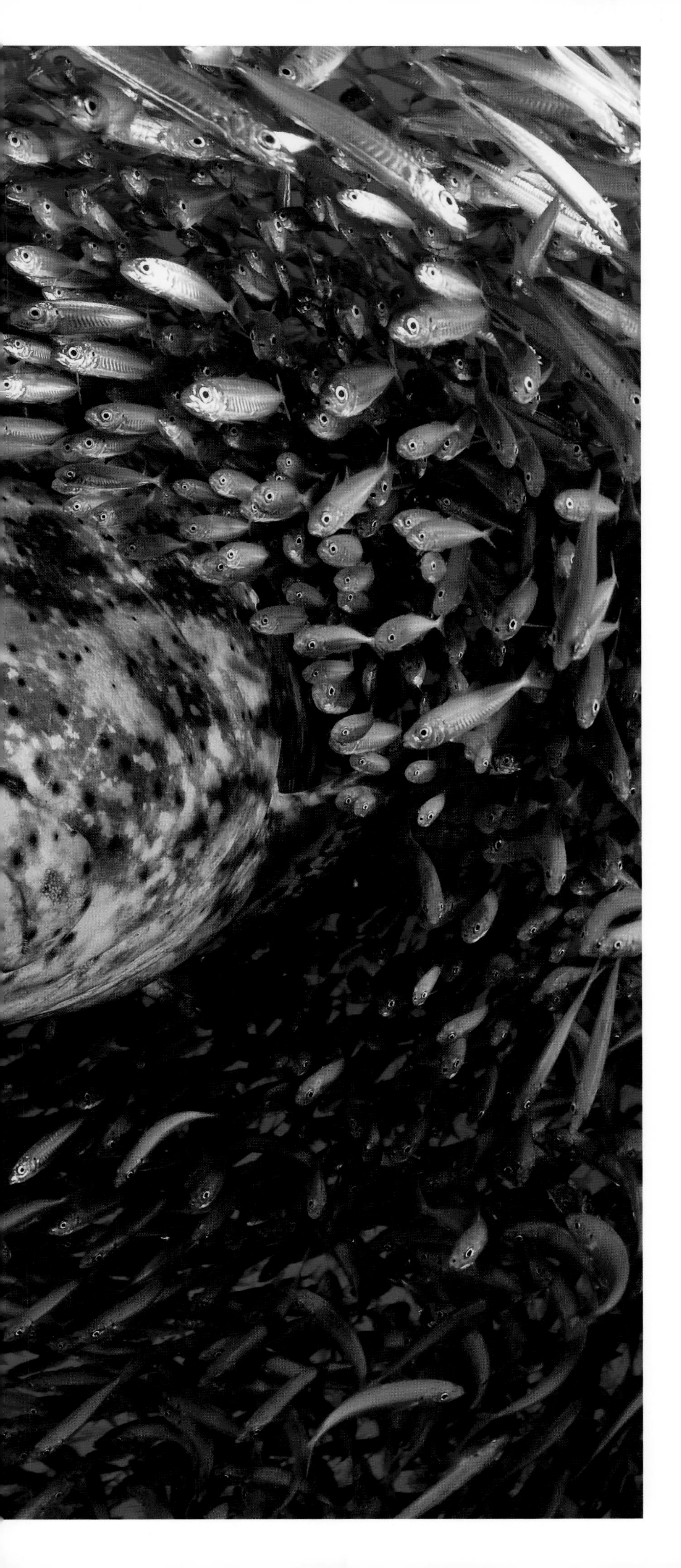

LEFT: Underwater photographer and goliath grouper (*Epinephelus itajara*) during a spawning aggregation in Jupiter, Florida, USA. **Photograph by Michael Patrick O'Neill**

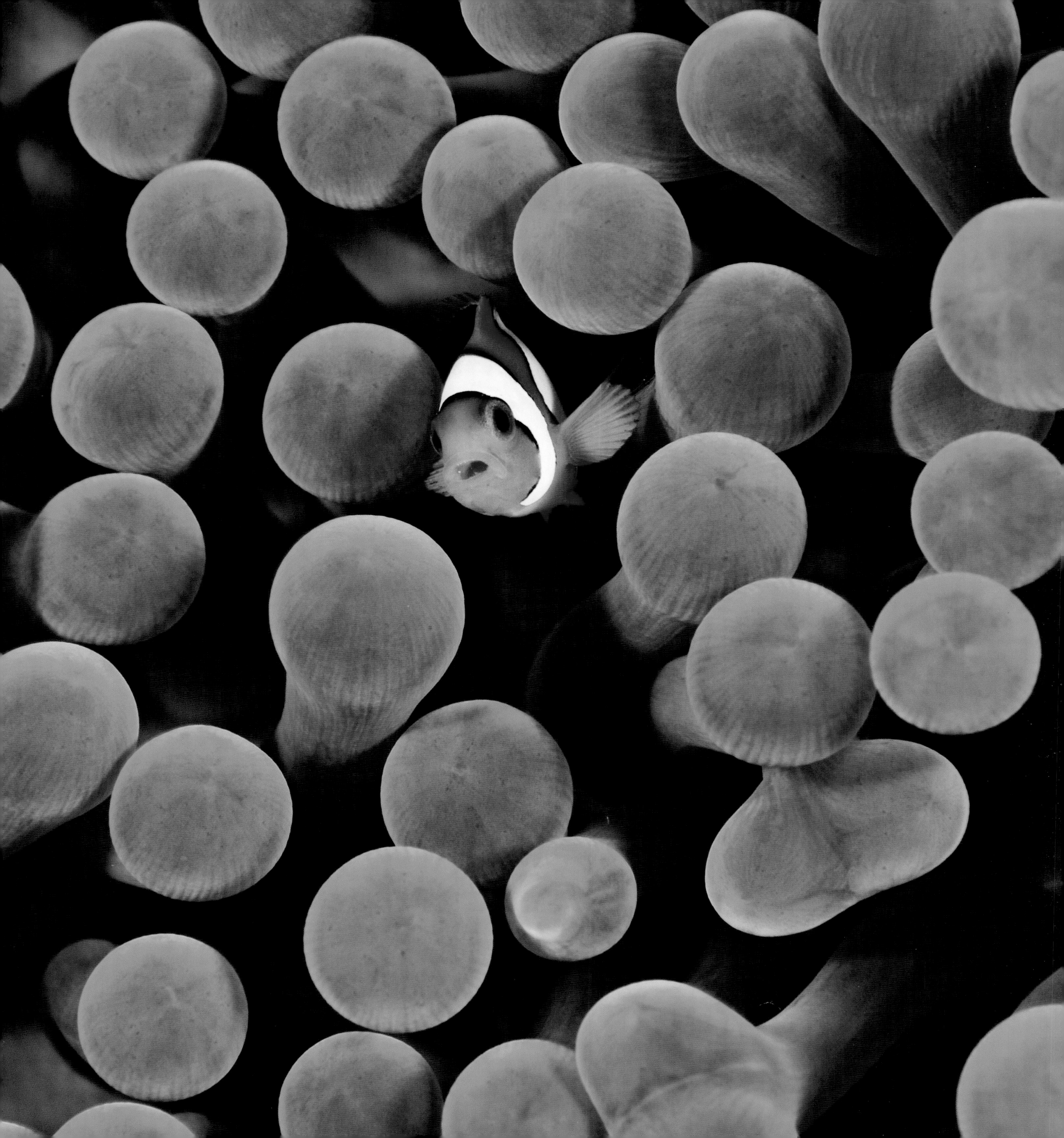

STAFF CREDITS

Series Editor—Cristina Mittermeier/Fellow iLCP

Project Manager/Design Director and Editorial Director—Abbie Williams/Earth in Focus

Consulting Editors—Russell A. Mittermeier, Gregory S. Stone

Art Direction, Book and Jacket Design—Stefan Gutermuth

Photo Editor—Meghan Lamb/iLCP

Text Editors—Ann Downer-Hazell and Ellen Peixoto

Translator—Francisco Malagamba

Pre-Press Editor—Jerry Dodrill

Illustrations—Kerry Lagueux

Assistant to the Publisher—Deborah Petersen/Earth in Focus

LEFT: A baby clownfish (*Amphiprion percula*) in its anemone home. **Photograph by Jürgen Freund/ iLCP**

FOLLOWING SPREAD: Mangroves at sunrise, Everglades National Park, Florida, USA. **Photograph by Carr Clifton/ iLCP**

GAIA AND OKEANOS

The modern environmental movement has often borrowed from the story of the Greek goddess Gaia to illustrate the intimate relationship that humans have, or ought to have, with the Earth. According to the story related in Hesoid's eighth-century poem, *Theogony,* or *Birth of the Gods,* the Titan Gaia made herself into a world for the enjoyment of humans, becoming Mother Earth. Conversely, human beings, as *Gaian-oxos* or inhabitants of Gaia, were created for the purpose of enjoying Gaia. (In his 1979 book *Gaia: A New Look at Life on Earth* scientist and futurologist James Lovelock proposed that the biosphere is in effect a living organism that acts to sustain life. Known as the Gaia Hypothesis, this idea and was further elaborated by later scholars.)

Such poetic license is not so farfetched if we recognize that all creatures, or species, exist only if they are adapted to their environment. No living thing can possibly exist out of harmony with its ecosystem. Seen in this way, each organism becomes a byproduct of its environment in which it lives. If we allow ourselves to think in this manner, we can accept that the marvelous variations and manifestations of biodiversity are not only possible, but in fact fitted to and codependent upon their environment. Thus, every life form is "created" to enjoy its environment, and is possible only as a result of its adaptation to it.

Speciation itself is an environmental relationship. Every species manifests itself in its adaptive characteristics to every particular environment. Polar bears have adapted to the Arctic with white coloring and dense fur because the harsh polar environment demands it. We can view this as a reciprocal relationship; while the polar bear has developed these characteristics to succeed in a cold environment, the bear also plays an important role in the ecosystem as the apex predator, thus "giving back" to the environment to which it has adapted. Every species is thus equipped to cope with the place it calls home. The long-neck of the giraffe, the claws of a fiddler crab, the tentacles of octopi, the sleek hydrodynamic shape of dolphins, the wings of birds: all these adaptations have been shaped as a perfect fit between organism and environment thus creating a single living thing: a living, breathing planet.

Understood in such a way, the Gaia analogy makes perfect sense as a relationship of reciprocity where life, as we know it, can only be manifested in its specific way, as a byproduct of the relationship of the environment to individual organisms.

Until fairly recently humans were the dominant players in Gaia's paradise. People rejoiced and adapted to such a garden of Eden, if you will, but now we have dramatically altered and changed our environment, stretching natural resources to the limit in our quest for ever more raw materials and consumer goods. This change in the human-Gaia relationship is taking us from a simple myth to a tragedy of Greek proportions. For all of human history, we had confronted the challenge facing any and all species: to form themselves, change, and adapt to the environment. But with the advent of the Industrial Age, humankind began to alter its relationship with Gaia, and shape Gaia, Earth, the environment, to its needs. In this way we have begun to write the history of what is now called the human-focused or Anthropocentric Era. The changes we have made to our planet are profound, a result of our voracious consumption. We have consumed the forests; removed whole mountaintops to extract their minerals. We have depleted our ocean and polluted the air, water, and soil. The list goes on.

Twelve hundred years after Hesiod, Johann Wolfgang von Goethe wrote a compelling follow up to the Greek myth of Gaia in his epic poem, *Faust*. Ever thirsty for the secrets of nature, Faust makes a pact to sell his soul to the devil. In return, the demon Mephistopheles grants Faust unlimited knowledge and far-reaching powers. Towards the end of his life, Faust orders the construction of the ultimate metropolis. Now blind, he hears the noise of workers toiling to build dams and great buildings. Imagining it to be the sound of his crowning achievement, Faust does not realize that the noise he hears is the construction of his own grave.

At the heart of these analogies lies our lack of generosity to our environment, to mother Earth. Our gigantic moral failure—to be stewards of the very environment which made us possible—is leading us to blindly build our own grave.

This cataclysm reminds me of Jared Diamond's book *Collapse: How Societies Choose to Fail or Succeed* (2005), in which he uses the collapse of the Rapa Nui civilization on Easter Island as a case study. In one passage, Diamond poses a brilliant hypothetical question: "What did the Easter Islander who cut down the last palm tree say as he was doing it?" (p 426). Unless we mitigate the damage already made, and adopt measures to curtail our destructive consumption, Diamond warns, Earth will become a larger version of Easter Island. We will devour our world and in doing so doom ourselves to extinction.

The cradle of all life, the ocean is where it all began, and the ocean is Gaia's vastest environment, covering 70% of the planet's surface. According to the International Union for the Conservation of Nature, half of Earth's population lives on or near the coast. Furthermore, the ocean is the most significant force in stabilizing climate, $CO2$ intake, and oxygen production. Without healthy oceans to regulate our climate and provide food and other resources to our planets billions, our very existence as a species is under siege. There is no more significant peril to our humanity's future than the damage we are doing to the ocean.

Our word *ocean* comes from the Greek *okeanos*. In Greek myth, Okeanos was, like Gaia, another of the Titans. He was the god who oversaw the rising and setting of the sun and moon. The ancient Greeks believed the heavenly bodies set into Okeanos, an endless river that flowed all the way around the earth. This endless body of water symbolized for the Greeks the eternal flow of time.

In the Iliad, Homer writes of the enormous strength of Okeanos, "with his deep running waters, Okeanos, from whom all rivers are and the entire sea and all springs and all deep wells have waters of him" (21. 194 ff). If indeed Okeanos is, as per Homer, the realm whence gods and men first emerged, and it is the cradle of life, to neglect it, as we do, is a matricide, a crime for which we will pay dearly.

In this Anthropocentric Era we are acting as if we possessed god-like powers, forging our destiny by taking over our environment. But we have done so blindly, without assuming any moral responsibility for our actions. Instead of caring for and being generous to our own cradle of life, we have opted to view the ocean as an inexhaustible cornucopia of resources. Without a doubt, our mighty technological advances give us almost god-like powers, and we enjoy great progress and comfortable life styles, but our lack of reciprocity to our environment has now depleted most of the ocean's bounty, and we now face the real possibility of depleting the sustenance necessary for even our most basic needs. This basic lack of understanding that indeed, our existence is one of reciprocity with our environment, may very well mean our demise.

In our new role as purveyors of the earth, we are writing the most apocalyptic of all tragedies. We now face the daunting task of curbing our blind enthusiasm for mindless consumption. Titanic measures will be required to remedy the damage we have already done and change the way we live, produce, and consume. It is only thus, and with great common resolve and sense of urgency, that we have a chance to rewrite our destiny from a tragedy into the story of the Phoenix rising from the ashes. Let us make no mistake; either we measure up to this overwhelming task, or we perish.

We need to make a daily vow to recommit ourselves to sustaining Gaia and Okeanos, and by doing so, ourselves. In the words of Homer's hymn:

> Okeanos, whose nature ever flows,
> from which at first both gods and men arose;
> sire incorruptible, whose waves surround,
> and Earth's all-terminating circle bound;
> hence every river, hence the spreading sea,
> and Earth's pure bubbling fountains spring from thee.
>
> Hear, mighty sire, for boundless bliss is thine,
> greatest cathartic powers divine;
> Earth's friendly limit, fountain of the pole,
> whose waves wide-spreading and circumfluent roll.
> Approach benevolent, with placid mind,
> and be forever to thy mystics kind.
> —Homer's Orphic Hymn 83 to Okeanos, trans. Taylor

Dr. Richard Sneider
Eitan Sneider

LEFT: This photo of a primitive looking Columbine sea krait (*Laticauda colubrina*) was taken in October of 2009 off the coast of Papua New Guinea. These snakes still need fresh water to survive and regularly come on to land to drink. **Photograph by Claudia Pellegrini**

FOLLOWING PAGE: Glassy sweepers (*Parapriacanthus Pempheris*) look out at the lens of the camera in the Red Sea. **Photograph by David Doubilet/ iLCP.**